Huber's New Observations Upon Bees

The Complete Volumes I & II
Bicentennial Edition
1814-2014

by Francis Huber
Translated by C.P. Dadant

Huber's New Observations Upon Bees
The Complete Volumes I & II
Bicentennial Edition 1814-2014

Written by Francis Huber between 1789 and 1814 and published in French as *Nouvelles Observations Sur Les Abeilles*. Volume 1 was released in 1792 and a two Volume set (with the addition of Volume 2) was released in 1814.

Translated from the original French
by Camille Pierre Dadant 1926
(Past editor of the American Bee Journal, Hamilton Illinois, U.S.A.)

Contributors: Francis Huber; Francis Burnens; Pierre Huber; Maria Aimée Lullin Huber; Jean Senebier; Charles Bonnet; Christine Jurine; John Hunter

𝔛-𝔖tar 𝔓ublishing 𝔠ompany
Nehawka, Nebraska
xstarpublishing.com

ISBN 978-161476-056-6

673 pages
149 Illustrations

TRANSCRIBER'S NOTES

This edition of Huber's Observations by far surpasses any other edition ever printed in the English language.

First it is the most complete. It has both Volumes I and II, while every English edition currently in print that I am aware of is only Volume I of the 1809 edition, which is only a third of the final Huber book. The second volume was published in 1814 in French 5 years after that 1809 edition and contains Huber's research on the origin of wax, the construction of comb, the ventilation of the hive and much more. Also it contains all the letters from Huber I could find that were in the American Bee Journal from 1872 until 1924 that were also translated by C.P. Dadant (except for 3 translated by Dr. Ehrick Parmley) .

Second, it is the best English translation from the original French. C.P. Dadant, was uniquely qualified to do the translation. Dadant was born in France and French was his first language, yet he spent most of his life beekeeping; and writing and editing beekeeping articles and books in America in English.

Third, all of the English editions currently in print have only 2 plates (if any). Only the previous Dadant edition (1926) had all 14 of the original plates but unfortunately they were apparently only halftones of some old yellowed copies and are not very readable. This edition has new scans from a very good condition edition of the original 1814 French of both Volumes of *Nouvelles Observations Sur Les Abeilles,* so these are clearer than any previous edition other than the original 1814 French edition. An additional engraving of Huber's work from Cheshire's book, plus an engraving of Francis Huber from the Dadant edition have been included. In addition, 7 more photos of a museum quality reproduction of Huber's Leaf Hive have also been included. All figures have been split out and enlarged and put in the text where they are referred to. Photos of the original plates are included at the back for historic and artistic purposes.

Fourth, to put this book in context I have included a memoir of Huber by Professor De Candolle, a friend of Huber. This gives a bit of background on Huber's life.

Fifth, the only other edition to come close to this, the 1926 edition by Dadant, was in very small print. This one is 11 point and a typeface that appears to be larger and is very readable.

Some of the archaic spellings have been updated and notations were added to show measurements in modern English and Metric. Typographical errors that occurred in the Dadant version were checked against the original French and corrected without notes. Footnotes have been put where they occur in the text and flagged as "Note:" and put in smaller type, rather than the bottom of the page. Additional headings and subheadings have been added to make particular subjects easier to find in the text and these have been put in the Table of Contents to make it easier to scan there to find a particular item. A table of illustrations is also included.

To put this work in its historic context, much of Huber's initial conjecture was based on current thought about queens and their fertility. Parthenogenesis had not been proposed, let alone proven by Dzierzon, which was not published until 1845, so some of Huber's assumptions about the laying of drones are outdated. But as opposed to his conjecture, which he clearly delineates as conjecture, I think you will find all of his observations true and correct and he is ever vigilant to distinguish the one from the other. Also during the writing of the first volume Huber had not yet done his research on the origins of wax which appear in Volume II.

—Michael Bush, Transcriber

Introduction by the Translator

Is it necessary to mention the great value of Huber's observations? Very few beekeepers have failed to hear or read of the great naturalist. He enriched the public mind with a number of observations, very few of which have proven incorrect. Langstroth called him "The prince of apiarians". At the suggestion of leading students and beekeepers in America, of whom I will name only two, Dr. E.F. Phillips and Mr. E.R. Root, this complete translation was made. It is useless to recall how important a work Huber's "New Observations" has been. Many people imagine that they have discovered things in beekeeping that this wonderful man had already described, with the help of his faithful wife and devoted secretary, Burnens, for Huber was blind.

The translator's intention is not to make money out of it, but only to have the credit of a correct translation of this wonderful book. Let me add here, that credit must be given to Mr. Graham Burtt of England for his help in the translation of one chapter.

The Writer of this has both editions of Huber's "Nouvelles Observations," in the French language, dated 1792 and 1814. He also possesses two of the four so-called "original" translations into English of this famous work, the second (1808) and the third (1821). Reading them and comparing them with each other and with the French original, he discovered that they are far from complete. They appear to be different from each other, for they begin and end with different wording. But some of the most absurd errors in translation or type-setting are repeated in each. For instance, in the eighth letter, the words "strong hive" were printed as "strange hive" and this ridiculous printer's error is repeated in each edition of the translation, showing that they are a copy of each other, with just enough changes to make it appear that they are original translations. Moreover, the English translation has but 5 plates instead of the 12 in the original French editions. It is very incomplete, being very much abridged in many parts.

—C. P. Dadant, Translator

TABLE OF CONTENTS

TABLE OF FIGURES

VOLUME I

PREFACE BY THE AUTHOR

In publishing my observations upon honeybees, I will not conceal the fact that it was not with my own eyes that I made them. Through a concourse of unfortunate accidents, I became blind in my early youth; but I loved sciences, I did not lose the taste for them when I lost the organs of sight. I caused the best works on physics and natural history to be read to me: I had for reader a servant (Francis Burnens, born in the canton of Vaud), who became extraordinarily interested in all that he read to me: I judged readily, from his remarks upon our readings, and through the consequences which he knew how to draw, that he was comprehending them as well as I, and that he was born with the talents of an observer. This is not the first example of a man who, without education, without wealth, and in the most unfavorable circumstances, was called by Nature alone to become a naturalist. I resolved to cultivate his talent and to use it someday for the observations which I planned: with this purpose, I caused him to reproduce at first some of the most simple experiments of physics; he executed these with much skill and intelligence; he then passed to more difficult combinations. I did not then possess many instruments, but he knew how to perfect them, to apply them to new uses, and when it became necessary, he made himself, the machines which we needed. In these diverse occupations, the taste which he had for the sciences soon became a veritable passion, and I hesitated no longer to vie him my entire confidence, feeling sure to see well when seeing through his eyes.

The continuation of my readings having directed me to the beautiful memoirs of Mr. de Réaumur upon bees, I found in this work so beautiful a plan of experiments, observations made with so much art, so wise a logic, that I resolved to study especially this celebrated author, to shape my reader and myself at his school, in the difficult art of observing nature. We began by studying bees in glazed hives, we repeated all the experiences of Mr. de Réaumur, and we obtained exactly the same results, when we used the same processes. This agreement of my observations with his own gave me extreme pleasure, for it proved to me that I could depend absolutely upon the eyes of my pupil. Emboldened by his first trial, we attempted to make upon the bees some entirely new experiments; we devised diverse hive constructions of which no one had ever thought, and which presented great advantages, and we had the good fortune to discover remarkable facts which had been unobserved by Swammerdam, Réaumur and Bonnet. These facts I publish in this work: there is not one of them that we have not seen over and again several times, during the eight years in which we have occupied ourselves with researches upon bees.

One cannot have a correct idea of the patience and skill with which Burnens executed the experiments which I am about to describe: it often happened that he followed, for 24 hours, without allowing himself any relaxation, without taking rest or food, and few worker bees of our hives, which we suspected of being fertile; in order to detect them in the laying of eggs. At other times, when it was necessary to examine all of the bees which inhabited a hive, he did not have recourse to the operation of a bath which is so simple and easy, because he had noticed that a sojourn in water disfigures the bees to a certain point, and does not enable one to perceive the little differences of structure which we wanted to ascertain; but he would take all the bees, one after another, in his fingers, and examine them with attention, without fearing their anger: it is true that he had acquired such dexterity, that he usually avoided the strokes of the sting; but he was not always so lucky, and when he was stung, he continued his inspection with the most perfect calm. I often upbraided myself for putting his courage and patience to so hard a test, but he was as interested as I in the success of our experiments, and through the extreme desire which he had to become informed of the results, he counted as nothing the trouble, the fatigue and the temporary pains of the stings. Therefore, if there is any merit in our discoveries, I must divide the honor with him; it is a great satisfaction for me to insure this reward for him, by acknowledging the justice of it publicly.

Such is the faithful account of the circumstances in which I found myself; I realize that I have to do much to secure the confidence of naturalists; but in order to be more sure of obtaining it; I will take the freedom of a little self-conceit. I communicated successively my principal observations upon bees to Mr. Bonnet; he found them correct, he advised me to publish them and it is with his approval that I publish them under his patronage. This testimony of his approval is so glorious for me, that I could not forego the pleasure of informing my readers of it.

I do not ask that I be believed upon my work: I will recount our experiments and tell all the precautions taken: I will detail so exactly the processes that we have employed, that all observers will be enabled to repeat these experiments; and if then, as I do not doubt, they secure the same results as I did, I will have consolation of knowing that the loss of my eyesight did not render me altogether useless in the progress of Natural History.

1ˢᵀ Letter—Upon the Fecundation of the Queen Bee

Pregny, August 13, 1789

Sir, when I had the honor of giving you, at Genthod, an account of my principal experiments upon bees, you expressed the desire, that I should write all the details and that I should send them to you, so that you might judge them with more attention. I therefore hastened to extract the following observations from my journal. Nothing could be more flattering for me than the interest you are kind enough to take in the success of my researches. Therefore permit me to remind you of the promise you have made to suggest new experiments to undertake.

Observation Hives

After having for a long time watched the bees in glazed hives, constructed in the way indicated by Mr. de Réaumur, you perceived, Sir that their shape was not favorable to the observer, because these hives are too wide, the bees building in them two rows of parallel combs, and consequently all that happens between those combs is lost for the observer: from this correct remark, you advised the use for naturalists of much narrower hives, the panes of which should be so close together that there would be room between them for only one row of combs. I followed your advice; I made hives an inch and a half (38mm) only in thickness and I had no trouble in hiving swarms in them. But we cannot rely upon the bees to construct a single comb; they never derogate, when they are not constrained by some particular disposition: therefore if left to themselves in our thin hives, as they could not build two parallel combs in the length of the hive, they would construct several small ones perpendicular to it and all that would happen between them would be equally lost for the observer: one must therefore arrange the combs beforehand. I have them placed so that their plan is perpendicular to the horizon and their lateral surfaces three or four lines (3 lines=¼ in.=6mm. 4 lines=1/3 in.=8.5mm) from the panes of the hive, on each side. This distance gives the bees sufficient freedom, but prevents them from collecting in too thick clusters upon the surface of the combs. With these precautions, the bees establish themselves easily in such narrow hives; they do their work with the same assiduity and order, and as there are no cells which are not exposed to view, we are sure that they cannot conceal any of their actions.

Volume 1 Plate I Fig 1—Leaf Hive, one frame.

Description of Hive Invented by the Author

It is true that by compelling these bees to be content with a habitation, in which they could build but one single row of comb, I had, to a certain point, changed their natural condition, and this circumstance might alter their instinct more or less. Therefore, to obviate any kind of objection, I devised a hive which, without losing the advantage of thin hives, approached the shape of the common hives in which bees construct several parallel rows of combs. I will give here the description in a few words:

Volume 1 Plate I. Explanation.

The book hive is composed of the putting together of 12 frames placed vertically and parallel to one another.

Fig. 1 represents one of these frames: the uprights fg, fg, should be 12 inches (30 cm) in length, and the cross pieces ff, gg, 9 or 10 inches approximately 23 to 25 cm) (Transcriber's note: elsewhere Huber says "one foot square", so it appears he built them both sizes); the thickness of the uprights and of the cross pieces should be 1 inch (2.5 cm) and their width 1 ¼ inches (32 mm). It is important that this last measurement be exact.

aa, piece of comb which serves to direct the bees in their work.

bb, bb, pegs which serve to fasten the comb within the frame: there are four on the other side which do not show in this cut, but figure 4 shows how they are to be placed.

d, movable cross piece which serves also in supporting the comb.

ee, pegs driven into the uprights under the movable cross piece to support it.

Figure 2 represents a book hive, composed of 12 frames all numbered. Between the 6th and 7th frames are 2 boards each with shutter which may divide the hive into two equal parts, but which are to be used only when wanting to separate the hive in two for the making of an artificial swarm. They are designated by a a.

b b, boards which close the ends of the hive with shutters

There are openings at the lower end of each frame; all must be closed with the exception of Numbers 1 and 12; but they must be disposed so as to be opened at will.

Fig. 4.

Fig. 1.

Fig. 2.

Fig. 3.

Volume 1 Plate I—Leaf Hive.

Volume 1 Plate I Fig 2—Leaf Hive, closed.

Volume 1 Plate I Fig 3—Leaf Hive, open.

Figure 3 exhibits the hive as an open book in part to show that the frames of which it is composed may be joined together, and opens like the leaves of a book. a a, are shutters which close it at each end.

Fig. 4.

Volume 1 Plate 1 Fig 4—Leaf Hive, cutaway side view of the frame in Fig 1.

Figure 4 is the same as figure 1 shown in a different way.

a a, piece of combs to direct the work of the bees.

bb, bb, pegs arranged in wedge shape to hold the comb within the frame.

c c, end of two slats which serve in holding the comb, the upper one stationary, the lower one movable.

I procured several small frames of pine, a foot square, and an inch and a quarter thick; I caused them to be all joined together with hinges, so that they might open and close at will. Like the leaves of a book, and I had the two outside frames covered with panes of glass, representing the covers of the book. When we used hives of this shape, we had a comb of cells fastened within each of the frames; we then introduced the number of bees needed for each particular experiment; then, by opening successively the different frames, we inspected, several times each day, each comb on its two sides: there was not a cell, therefore, in which we could not examine what took place at any moment; I might almost say that there was not a single bee with which we did not get personally acquainted. In fact, this construction is nothing but the union of several narrow hives, which may be separated at will: I acknowledge that bees must not be examined, in such a hive, before they have fixed their combs securely in the frames; otherwise they might fall out of the frames, upon the bees, crush or maim some of them and irritate them to such a point, that the observer could not avoid stings, which are always unpleasant and sometimes dangerous: but they soon become accustomed to the situation; they are in some way tamed by it, and at the end of three days one may open the hive, carry away parts of combs, substitute others, without the bees exhibiting too formidable signs of displeasure. Kindly remember, sir, that when you visited my retreat, I showed you a hive of this shape which had been a long time in Experiment, and that you were much astonished at the peaceableness with which the bees permitted us to open it.

I have repeated all my observations in hives of this shape and the results were exactly the same as in the thinnest hives. I thus believe that I have obviated all the objections that might be made upon the supposed inconveniences of my flat hives. Besides, I have no regret of having repeated all my work; by going over the same observations several times, I am much more certain of having avoided error, and I have found in these hives (which I will call *book* or *leaf hives*) several advantages which make them very useful in the economic treatment of bees. I will detail them afterwards, if you permit me.

I come now Sir, to the particular object of this letter, the fecundation of the queen-bee.

Note: I do not dare insist that my readers, in order to better comprehend what I have to say, should read the memoirs of Mr. de Réaumur upon bees and those of the Lusatian Society, but I urge them to study the extract that Mr. Bonnet has given of them in his work, tome X of the octavo edition, and tome V of the quarto edition. They will find in it a short and clear summary of all that naturalists had hitherto discovered on those bees.

Opinions on the Fecundation of Bees

I will first examine in a few words, the different opinions of naturalists on the peculiar problem which this fecundation presents; I will mention to you the most remarkable observations which their conjectures caused me to make, and will then describe the new experiments through which I believe that I have solved the problem.

Swammerdam's Opinion

Swammerdam, who had observed bees with constant assiduity, and had never been able to see a real mating of a drone with a queen, was satisfied that mating was unnecessary for the fecundation of the eggs; but as he noticed that the drones exhaled, at certain times, a very strong odor, he imagined that this odor was an emanation of the *aura seminalis,* or the aura seminalis itself, which penetrating the body of the female, operated fecundation. He become confirmed in this conjecture, when he dissected the organs of generation of the males; he was so struck with the disproportion which they present compared with the organs of the female, that he did not believe that copulation was possible; his opinion upon the influence of the odor of the drones had the advantage that it explained very plausibly their prodigious multiplication. There are often 1,500 to 2,000 of them in a hive, and according to Swammerdam, it was necessary that they be there in great numbers, that the emanation proceeding from them be sufficiently intense or energetic to effect fecundation.

Mr. de Réaumur has already refuted this hypothesis by just and conclusive reasoning; but he has not made the sole experiment which could verify or overturn it in a decisive manner. It was necessary to confine all the drones of the hive in a box perforated with very minute holes, which would allow the passage of the odor, without permitting the passage of the organs of generation; place this box in a well peopled hive, but entirely deprived of males of either large or small size, and observe the result. It is evident that, after having thus disposed matters, if the queen had laid fertilized eggs, Swammerdam's hypothesis would have acquired much probability, and on the contrary, it would have been entirely overthrown, if the queen had not laid any eggs or only sterile ones. We made the experiment as I have just indicated it, and the queen remained barren. It is therefore certain that the odor of the drones is insufficient to impregnate her.

Mr. de Réaumur's Opinion

Mr. de Réaumur had a different opinion: he believed that the fecundity of the queen-bee was the result of actual mating; he enclosed a few drones with a virgin queen, in a glass sand-box; he saw her make many advances to the males, but as he could not seen any connection sufficiently intimate to call it a mating, he made no decision, leaving the question open. We have repeated the experiment after him, we enclosed, at different times, virgin queens, with drones of all ages, we made the experiment in all seasons; we saw the advances made by the queen: we have even at times thought we detected between them a sort of union, but so short and imperfect that it was not likely that it had operated fecundation. However, as we did not wish to neglect anything, we confined to her hive the queen which had been approached by the male and observed her for several days. She was imprisoned for more than a month, she did not lay a single egg during that time, therefore she had remained sterile. Those momentary junctions do not operate fecundation.

Mr. de Braw's Opinion

In the *Contemplation de la Nature*, part XI, chapter XXVII, you have reported the observations of an English naturalist, Mr. de Braw. They appeared made with accuracy and seemed, at last to clear the mystery of the fecundation of the queen-bee. See Volume LXVII of the *Transactions Philosophiques*. This observer favored by chance, one day perceived at the bottom of some cells containing eggs, a whitish liquid, of spermatic appearance, distinct at least from the jelly which the workers usually gather around the newly hatched worms. Curious to learn its origin, and conjecturing that it was drops of the prolific masculine liquid, he undertook to watch in one of these hives the actions of the drones, so as to detect them at the time when they would be sprinkling the eggs. He asserts that he saw several of them insinuating the posterior part of their body in the cells, depositing the liquid there. After repeating this observation several times he undertook a long series of experiments: he confined a number of workers with a queen and a few drones in a glass bell; he supplied them with pieces of comb containing honey but no brood and he saw this queen lay eggs which the drones afterwards sprinkled and from which worms hatched. On the other hand, when he failed to enclose drones within the prison with the queen, she did not lay or laid only sterile eggs. He did not hesitate to give, as a demonstrated fact, that the males of bees fecundate the eggs of the queen in the manner of fishes and frogs, that is to say, externally after they have been laid.

This explanation appeared specious; the experiments upon which it was based appeared well made, and it especially accounted for the prodigious number of males which are found in hives. However there remained a very strong objection which the author had overlooked. Larvae are born when there are no longer any drones. From September until April the hives are, usually, deprived of drones and notwithstanding their absence, the eggs which the queen lays in that interval are not sterile: this they have no need to be fertile, of the influence of the drone's sperm. Should we suppose that it is needed at a certain time of the year and that in other seasons it becomes useless?

To discover the truth amid these apparent contradictory facts, I resolved to repeat the experiments of Mr. de Braw and to take greater precautions than he had taken himself. First, I sought, within the cells which contained the eggs, to see the liquid of which he speaks, and which he mistook for drops of sperm; we found, Burnens and I, several cells containing an appearance of liquid, and I must acknowledge that, during the first days, after making this observation, we had no doubt of the reality of this discovery: but we recognized the illusion afterwards, caused by the reflection of the rays of light; for we could see traces of this liquid only when the sun was sending its rays to the bottom of the cells. That bottom is usually lined with debris of different cocoons of the worms which have successively hatched in it. Those cocoons are sufficiently bright and when strongly lighted there results an illumination, which is quite deceiving. We became convinced of this when we examined the matter more closely. We detached the cells which presented this peculiarity; we cut them up in different ways and saw very clearly that there was not the least trace of liquid in them.

Although this observation inspired us with a sort of distrust of Mr. de Braw's discovery, we repeated his other experiments with the greatest care. On the 6th of August 1787, we immersed a hive and examined all of the bees while they were in the bath. We made sure that there was not a single drone in it, either of the large or of the small size. We examined all of the combs and we made sure that there were neither nymphs nor larvae of males in them. When the bees were dry we placed them all back with the queen in their hive; and transported this hive into my cabinet. As we wished them to enjoy full liberty, we did not close them up; they went into the fields and made their usual harvest; but as it was necessary that, during the entire time of the Experiment, there should be no drones among them, we adapted a glass tube to the entrance, the dimensions of which were such that two bees only could pass at once, and we watched this tube attentively during the four or five days that the experiment lasted. Had a drone appeared, we would have recognized him instantly and removed him so that the result of the experiment be not disturbed. We can affirm that not one was seen. However, the queen laid, from the first day (6th of August), 14 eggs in worker cells and all the worms hatched on the 10th of the same month.

This experiment is decisive. Since the eggs were fertile that the queen laid in the hive containing no drones, and where no drones could possibly have been introduced, it is very certain that they do not need to be sprinkled with the sperm of the drones in order to hatch.

It appears to me that no reasonable objection can be brought against this inference. However, as I have accustomed myself, in all my experiments, to seek the most trifling difficulties which might be raised against their results, I thought that Mr. de Braw's partisans would say that the bees, deprived their drones might seek those living in other hives, remove the fertilizing liquid from them, and bring it to their own home to deposit it upon the eggs.

It was easy to appreciate the value of this suspicion. It was only necessary to repeat the previous Experiment, confining the bees in their hive so closely that not one of them could escape. You know, Sir, that the bees may live for three or four months in confinement in their hive, otherwise well provisioned with honey and wax, and in which small openings have been left for the passage of air. I made this experiment on the 10th of August; I had made sure, by means of immersion, that there was not a single drone among them; they were kept prisoners, in the closest manner, for four days, and at the end of that time I found forty worms newly hatched on their bed of jelly. I went to the length of immersing this hive again to make sure that no male had escaped my search; we examined all of the bees separately and we can assure that there was not a single one which did not show us her sting. This result, coinciding with the first Experiment, demonstrated that the eggs of the queen-bee are not fecundated externally.

In order to conclude the confutation of Mr. de Braw's opinion, I need only to indicate that which lead him into error. In his different observations he used queen-bees with which he was not acquainted from their birth. When he saw the eggs hatch which were laid by a queen confined with males, he determined that they had been sprinkled with the prolific liquid; but to have a just conclusion, he should have ascertained that this female had never mated and this he neglected. The fact is, that without knowing it, he had employed in this experiment a queen which had had commerce with a male. Had he used a virgin queen and enclosed her with the drones within his glass bells, at the moment of her emerging from the royal cell, he would have had an entirely different result. For even amidst this seraglio of males, she never would have laid as I will prove in the sequel of this letter.

Mr. Hattorf's Opinion

The Lusatian observers, and Mr. Hattorf in particular, thought that the queen was fertile, of herself, without the concourse of the males. Note: See in Schirach's history of bees a memoir of Mr. Hattorf, entitled: Physical researched upon this question: Does the queen-bee require fecundation by drones? I will recall here the experiment upon which this opinion was founded.

Mr. Hattorf took a queen of whose virginity there could not be any doubt; he confined her to a hive from which he excluded all the males of the large or small size and a few days after he found in it eggs and worms. He asserts that, in the course of this experiment no drones were introduced within this hive, and, since in spite of their absence the queen laid eggs from which worms hatched, he concluded that she is fertile by herself.

Reflecting on this Experiment, I did not find it sufficiently exact. I knew that drones pass easily from one hive to another and that Mr. Hattorf had taken no precautions to prevent any of them from being introduced within his hive; indeed he says that no males came, but he does not say by what means he made sure of this fact: even though he might have made sure that no drones of the large size had entered, it might have been possible that one of the small size had entered, escaping his diligence, and had fecundated the queen. To clear up this doubt, I resolved to repeat the experiment of this observer, as he described it, without greater care or precautions.

I placed a virgin queen within a hive from which I removed all the drones, and left entire freedom to the bees: a few days after, I visited this hive and found newly hatched worms in it. Here then was the same result as Mr. Hattorf had obtained; but to draw similar consequences, it was necessary to make sure that no males had been introduced. It was necessary to immerse the bees and examine them separately. We performed this operation and after careful search we found four small males. It results from this, that to render an experiment decisive on this question, it is not only necessary to remove all the drones, but one must also, by some sure method, prevent any from being introduced, which the German observer had neglected to do.

I prepared to repair this omission. I placed a virgin queen in a hive from which I carefully removed all the males, and to be physically certain that none would come, I adapted to the entrance of the hive a glass tube of such dimensions that the worker bees could easily pass through, but which was too small for even a drone of the small size. Matters remained thus for thirty days; the workers, going and coming, did their usual work, but the queen remained sterile; at the end of the thirty days, her belly was as slender as at the time of her birth. I repeated this experiment several times and the result was the same.

Therefore, since a queen remains sterile which is rigorously separated from all commerce with the males, it is evident that she is not fertile by herself. So the opinion of Mr. Hattorf is ill-founded.

Hitherto, when seeking to verify or destroy the conjectures of all the previous observers by new experiments, I had acquired the knowledge of new facts; but these facts were apparently so contradictory that they rendered the solution of the problem still more difficult. While working upon Mr. de Braw's hypothesis, if I confined a queen within a hive from which I had excluded all drones; she did not fail in fertility. On the contrary, if, while examining the opinion of Mr. Hattorf, I placed in the same conditions a queen of whose virginity I was positively certain, she remained sterile.

Difficulty of Discovering the Mode of Impregnation

Embarrassed by so many difficulties, I was on the point of abandoning this subject of researches, when at last, in reflecting more attentively upon it, I thought that these apparent contradictions were due to my bringing together experiments made on virgin queens and others executed upon females which I had not observed from their birth, and which had perhaps been fecundated unknown to me. Impressed with this idea, I undertook to follow a new plan of observation, not on queens taken haphazard from my hives, but on positively virgin females, whose history was known to me from the moment of their leaving the cell.

Experiments on the Fecundation of Bees

I had a great number of hives: I removed all the reigning females and substituted for each of them a queen taken at the moment of her birth; I removed all the males of both large and small sizes, and adapted to the entrances a glass tube so narrow that no drone could enter, but large enough for the free ingress and egress of the workers. In the hives of the second class, I left all the drones that were there and even introduced new ones, and to prevent them from escaping, I placed on these hives, as with the first, a glass tube too narrow for the passage of the drones.

I followed with great care, for over a month, this experiment made on a large scale, and was very much surprised at the end of that time, to see my queens equally sterile.

It is therefore absolutely certain that queens remain unfertile, even amidst a seraglio of drones, when one confines them to the hive. This result led me to suspect that the females cannot be fecundated in the interior of their hives, and that they must go out in order to receive the approaches of the males. It was easy to ascertain this by a direct experiment. As this is important, I shall relate in detail that which we made, my secretary and I, on the 29th of June, 1788.

We knew that, during the fine season, the drones usually emerge from their hives at the warmest hour of the day. It was therefore natural to conclude that, if the queens are also compelled to emerge in order to be fecundated, they would be induced to select the hour of the drones' flight.

We therefore stationed ourselves in front of a hive whose unfertile queen was five days old. It was 11 o'clock in the forenoon: the sun had been shining from its rising, the air was very warm; the drones began to fly from several hives, we then enlarged the entrance of that selected for observation; then fixed our attention upon that entrance and the bees that issues from it. We first saw a few males appear, which took flight as soon as released. Soon afterwards, the young queen appeared at the entrance of the hive; she did not fly at once. We saw her promenading on the stand of the hive for a few instants, brushing her belly with her posterior legs: neither the bees nor the males that emerged from the hive appeared to bestow any attention upon her: at last the young queen took flight. When a few feet from the hive, she turned and approached as if to examine the point from which she had left; (it seemed that she judged this precaution necessary to recognize it on her return) she then flew away, describing horizontal circles twelve or fifteen feet above the earth. We then contracted the entrance of the hive, so that she might not re-enter unobserved, and we placed ourselves in the center of the circles which she was describing in her flight, to be better able to follow her and witness all her actions. But she did not remain long in a situation so favorable for observation; soon she took speedy flight and arose out of sight: we returned immediately to our place in front of the hive, and in seven minutes we saw the young queen return and alight at the entrance of this hive from which she had emerged only once. We took her in our hands to examine her and having found no signs of fecundation upon her we allowed her to re-enter the hive.

She remained inside nearly a quarter of an hour, when she appeared again; after having brushed herself as before, she took flight, turned to examine the hive, and rose so high we lost sight of her. This second absence was much longer than the first; it was only after twenty-seven minutes that we saw her return and alight on the board. We found her then in a very different state from that in which she was after her first excursion: the posterior part of her body was filled with a whitish substance, thick and hard, the interior edges of her vulva were covered with it; the vulva itself was partly open and we could readily see that its interior was filled with the same substance. This substance very much resembled the liquid contained in the seminal vesicles of the males, completely similar to it in color and consistency;

Note: It will be shown in the following letter that what we took for drops of coagulated sperm was really the male organs, which the mating fixes into the body of the female. We owe this discovery to a circumstance that I will here relate. In order to shorten this work, perhaps I should have omitted all the accounts I give of my first observations on the fecundation of the queen-bee, and pass directly to the experiments which prove that she brings home with her the genital organs of the male; but in observations of this kind, which are both new and delicate, it is so easy to be deceived, that I believe I serve my readers by exposing candidly the errors which I committed. It is an additional proof, added to so many others, of the necessity for an observer, to repeat his experiments thousands of times, to obtain the certainty of seeing facts in their true light.

But we needed stronger proof than this resemblance, to make sure that the white liquid, with which she was impregnated, was really the fecundating liquid of the drones; it was necessary that it should operate fecundation. We then allowed this queen to enter the hive and confined her there. Two days later we opened the hive and saw the proof that she was fertile. Her belly was perceptibly enlarged and she had already laid nearly a hundred eggs in worker cells.

To confirm this discovery, we made several other experiments, with the same success. I will transcribe this one from my journal: The second of July, the weather being very fine, the males came out in numbers. We set a liberty a queen which had never lived with drones (for her hive had always been entirely deprived of them.) She was eleven days old and positively not fertile; We soon saw her leave the hive, turn to examine it, and rise out of sight: she returned after a few minutes, without any exterior signs of fecundation; she flew again for the second time, at the end of a quarter hour, but with so rapid a flight that we were able to follow her only an instant; this new absence lasted thirty minutes. The last ring of her abdomen was open and the vulva was filled with the whitish matter already mentioned. We replaced her in her home, from which we continued to exclude all males. We examined her two days later and found her fertile.

These observations at length taught us why Mr. Hattorf had obtained results so different from ours. He had had fertile queens, in hives which were deprived of drones, and he had concluded that their intercourse was not necessary for fecundation, but he had not deprived his queens from the liberty of flight and they had taken advantage of this to join the drones. We, on the contrary, had surrounded our queens with a great number of males and they had remained sterile, because the precautions which we had taken for confining the males to the hives had also prevented the queens from departing and seeking *outside,* the fecundation which they could not obtain within.

We repeated these experiments upon queens aged twenty, twenty-five, thirty, thirty-five days. All became fertile after a single impregnation. However, we have observed some essential peculiarities in the fecundity of those queens which were fecundated after the twentieth day of their life; but we defer speaking of it until we can offer to naturalists some observations sufficiently positive and sufficiently numerous to better merit their attention.

However, allow me to add a word here. Although we did not witness a real mating between the queen and a drone, we believe that, after the details which we have just given, there will remain no doubt of the actual mating and of the need of it for fecundation. The sequel of our experiments, made with every possible precaution, appears demonstrative. The uniform sterility of queens in the hives containing no males and in those in which they were confined with males; the departure of these queens from their hives and the very conspicuous signs of impregnation which they exhibited on their return, are proofs against which no objections can stand. We do not despair of being able, next spring, to secure the last complement of this proof, by seizing the female at the very instant of copulation.

Naturalists had always been much embarrassed to account for the great number of drones found in most of the hives and which seem to be only a burden on the community of bees, since they fulfill no functions there. But we may now begin to discern the intentions of Nature in multiplying them to such an extent: since fecundation cannot take place within the hives, and the queen is compelled to fly in the expanse of the air to find a male who may fecundate her, it was requisite that these males be in sufficient number for the queen to have the chance of meeting one; were there only one or two drones in each hive, the probability of their issuing at the same time as the queen and of meeting her would have been very scanty and the majority of the females would have remained sterile.

But why has Nature forbidden fecundation within the hives? It is a secret which has not been unveiled to us. Some favorable circumstance may enable us to penetrate it in the course of our observations. One might make diverse conjectures but today we require facts and we reject gratuitous suppositions. We will remember only that the bees do not form the sole republic of insects presenting this singularity; female ants are also compelled to leave the ant-hills in order to be fertilized by the males of their species.

I dare not beg you, Sir, to communicate to me the reflections which your genius will suggest to you upon the facts that I have just related to you. I have not yet any right to this favor. But if, as I have no doubt, some new experiments to be tried come to your mind, upon the fecundation of the queen-bee or upon other points of the history of bees, be so kind as to suggest them to me: I will bring in their execution all the care of which I am capable and I will consider this mark of your friendship and interest as the most flattering encouragement which I may receive in the continuation of my labor.

I am, Sir, with the greatest respect,

Yours etc.

Letter from Mr. Bonnet to Mr. Huber Upon Bees

You surprised me, Sir, very agreeably, with your communication upon the fecundation of the queen-bee. You had a very fortunate idea, when you surmised that she left the hive to be fecundated, and the method to which you resorted to ascertain it was very appropriate to the end.

I will remind you that the males and females of ants mate in the air, and that after fecundation the females return to the ant-nest to deposit their eggs. *Contemplation de la Nature, part XI, Chapitre XXII, note I.* It would still be necessary to seize the instant when the drone unites with the queen-bee, but how can we ascertain the manner in which the copulation takes place, in the air, far from the eyes of the observer! Since you have good proofs that the liquid which moistened the last rings of the queen upon her return is the same as that which the males supply, it is more than a simple presumption in favor of mating. Perhaps it is necessary, for its operation, that the male may seize the female under the belly which cannot easily take place except in the air. The large opening that you have observed in a certain circumstance at the extremity of the queen's belly appears to correspond with the singular volume of the sexual organs of the male.

You desire, Sir, that I should indicate some new experiments to try upon our industrious republicans; I shall do it with the greater interest and pleasure, since I know to what extent you possess the precious art of combining ideas and drawing from this combinations results adapted to the discovery of new truths. A few at this moment come to mind.

Mr. Bonnet's suggestion's for experiments on the Fecundation of Bees

Artificial fecundation

It would be suitable to try to fecundate a virgin queen artificially, by introducing, within the vagina, at the end of a hair pencil, a little of the prolific liquid of the male, taking every precaution to avoid error. You know how much artificial fecundations have been worth to us already in more than one way.

Assure the queen returning is the one that left

In order to make sure that the queen that left the hive for fecundation is the same one that returns to deposit eggs, it would be necessary to paint her corselet with a moisture-proof varnish. It will be well also to paint the corselet of a good number of workers to discover the duration of the life. One would succeed still better by mutilating them slightly.

Required position for egg to hatch

In order to hatch, the little egg must be fixed almost vertically by one end near the bottom of the cell; this brings one question to mind: is it very certain that it may not hatch unless it is fixed in that position? I would not dare affirm it, and I leave the decision to experiment.

Are they true eggs?

I said to you once that I long doubted the real nature of those small oblong bodies that the queen deposits in the bottom of the cells: I was inclined to consider them as minute worms that had not yet begun their development. Their very elongated shape favored my conjecture; it would be advisable to watch them with the utmost assiduity from the time of their being laid until they hatch. If one can see the shell burst open and the little worm emerge from the aperture, there will no longer be any doubt that these little bodies are real eggs.

Suggestions to observe true mating

I return to the manner in which the mating takes place. The height to which the queen and the males rise in the air prevents us from distinctly seeing what passes between them: it would then be necessary to try enclosing the hive in a room with a very high ceiling. It would also be advisable to repeat the experiment of Mr. de Réaumur, who confined a queen with several males in a glass sand-box; and if, instead of a glass sand-box, one used a glass tube several inches in diameter and several feet long, perhaps one could observe something decisive.

Laying workers or small queens?

You had the good fortune to observe some of the small queens mentioned by Abbé Needham, but which he had not seen. It would be important to dissect with care some of these queens for the purpose of discovering their ovaries. When Mr. Riems informed me that he had confined about 300 workers in a box, with comb that did not contain any eggs and that some time after he found hundreds of eggs in that comb, which he credited to the laying of the workers, I strongly recommended to him to dissect the workers: he did so, and informed me that he had found eggs in three of them. They were apparently small queens which he had dissected without knowing it. Since small drones are produced it is not astonishing that small queens are produced also, doubtless by the same external causes.

These queens of the small size deserve to be known, for they may have great influence in diverse circumstances and embarrass the observer. We should ascertain whether they grow in pyramidal cells smaller than common or in hexagonal cells.

Does the Schirach method work with eggs?

Schirach's famous experiment on the pretended conversion of a common worm into a royal one could not be too often repeated, although the Lusatian observers have done so many times. But the discoverer maintained that the experiment succeeds only with worms three or four days old, and never with simple eggs. I would much like that this last assertion be tested.

The Lusatian observers and the one from Palatinate affirm that the common bees or workers lay only drone eggs, when they are confined upon combs containing no eggs at all: so there may be small queens that lay only drone eggs; for it is evident that those eggs, which they believed had been laid by workers, must have been produced by queens of the small size. But how can we conceive that the ovaries of those small queens contain only drone eggs?

Mr. de Réaumur informed us that we may prolong the life of chrysalides by keeping them in a cold place, such as an ice-house: it would be advisable to try the same experiment upon the eggs of the queen-bee and upon the nymphs of drones and workers.

Effects of cell size on bee size?

Another interesting experiment would be to remove all the combs composed of common cells, leaving only those made of cells intended for drones. One would ascertain whether the eggs which the queen would lay in those large cells would produce workers of a larger size. But it is quite probable that the deprivation of common cells would discourage the bees; because they need this sort of cells for their honey and wax. Perhaps however, if we removed only a part of these common cells, the mother might be compelled to lay common eggs in drone cells.

Queen larvae in common cell?

I should also desire that an attempt be made to gently remove from a royal cell the worm which is housed in it and place in it at the bottom a common one, in which some of the royal jelly would have also been deposited.

Ideal size and shape of hive?

As the shape of hives has a great influence upon the re-spective disposition of the combs, it would be a desirable experiment to vary their shape and internal dimension. Nothing would be better adapted to inform us of the manner in which bees modify their work and apply it upon circumstances.

This might enable us to discover particular facts which we do not divine.

Can drone, worker and queen eggs be distinguished?

They have not yet compared with care the royal egg and the drone egg with the eggs from which common workers are produces. It would be well to make this comparison to ascertain whether these different eggs contain distinctive characters.

Feeding royal jelly to workers

The pap supplied by the workers to the royal worm is not the same with that given to the common worms. Could we not endeavor to remove a little of the royal pap with a hair pencil and feed it to a common worm which would be placed in a common cell of greater size. I have seen common cells hanging almost vertically in which the queen had laid common eggs. These cells I would prefer for the experiment which I suggest.

Facts from Bonnet's book that require verification

I have gathered, in my *memoires sur les Abeilles*, diverse facts which would need verification; the same would be required of my own observations; you will know, sir, how to select, among these facts, the ones which are most worthy of your attention; you have already enriched the history of bees so greatly that everything may be expected from your sagacity and perseverance. You know the sentiments with which you have inspired the Contemplator of Nature.

Genthod, August 18, 1789

2ND LETTER—FECUNDATION OF THE QUEEN BEE CONTINUED

Pregny, August 17, 1791

The queen is impregnated by copulation, which never takes place in the hive

Sir, it was in 1787 and 1788 that I made the experiments related to you in my previous letter. They seem to establish two facts upon which only vague indication had been secured previously.

1st. The queen bees are not fertile of themselves; they become so through mating with a drone.

2nd. Mating is accomplished outside of the hive, and in the air.

The latter fact was so extraordinary, that notwithstanding all the proofs which we had acquired we keenly desired to see the queen in the act. But as she arises to a great height in this circumstance our eyes could never reach it. It was then that you advised us, sir, to cut off some part of the wings of virgin queens to prevent them from flying as rapidly and to so great a distance. We endeavored in every manner to profit by this advice, but to our great regret, when we mutilated their wings very much, they could no longer fly, and when we cut off but a small part, it did not diminish the speed of their flight. There is, probably, a medium between these two extremes; we were unable to attain it. We tried also, upon your recommendation, to render their sight less acute, by covering a part of their eyes with an opaque varnish; this attempt was also useless.

Experiments on artificial fecundation have not succeeded

At last, we tried to artificially fecundate some queen-bees by introducing into their posterior parts the liquid of the drones.

We took in this operation all imaginable precautions to insure its success, but the result was not satisfactory. Several queens were the victims of our inquisitiveness; the others which survived remained sterile nevertheless.

Although these diverse attempts were fruitless, it was proved that the females emerge from their hives to seek the males, and that they come home with the most evident signs of fecundation. Being satisfied with this discovery, we hoped for time or accident to give us decisive proof, a real mating, taking place under our eyes. We were far from suspecting a most singular discovery, which we made this year in the month of July and which gives a complete demonstration of the supposed mating.

Explanation of Plate II

Fig. 1 represents the organs of the male bees, such as they are after they have been drawn out of their body and stretched, so that no part of them should hide the rest.

a, the posterior of the body, the top of the last ring.

s, s, the seminal vesicles.

d, d, the deferent vessels (vas deferens)

q, q, constricted passage connecting the vas deferens with the seminal vesicles.

x, x, tortuous vessels, which are longer than they appear here and connect with the testicles.

Volume 1 Plate II Fig 1—Drone Organs.

t, t, testicles.

r, duct into which the seminal vesicles may empty their milky product, and which Swammerdam calls the "root of the penis".

l, junction point of the duct with the body that we call the lentil.

li, the lentil.

ie, ie, two brown, scaly or chitinous plates, which strengthen the lentil at its edges.

N, another chitinous plate.

On that surface of the lentil which cannot show in this cut, there are also two plates similar to those marked ie, and n; they are similarly located.

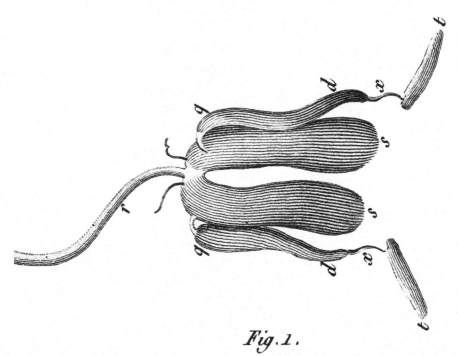

Fig.1.

Volume 1 Plate II Fig 1—Drone Organs (continued).

k, duct composed of folded membranes, emerging from the posterior part of the lentil.

p, plaited palet.

u, the arch; it shows through the membranes which cover it.

m, membranes forming a fleshy bag, which when out of the body, forms a sort of wooly mask.

c, c, the two horns, one of which is stretched out, the other folded; they are both ordinarily more folded even than this one is.

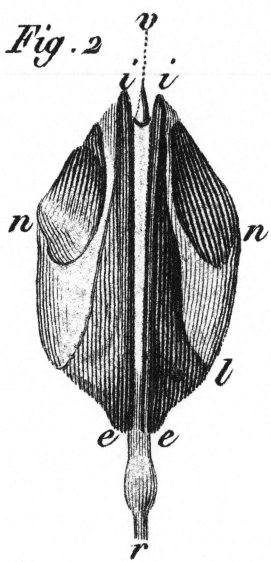

Volume 1 Plate II Fig 2—Drone organ, part that remains in queen.

Fig. 2 represents that part of the drone organ which remains within the posterior part of the females after mating, and which Mr. de Réaumur has called "the lentil".

li, lenticular body, shown from the edge, from magnifying glass.

r, fragments of the duct which Swammerdam called the "root of the penis" and which breaks at that spot, when the male separates from the female after mating.

ie, ie, two scaly plates which act as pincers.

n, n, two chitinous plates, shorter than the former and adjoining them.

v, part which I called the verge or penis.

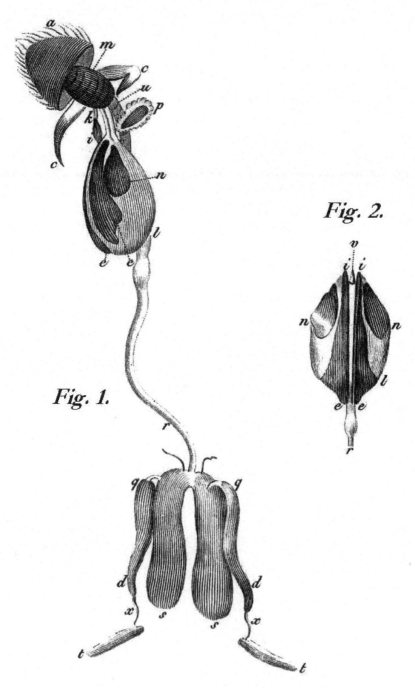

Volume 1 Plate II—Drone organs.

Anatomical Observations on the Sexual Organs of Bees

Note: Swammerdam, who gave us the description of the ovary of the queen-bee, has left it incomplete. He says that he could not see where the egg canal emerges from the belly, nor what parts may be perceived, outside of those which he described.

> "However much pain I took." Says he (Bible of Nature). "to discover distinctly the vulva opening, I was unable to do so, partly because I was then in the country and did not have all my instruments with me, partly because I did not wish to force the vulva out of the abdomen of the female, for fear of damaging some other parts which I needed to examine at the same time. However, I saw plainly enough that the excretory duct of the eggs forms a muscular enlargement, at the place where it is near the last ring of the abdomen; afterwards shrinking and again enlarging when it becomes membranous. I could not follow it farther, because I desired to preserve the venom vesicle, with the few muscles which serve for the play of the sting. But in another female, it seemed to me, that the vulva, when the bee is lying on her belly, opens in the last ring under the sting, and that it is very difficult to penetrate in this opening, unless these parts stretch and extend at the time when the bee lays."

We tried sir, to see what indefatigable Swammerdam had failed to see; he put us on our way by indicating to us the time of laying as the most advantageous for this research: we then saw that the excretory canal of the eggs did not open directly to the outside of the body; and that the eggs, when emerging from the womb, fell in a cavity, in which they were held for a time, before issuing out of the belly though of the lips of the last ring.

On the 6th of August 1787 we took out of her hive a very prolific queen: holding her carefully, overturned, by the wings, her entire belly was uncovered; she seized the extremity of it with the second pair of legs, and bringing it in this way towards her head, she bent it as much as she could, giving it the shape of a bow. This posture appeared to us opposed to free laying;

by the use of a straw we compelled her to take a more natural attitude and to straighten out her belly. Pressed to lay, she could not withhold her eggs any longer: we saw her make an effort and stretch out her belly; the interior part of the last ring spread away from the upper sufficiently to make an opening which uncovered a part of the interior of the belly. We saw the sting within its sheath in the upper part of this cavity. The queen then made further efforts, and we saw an egg emerge from the end of the ovary duct and drop into the cavity which we have mentioned; then the lips closed again and after a few instants they opened, but much less than the first time yet sufficiently to allow the egg which we had seen, to fall out of this cavity.

The male loses the sexual organs in copulation

We knew by our own observations that the sperm of the drone coagulates as soon as it is exposed to air; several experiments, by confirming this fact, left so little doubt on that score, that whenever we saw the females return with their exterior signs of copulation, we thought that we recognized the drops of the male sperm in the white substance with which their vulva was filled. We did not even think of dissecting one of those females to make ourselves more positively certain of the fact.

But this year, in order to neglect nothing and also to take note of the development which we supposed was produced in the organs of the queens by the injection of the coagulated sperm left by the drones, we undertook the dissection of several; to our great surprise we found that what we had mistaken for the prolific liquid, was really the generative organs of the male, separated from his body at the time of copulation, and remaining planted within the vulva of the females: here are the details of this discovery.

After having resolved to dissect several queen-bees at the time when they would return to the hive with the exterior signs of fecundation, we procured several, by the Schirach method, and allowed them successively to fly out to hunt for drones; the first one that took advantage of it was caught at the instant when she was about to re-enter the hive, and without dissection, she displayed to us what we were so desirous of learning. We had seized her by her four wings, and examined the underside of her belly. Her partly open vulva showed the almost oval end of a white body which, by its volume and position, prevented the lips from closing altogether; the belly of the queen was in continuous motion; it stretched, shrank, lengthened shortened, bent and straightened successively. We were making ready to cut open her rings, and seek, by dissection, the cause of all those motions when we saw her bend her belly sufficiently to reach its extremity with her posterior legs, and seize, with the hooks upon her claws, that part of the white body which was within the lips of her vulva and which held them apart; she was evidently making efforts to draw it out; she soon succeeded and dropped it into our hands. We were expecting to see the shapeless mass of some coagulated liquid; but our surprise was great when we found that it was a part of the body of the drone who had made her a mother. At first we did not believe our eyes; but after having examined that substance on all sides, both with the naked eye and with a good magnifying glass, we recognized distinctly the part of a drone which Mr. de Réaumur calls the "lenticular part" or "lentil," of which I here give the description copied from his own work (Ninth Memoir upon Bees, quarto edition, page 489)

> "When we open the body of a drone either from above or from below, we notice a substance formed from the assembling of several parts, often of a white color surpassing that of milk: If we spread out this substance, we find it composed principally of four oblong bodies; the two largest of these bodies are fastened to a sort of tortuous cord which Swammerdam called "the root of the penis (Plate II fig. 1), and he gave the name of *seminal vesicles* s s, to the two white, long bodies which we have just mentioned. Two other bodies, oblong like these, but with a diameter only about half of the others, and shorter, are called by the same author *deferent vessels* d d. Each of these communicates with one of the seminal vesicles, near the spot q q. which the latter are joined to the tortuous duct r; at the other end of each of these deferent vessels, a slim duct is found x x, which, after a few curves, ends in an en-

larged body t, a little larger, but difficult to separate from the trachea which surrounds it. Swammerdam considers these two bodies as the testicles. So we have two bodies of considerable volume
which join with two larger and longer ones still longer and larger.
These four bodies have a cellular tissue filled with a whitish liquid,
which may be forced out by pressure. The long and tortuous duct
r, to which the two largest bodies are fastened, which are called the
seminal vesicles, is undoubtedly the duct through which the milky
liquid can escape. After several turns it widens or rather terminates in a sort of bladder l, i, a fleshy bag. This part is more or
less stretched and more or less flat in different drones; by giving it
the name of *lenticular body* or *lentil*, we describe its appearance in all
the drones whose organs have been hardened in alcohol. *(Note:
this is referring to the food product "lentil", a small legume seed which is what
its shape resembles.—Transcriber)* This bag l, i, is then a rounded lentil, half of whose circumference is bound by two scaly plates e i, e
i, of chestnut color which follow the curves of its contour. A little whitish cord, on the border of the lentil, is visible and separates
them from one another. As this lentil is oblong we will give its
two ends the names of posterior and anterior. The anterior end l,
nearest to the head, is the one into which the duct r is inserted
coming from the seminal vesicles. The posterior end i, nearest to
the anus gives rise to the two scaly plates e i, e i, each of which
widens so as to cover a part of the lentil. Below the spot where
each of these scaly plates is widest, there is a notch which makes
two rounded points of uneven lengths, the longer being upon the
circumference of the lentil. Besides these two plates, there are two
others n n, Fig. 2, of the same color, but narrower, and shorter by
half, each of which is near the others, with their end at the same
end as the others, at the posterior part of the lentil, fig. 2. The
rest of the lentil is white and membranous; at its posterior end is a
tube k, also white and membranous, the diameter of which is difficult to determine, for the membranes which compose it are visi-
bly folded. At one side of this tube a fleshy body, p, is fastened
which resembles a palet *(palet=a disk or a small plate or scale—
Transcriber)*, one side concave with plated edges; the other side
convex; in some cases the plaits turn up and their edges project
beyond the circumference; they form rays which give the palet the

appearance of pretty work. This palet lies upon the lentil, and rests upon it on its concave side, but it does not adhere to it.

"The parts which we have just mentioned and which are the most visible in the body of the drones, are not those that emerge first out of the body, nor those that are most remarkable, outside of the body. If we consider the tube k, or the sac which begins at the posterior end of the lentil which separates the two scaly plates, we can easily see the part, u, which we have named the arch; one may see five wooly bands disposed crosswise, they are of tawny color, while the rest is white. This arch even seems to be outside of the membranous tube, for it is covered only by a very transparent membrane; at one end it almost touches the lenticular body while at the other it terminates where the membranous canal joins the membranes m, which are wrinkled and yellowish, making a sort of sac resting upon the edges of the opening from which the generative organs are to issue. The tawny-colored membranes mentioned are those which pressure forces out first, they form the elongated mass the end of which resembles a woolly mask. Lastly, this sac, composed of tawny membranes, holds two appendices c c, of reddish yellow color, even red to the tip; and these are the appendices which project to the outside in the shape of horns.

"When we press the belly of a drone gradually, with care, we cause other parts also to be ejected; these parts show themselves on the opposite side from their position in the body. The surface of these parts, which was the inside, becomes the outside; the same thing happens to them as to a stocking which is drawn inside out. If the opening of the stocking which we try to turn inside out was fixed upon a hoop, and if we began to evert it by beginning at the part nearest the opening, so that the heel and toe came last, we would have in this eversion of the stocking an exact illustration of the manner in which the organs of the male bee are turned to project outside.

"When we know the position of these parts in the interior of the body, it is easy to figure the order in which they must appear at their ejection. The tawny sac, which is nearest the opening, appears first and as a portion of its interior part is woolly, it provides the woolly mask. The base of the horns then show themselves; the arch next. When the arch is entirely extruded, it is necessary to increase the pressure to bring out the other parts; for it is through the end of this arch that the lenticular body passes which then assumes a very lengthened appearance. In spite of this, it is easily recognized, and it is evident that it has been everted inside out, since we see, upon one of its sides, the scaly plates already described, and that the side on which they are seen is concave, while when in the body of the drone it is convex."

The lenticular body l, is covered with the scaly plates i e, i e, is the only one of the parts described by Mr. de Réaumur which we have found within the vulva of the queens.

The canal r, which Swammerdam has called the *root of the penis*, is torn after fecundation; we saw fragments of it at the place where it joins the end l of the lentil, near its forward extremity, but we have never found any trace of the tube k, made of folded membranes, nor of the plaited palet p, which adheres to this tube, and which Swammerdam had called the penis, on account of its resemblance to that of other animals, although he did not believe this part, which is not perforated, could fulfill these functions. It must be that the tube k, and all that belongs to it break apart at i, near the posterior end of the lentil, and that these parts remain within the body of the male.

When we dissect a drone, we see, at the upper end of the canal r, two very apparent nerves which are inserted in the seminal vesicles, and divide among them as well as in the penis a number of ramifications.

According to Swammerdam these nerves and their ramifications may serve, at the same time, for the action of the parts, the emission of the sperm and the pleasure of feeling at the instant of this emission.

We perceive also, near these two nerves, two ligaments intended to retain in place the generative organs, so that they may not be drawn out without effort, excepting however the root of the penis and the lentil which may extrude naturally and which are in fact expelled from the body of the drone during the mating.

The canal r is not stretched out in the body of the males as it is in the engraving which is shown here; but this long and tortuous duct folds upon itself several times between the vesicles s s from which it emerges to the lenticular body to which it carries the seminal liquid. So, it may unfold, extend, and lengthen as far and farther than is necessary for the lentil to move within the body of the drone, emerge from it and pass into the body of the female.

When we open the body of a drone, we see that this is possible, for if we grasp the lenticular body and try to displace it, the folds of this canal disappear, it stretches considerably, and if we draw it farther it breaks at i, close to the lentil, and precisely at the same spot where it breaks in the mating.

A more or less intense pressure may force it out of the body of the drone like a glove, and show their inner side. Swammerdam and Réaumur admired this structure and described it with the greatest precision. We have also, like them, squeezed a great number of drones; we have often seen this marvelous eversion and understood how it might be operated under air pressure. But we are unable to believe that the generative parts turn inside out during mating, as happens with an unusual pressure; for not one of the drones that we have thus pressed survived after the operation: it is singular that such an extraordinary circumstance should have been unobserved by these naturalists.

We have indeed seen drones which we had not touched, in which the generative parts were inverted, but they had evidently died instantly, without being able to draw back into their body any of the parts which perhaps an accidental pressure had forced out.

Another observation gives proof also what the everting in question does not take place in natural circumstances. When we examined the lentil of which the queen had rid herself, we saw clearly that it had not been everted, since the side of it which we saw was the same as what is seen within the body of the male; we recognized this by the position of the four scaly plates, which exhibited their convexity and which covered the lentil at its posterior end; had they been everted the contrary would have been the case.

We conjectured then that these plates, intended, according to Mr. de Réaumur, to strengthen the lenticular body, might have a more important use and serve as pincers or hooks. The respective position of these plates, their appearance their scaly consistency, the space that they occupied upon the lentil, and especially the efforts that the queen was compelled to make to rid herself of them, seemed to strengthen this conjecture: but it was verified only when we had observed the position of these parts within the body of females which we killed to satisfy our inquisitiveness. For this purpose, we prevented several of these queens from displacing and pulling from their body the organs left by the drones that had fecundated them, and dissection showed us that those plates were true pincers or hooks, as conjectured by us.

The lentil was inserted beneath the sting of the queen and pressed against the upper part of her body; it thus filled the cavity of the vulva and rested at its posterior end against the end of the vagina or excretory canal of the eggs. It was there that we saw the action and use of the scaly plates; they were a little farther apart than they are in the body of the male. They were inserted below the orifice of the vagina and pressed between them some parts which their infinitely small size did not allow us to distinguish; but the effort required to separate them and remove the lenticular body left no doubt to us of the use of those scaly hooks.

The lentils taken out of the body of the males always seemed smaller than those found in the vulva of females; we also noticed, as did Mr. Réaumur, that those parts, in different drones, are not always of the same size; but we discovered another part, which escaped his notice or that of Swammerdam, which probably plays the main role in fecundation. We will mention it when giving account of the experiment which caused us to notice it.

Experiments Proving the Copulation of the Queen
1st Experiment: showing more than one mating flight is sometimes necessary.

On the 10th of July, we released, one after another, three virgin queens, four or five days old. Two of those queens took flight several times; their absences were short and unsuccessful; the one which we released last succeeded better, she flew three times: her first trips did not last long, but the last trip lasted thirty-five minutes. She came back in a very different condition , which permitted no doubt of the use she had made of the time; for her vulva partially open exhibited the organs, which the male had left in her body, that had fertilized her.

We caught her in one hand by her four wings, and with the other we obtained the lenticular body which she pulled out of her vulva with the claws of her posterior legs; the posterior end of this was armed with two scaly and elastic pincers; one could spread them apart, but when they were released they came back into the same position.

Towards the anterior end of the lentil, one could see a fragment of the root of the penis; this tube had broken, half a line (3/64th in.=1 mm) from the lenticular body: is it fragile at that spot in order to facilitate the separation of the female from the male? One would be tempted to believe it. We allowed this queen to re-enter her hive and arranged the entrance so that she might not emerge, unknown to us.

On the 17th we opened her hive, but found no eggs there; the queen was as slender as on the day of her flight. The drone that had mated with her evidently had not fecundated her. We gave her liberty again; she took advantage of it, and after two absences, she again brought to the hive evidences of mating; we confined her again, and the eggs which she laid afterwards gave us evidence that the second mating had been successful, and that some drones may be more fit for mating than others.

It is however very rare that a first mating is insufficient; in the course of our numerous experiments, we have seen but two queens that needed more than one to become fertile; all the others were fertile after the first mating.

2nd Experiment: Caused us to believe the drone's organ was broken off.

On the 18th, we gave liberty to a young queen, twenty-seven days old; she flew twice, her second absence lasted twenty-eight minutes and upon her return she brought the evidence of her mating. We did not allow her to enter the hive but placed her under a tumbler to see in what manner she would rid herself of the male organs which prevented the closing of her vulva; she would not succeed in it, as long as she had nothing but the table and smooth glass to rest upon. We enclosed under the glass a little piece of comb, in order to give her the same conveniences as she would have had in her hive, and to see whether, with this help, she could do without the help of the bees. She climbed promptly upon it, held to the edges of the cells with her four front legs; then stretching her two hind legs along her belly, she appeared to press it by rubbing with the legs up and down on each side, at last passing the hooks of her feet in the opening of the last ring of her abdomen, she clasped the lenticular body and allowed it to drop on the table; we took it up then: its posterior end was armed with the two scaly plates, under which in the same direction, we saw a cylindrical body, of grayish-white color; the end of this body, farthest from the lentil appeared perceptibly larger than the end next to it; beyond this enlargement it terminated in a point; this point was double and open like the beak of a bird, which caused us to believe that this body had been broken and torn; the following experiment sustained this conjecture.

3rd Experiment: Seemed to indicate that it was the male organ and the lenticular body was only an appendix.

On the 19th we released a virgin queen four days old. She flew twice, the second absence, longer than the first, lasted thirty-six minutes; she returned with the signs of fecundation. We wanted to secure in their entirety the parts which the drone had left in her vulva; for this purpose it was necessary to prevent her from breaking them by drawing them out with her claws: after having killed her as promptly as we could, we cut open her last rings to uncover the vulva; but in depriving her of life we had not deprived her of motion; there was so much of this in these parts that the lenticular body dropped out spontaneously, and the part which we were interested in was broken as it had been the previous time; we were thus compelled to repeat the test: I will give only the results of this.

In several instances, when we separated the lenticular body from the orifice of the vagina, against which it was pressed, we found with it a white body which adhered to it by one of its extremities; the other being engaged in the excretory canal of the eggs.

This body appeared cylindrical at its end near the lentil; it became enlarged farther along, then shrunk and again enlarged more than at first; it thus formed a sort of acorn, after which it terminated in a sharp point.

These details were not perceptible with the naked eye; a magnifying glass was needed to perceive them.

The shape of this body and its position seemed to indicate that it was the special male organ of which the lenticular body was only an appendix; but the last queen that we had under our control destroyed this conjecture.

4th Experiment: Disproving the previous conjecture from the 3rd experiment.

On the 20th, we liberated two virgin queens: the first one had already taken flight the previous days, but had not been fecundated; we seized her upon her return; her vulva was open and the lentil of the drone appeared between its lips: we wanted to prevent her from getting rid of it, but she removed it with her legs so quickly that we could not forestall her, and we allowed her to re-enter the hive.

The second queen liberated flew twice; her first absence was as short as usual: the second lasted about a half hour; she returned fecundated, and we caught her at her arrival. We opened her promptly after having killed her. We found the lenticular body placed as in all the queens observed before: its pincers penetrated to the base of the vulva; the dull points which terminate them appeared to be implanted under the excretory canal of the eggs; they pressed between them some parts which their infinitely small size did not permit us to distinguish: the resistance which they offered, in trying to loosen them, convinced us that these hooks serve to bring the end of the lentil against the orifice of the vagina and to hold it there. Through this precaution, of which we see examples in other insects, as the drone and the queen cannot pull apart until the requirement of Nature are accomplished, the success of their union is assured.

Before disturbing these parts, we placed them under the lens of the microscope: we then saw a peculiarity which had escaped our observation: when drawing back the lenticular body, there emerged from the vagina a small body (Figure 2 v), adhering to the posterior end of the lentil and located under the scaly plates. It drew back of itself within the lentil, like the horns of a snail. This part is very short, white and apparently cylindrical: there was, under the plates, a little of the seminal fluid half clotted at the bottom of the vulva. Looking farther in the vagina, we did not find any other hard substances: we pressed out much sperm: it was almost liquid, but soon clotted and became a shapeless whitish mass. This careful observation put an end to our doubts and convinced us that what we had mistaken for the characteristic organ of the drone was the semen itself which had clotted in the interior of the vagina and assumed the shape of the latter.

Thus the only hard part that the male had introduced within the vagina of the female was this short cylindrical point which had withdrawn into the lentil when we had drawn it out. Its action and situation prove that it is there that we must seek the escape of the seminal liquid if it is possible to find it open at any other time than during mating.

We sought this new part in the drones and found it in the first one dissected; by pressing the seminal vesicles s s, Figure 1, from above, we forced the white liquid with which they were filled to flow and run down into the root of the penis r, and into the lenticular body l, i, which was then considerably enlarged. We prevented this liquid from flowing back and forced it forward by a renewed pressure. However, the liquid did not flow out when we pressed the lentil, but we saw at its posterior end and under the scaly plates, a small white body, short, cylindrical and with the same appearance as that which we had found in the vagina of the queen. When we ceased to press the lentil, this part re-entered it, but reappeared every time that we pressed it.

I ask you Sir, when you read this letter, to glance at the figure which Mr. de Réaumur has published of the sexual organs of the drones, and which I caused to be copied (Volume 1 Plate II); the descriptions that accompany it appear quite correct, and give a proper idea of the position of these parts. Upon examination of these figures one easily conceives the appearance which they present within the vulva of the female, when they are implanted in it after mating.

The details which I have exposed, help to fix the idea of the reader and sufficiently indicate the shape and position of the organ which I discovered and which must be considered as the penis of the male bee, of which the lentil must be only an appendix.

I have no doubt that the drones perish when they lose their sexual organs after mating. While reflecting one day upon the discovery which is the subject of this letter and upon the impossibility of witnessing a mating which takes place in the air, it seemed to us that one could add another proof to those that we had, if one could find the male which had fecundated one of our queens and catch him on his return; but we could hope for this only in case he did not die suddenly after mating, and if he had time to return to the hive.

Burnens thought that it would be easy to distinguish such a male from those that die without having mated and without having suffered any mutilation. So he condemned himself to examine, one after another, all the drones that he would find dead near the hives during the swarming season.

After long and useless researches, he found a few that had died in front of the hives and were evidently mutilated, for they had lost those of the genital parts that remain within the body of the queens. The root of the penis had protruded out of their body after mating, a piece of this canal ten or twelve lines long (7/8ths in. to one in. or 21 to 25 mm) was hanging at the extremity of their belly and had dried there. None of the parts which pressure may force out showed itself in that case.

These observations, made with greatest care, confirmed the conjecture which I had already stated, that is: that no other part than the penis and its appendages extrudes from the body of the male during mating. They proved also that the males perish after having lost their sexual parts, and that their death is not as prompt as one might have expected.

By coming back to die at the front of the hive, they bring back, as the queen does, the evidence of their union and of a long unknown fact.

But for what reason has nature required from the drone so great a sacrifice? It is a mystery which I will not attempt to penetrate. I do not know of any similar fact in the history of animals; but as there are two kinds of insects whose mating can only take place in the air, the ephemerides and the ants, it would be very interesting to learn whether their males also lose their sexual organs in those circumstances and whether, while making love upon the wing, like drones, the enjoyment of it is also for them a harbinger of death

Accept the assurance of my respect, etc.

Note from May 29th 1813

Note Well: **I have not observed the matings of ephemerides but Mr. Degers who has witnessed them, does not speak of the males as being mutilated. So remarkable a circumstance could not have escaped him.**

As to the ants, their drones lose so small a part of their sexual organs that they are able to fecundate several females in succession, and I have made sure of this through repeated observations.

3RD Letter—Queens Whose Fecundation Is Delayed

Pregny, August 21, 1791

Retarded impregnation affects the ovaries of the queen so that she lays only the eggs of males

Sir, I wrote you in my first letter that when the young queens were not permitted to mate until the twenty-fifth or thirtieth day after their birth, the result of this fecundation presented some very interesting peculiarities. I did not then give you the detail of these, because at the time when I had the honor of writing you my experiments upon this subject had not been sufficiently multiplied. I have repeated them so many times since, and their results have been so uniform, that I am not afraid of announcing to you, as a positive discovery, the singular effect that retarded fecundation produces upon the ovaries of the queen. When a queen is mated within the first fifteen days of her life, she becomes able to lay worker or drone eggs; but if her fecundation is delayed up to the twenty-second day, her ovaries become viciated so that she will be unable to lay worker eggs; she will lay only male eggs.

I was occupied with researches relative to the formation of swarms, when I had, for the first time, occasion to observe a queen that laid only drone eggs. It was June, 1787. I had found out that, when a colony is ready to swarm, the time of issue is always preceded by a very lively agitation, which first affects the queen, is then communicated to the workers, and excites among them so great a tumult that they abandon their labors and issue in disorder through all the entrances of the hive. I then knew well the cause of the queen's agitation (I will describe it in the history of swarms); but I was still ignorant how this delirium is communicated to the workers and this difficulty interrupted my work. To solve it, I thought of seeking, by direct experiments, whether when the queen was greatly agitated, even at other times than that of swarming, her agitation would be communicated similarly to the workers. I enclosed a queen in a hive, at the time of her birth, and prevented her issuing, by contracting the entrances in such a manner that they would be too narrow for her. I had no doubt that she would make great efforts to escape, whenever she would feel the imperious desire of joining the males, and that this impossibility might throw her into a kind of delirium. Burnens had the patience of observing this captive queen for thirty-five days. Every morning, towards 11 o'clock, when the sunshine invited the males to issue from the hives, he saw her traverse every corner of her habitation seeking an issue: but as she found none, her useless efforts threw her each time into an extraordinary agitation, the symptoms of which I shall describe elsewhere, and by which all the common bees were affected.

During the course of this long imprisonment, the queen did not go out a single time; she could not then be fecundated. On the thirty-sixth day, I at last set her at liberty; she quickly took advantage of it and soon returned with the most evident marks of fecundation. Satisfied with the success of this experiment for the particular object I had proposed, I was far from hoping that she would supply me also with the knowledge of a remarkable fact. How great was my surprise, when I found that this female, which began to lay, as usual, forty-six hours after mating, did not lay worker eggs, but only drone eggs, and that she continued, afterwards, to lay only this kind of eggs!

At first I exhausted myself in conjectures upon this singular fact; but the more I reflected on it, the more did it seem inexplicable. At last, by attentively meditating on the circumstances of this Experiment, it appeared to me that there were two points which I should try to weigh separately. On the one hand, this queen had suffered from long imprisonment; on the other hand, her fecundation had been extremely retarded. You know, sir, that the queen-bees usually have commerce with a male on the fifth or sixth day after their birth, and this one had not mated until the thirty-sixth day. I do not put great weight upon the supposition that this imprisonment had been the cause of this result. In natural conditions queen-bees fly out only to seek the males, a few days after birth: during the remainder of their life, excepting for the departure of swarms, they remain voluntary prisoners: it was therefore unlikely that captivity should have produced the result which I was trying to elucidate. However, as one must neglect nothing in so new a subject, I desired to ascertain whether it was the length of confinement or the retarded fecundation which brought about the singularity which I had observed in the laying of this queen.

But this was not an easy task. To discover whether captivity, and not retarded fecundation, had vitiated the ovaries of the queen, it would have been necessary to allow a queen to mate, while retaining her a prisoner; this could not be done since queen-bees never mate inside of the hive. For the same reason it was impossible to delay her mating without keeping her a prisoner. I was long embarrassed by this difficulty: at last I devised an apparatus which was not exactly what I wanted, but which filled the purpose fairly.

I took a queen at the end of her metamorphosis; I placed her within a well supplied hive, stocked with a sufficient number of workers and males. I contracted the entrance, so that it would be too narrow for the queen, but wide enough to give the workers free passage. At the same time, I made another opening for the passage of the queen and adapted to it a glass tube communicating with a large glass box measuring eight feet on each face. The queen could at all times come to this box, fly about and sport, breathing a better air than within the hive, in which nevertheless she could not be fecundated; for, although the males could also fly within this enclosure, the space was too limited for any mating between them. You know, Sir that the experiences which I have related to you show that the mating takes place only high in the air. I therefore found in this apparatus the advantage of retarding fecundation, while the queen had sufficient liberty that her condition of life was not too remote from the natural state. I followed this experiment for fifteen days. The captive female emerged from her hive every morning, when the weather was nice; she sported in her glass prison, and flew with ease and much motion. She did not lay during this time, for she had no connection with a male. At last on the sixteenth day, I set her at liberty: she flew from the hive, rose into the air and came back with all the signs of fecundation. Two days afterwards she began laying: her first eggs were worker eggs and from that time on, she laid as much as the most fertile queens.

It then follows:

First. That captivity does not alter the organs of the queen-bees.

Second. That when fecundation takes place within the first sixteen days after their birth, they lay eggs of both sorts.

This first experiment was important; it rendered my task more simple, by pointing out to me clearly the method to be pursued; it absolutely precluded the supposed influence of captivity and left nothing to seek but the effects of a longer delayed fecundation.

For this purpose, I repeated the previous experiment; but instead of giving her liberty to the virgin on the sixteenth day, I detained her until the twenty-first day; she flew then rose in the air, was fecundated and returned to her home. Forty-six hours afterwards, she began to lay, but it was male eggs, and although very prolific, she never laid any other kind. During the remainder of the year 1787, and two following years, I occupied myself with experiments on retarded fecundation and constantly had the same results. It is therefore true that, when the mating of queen-bees is delayed beyond the twentieth day, there is but a semi-fecundation, if one may thus call it: for instead of laying both worker eggs and male eggs, those queens lay male eggs only.

I do not aspire to the honor of explaining this strange fact. When the continuation of my observations on bees made known to me the fact that there are sometimes queens that lay only drone eggs, I sought for the proximate cause of this singularity, and ascertained that it was due to retarded fecundation. The proof that I acquired is demonstrative, for I can always prevent queens from laying worker eggs by delaying their fecundation until the twenty-second or twenty-third day. But what is the remote cause of this fact, or in other words, why does retarded fecundation prevent queens from laying worker eggs? It is a problem upon which analogy throws no light; in all the physiological history of animals I do not know of any observation bearing the least similarity to it.

This problem appears still more difficult, when we know how things happen in natural circumstances, that is, when fecundation has not been delayed. The queen then lays worker eggs 46 hours after mating and continues for the space of 11 months to lay almost only these. It is usually only at the end of these 11 months that she begins a considerable and uninterrupted laying of eggs of drones. Note: It appears that this period is not strict, and that the epoch of the great drone laying may be accelerated or delayed according to atmospheric circumstances more or less favorable to bees and to their crops. When on the contrary, fecundation is retarded beyond the 20th day, the queen begins to lay drone eggs from the 46th hour, in considerable numbers, and never lays any others during her entire life. Since she lays only worker eggs, during the first 11 months in a natural condition, it is clear that the worker eggs and drone eggs are not indiscriminately mixed in her oviducts: doubtless they occupy a situation corresponding to the laws that regulate her laying: those of workers are first, those of drones are behind them; it appears that the queen cannot lay drone eggs until she has discharged all the worker eggs that occupy first place in her oviducts. Why then is this order inverted by retarded impregnation? How does it happen that all the worker eggs that the queen should have laid, if fecundated in time, are withered and disappear, without obstructing the passage of the drone eggs, which occupy only second place in the ovaries?

One copulation impregnates all the eggs the queen will lay in two years

This is not all: I ascertained that a single mating is sufficient to fertilize all the eggs that a queen will lay in the course of two years at least: I have even reason to believe that this single act of fecundation is sufficient for the fertilization of all the eggs that she will lay during her life, but I have full evidence only for the two years. This fact, which is already very remarkable in itself, renders the influence of retarded fecundation still more difficult to conceive. Since a single mating is sufficient, it is clear that the masculine liquid acts from the first moment upon the eggs that the queen is to lay for two years.

According to your principles, Sir, it gives them that degree of animation which afterwards determines their successive development; after having received this first impulse of life, they grow, ripen, so to speak, progressively, until the day when they will be laid: and as the laws of laying are invariable, as the eggs laid during the first 11 months are always eggs of workers, it is clear that those eggs, which are to appear first, are also the first to mature; thus in the natural state, the space of 11 months is necessary for the male eggs to acquire the growth which they must have at the time they are laid. This consequence, which seems to me direct, renders the problem insoluble in my eyes. How can the male eggs which must grow slowly during 11 months, acquire at once their full development in the space of 48 hours, when fecundation has been retarded beyond 21 days, and by the effect of this delay alone? Observe, I beg you, that the supposition of the successive growing of eggs is not gratuitous: it is upon the principles of sound physics: besides, to be convinced that it is well founded, it is only necessary to glance at the figure given by Swammerdam of the ovaries of the queen: we see there that the eggs in that part of the oviduct contiguous to the vulva of the queen, are much farther advanced, larger than those contained in the part more remote of the same oviduct. The difficulty which I mention remains therefore in full force. It is an abyss wherein I am lost.

The only known fact which seems to have a semblance of connection with those just mentioned is the state in which some vegetable seeds are found, which although outwardly in good preservation, lose the faculty of germinating, through age; it might be, similarly, that the eggs of workers retain for only a short time the property of being fecundated by the seminal liquid, and that, after this period, which might be fifteen or eighteen days, they may be so disorganized as to be no longer susceptible of being animated by this liquid. I realize, sir that this comparison is very imperfect; and of making any new experiments; I will add but one reflection.

Up to this time, no effects had ever been observed of retarded fecundation upon the females of animals, excepting its rendering them absolutely sterile. The queen-bees offer us the first example of a female upon which this delay still leaves the faculty of engendering males. As no fact is unique in nature, it is very probable that we should find the same peculiarity in some other animals. So it would be a very curious object of research to observe insects under this new point of view. I say insects, for I do not conceive that anything similar would be found in other species of animals. It would even be necessary to begin these experiments upon the insects most analogous to bees, such as wasps, wooly bumblebees, mason bees, all kinds of flies etc. Some experiments might afterwards be made upon butterflies; finding perhaps some animal upon which retarded fecundation would produce the same effect as upon bees. If this animal were of a greater size than the bees, dissection would be easier, and we could discern what happens to the eggs, whose retarded fecundation prevents their development. At least we might hope that some fortunate circumstance would lead us to the solution of the problem. Note: The experiments which I suggest in this paragraph remind me of a singular reflection of Mr. de Réaumur. Speaking of viviparous flies, he says it might not be impossible for a hen to give life to a living chick, if after fecundation; the eggs that she might lay were retained for 20 days in her oviducts. (See Réaumur *sur les Insects, tome IV, Mémoire 10.*)

I now return to the recital of my experiments.

Drone laying queens continue to lay drones at least 9 months

In May 1789, I took two queens at the time when they were going through their last metamorphosis; I placed one of them in a leaf hive, well stocked with honey and wax, and sufficiently peopled with workers and males. The other was placed in a similar hive from which all the drones had been removed. I arranged the entrances of these hives for the freedom of the worker bees, but too narrow for the passage of females and drones. I kept those queens prisoners for 30 days. After that time, I liberated them. They departed eagerly and came back fecundated. In the beginning of July, I examined the two hives and found much brood: but this consisted entirely in worms and nymphs of males; there was not a single nymph, not a single worm, of a worker. Both queens laid without interruption until autumn, and uniformly eggs of drones. Their laying ended during the first fortnight of November, as did that of the queens of my other colonies. I was very desirous of ascertaining what would become of them in the ensuing spring; whether they would resume their laying, whether a new fecundation would be necessary, and, in case they should lay, of what sort their eggs would be; but as their hives were already much weakened I feared that they might perish during the winter. Fortunately, we succeeded in preserving them, and as early as April, they recommenced their laying: through the precautions we had taken we were sure that they had not received new approaches of the male; their eggs were still drone eggs.

It would have been very interesting to follow further the history of these females, but to my great regret, their workers abandoned them on the 4th of May, and on that same day we found both the queens dead. Yet there were no moth worms in the combs to cause any disturbance to the bees, and the honey was still fairly abundant, but, as in the course of the previous year no workers had been born, and as winter had destroyed many, they found themselves in too small numbers to engage in their ordinary labors, and in their discouragement they deserted their hives to join the neighboring hives.

I find, in my journal, the detail of a multitude of experiments on the retarded fecundation of queen bees: it would be an endless task to transcribe them all here: I repeat that there was not the least variation in the principal result and every time and whenever the matings of the queens was delayed beyond the 21st day, they laid none but male eggs. Therefore, sir, I will limit myself to expound to you those of my experiments which have taught me some remarkable facts not yet mentioned.

Cold weather can delay the start of laying

On the 4th of October 1789, a queen hatched in one of my hives: we placed her in a leaf hive. Although the season was well advanced there were still many males in the hives. It was important to learn whether, at this time of the year, they could equally effect fecundation, and in case of success whether the laying, begun in the middle of autumn, would be interrupted or continue during the winter. So we allowed this queen to leave the hive. She did, but made 24 fruitless trips before returning with the signs of fecundation. At last, on the 31st of October, she was more fortunate, she came back with most evident marks of success of her amours; she was then 27 days old, so that her fecundation had been much delayed. She should have begun laying 46 hours afterwards, but the weather was cold and she did not lay; which, let me say it in passing, proves that refrigeration of the temperature is the principal cause of the suspension of the queens' laying in autumn. I was very impatient to learn whether, on the return of spring, she would prove fertile, without the need of a new union. The means of ascertaining this was easy; for it only required contraction of the entrance of her hive, so that she might not escape. I confined her from the end of October until May. In the middle of March we examined her combs, and found many eggs, but as they were laid in cells of the small size, we had to wait a few days to pass judgment. On the 4th of April we again examined the hive and found a prodigious quantity of nymphs and worms. They were all of drones; the queen had not laid a single worker egg.

Here, as in former experiments, delayed fecundation had rendered the queen bee incapable of laying eggs of workers. This result is the more remarkable that the laying of the queen began four months and a half after fecundation. The term of 46 hours which usually elapses between mating and laying is therefore not a rigorous term; the interval may be much longer if the weather grows cold. Lastly, it follows from this experiment that; even when the cold retards the laying of a queen fecundated in autumn, she will begin to lay in the spring without the need of a new mating.

I may add that the queen whose history I have just given was of astonishing fecundity. On the first of May, we found in her hive, besides 600 males in full development, 2,438 cells, containing eggs larvae or nymphs of drones. Thus she had laid, during March and April, more than 3,000 male eggs, or about 50 per day. Unfortunately, she perished shortly afterwards and we were unable to continue our observations: I had intended to calculate the number of drone eggs that should would lay during that year, and compare it with eggs of the same sort that queens lay whose fecundation has not been retarded. You know sir, that the latter lay about 2,000 male eggs in the spring; and a second laying less considerable in August; in the intervals they lay almost exclusively worker eggs. It is otherwise with females whose mating has been delayed, for they produce no worker eggs; for 4, 5, or 6 months in succession they lay male eggs uninterruptedly, and in such great numbers that, in this short time, I presume that they give birth to more drones than a female whose fecundation has not been retarded would produce in the course of two years: I much regretted having been unable to verify this conjecture.

Drone laying queens are shaped differently

I should also, Sir, describe to you the remarkable manner in which the queens that lay only drone eggs deposit them sometimes in the cells. They do not always place them upon the lozenges forming the bottom of the cells, but often deposit them upon the lower side, two lines (11/64th in. or 4mm) from the mouth. The reason of this is that their belly is shorter than those of queens whose fecundation has not been retarded, their posterior extremity remains slender, while the first two rings next the corselet are extraordinarily enlarged: it results from this that, when they dispose themselves for laying, their anus cannot extend down to the lozenges at the bottom of the cells: the enlargement of the rings not permitting it; and consequently the eggs must remain attached to the part reached by the anus. The larvae proceeding from these spend their vermicular state in the same place, which proves that bees are not entrusted with the care of transporting the eggs of the queen, as had been presumed. But in this case they follow another plan; they lengthen the cells in which eggs are thus placed 2 lines beyond their opening. Note: This observation also teaches us that the eggs of bees need not be fixed by one end at the bottom of the cells in order to be fertile.

Bees Are Not Entrusted With Transporting Eggs

Permit me, Sir, to digress a moment from my subject, to narrate to you an Experiment, the result of which seems interesting. I said that the bees are not entrusted with the care of transporting eggs, misplaced by their queen, into convenient cells; and even judging by the sole fact which I mention here, you will think me well entitled to deny this feature of their industry. However, since several writers have affirmed the contrary and have even claimed our admiration of workers in conveying the eggs, I must prove to you clearly that they are mistaken.

I had a glass hive constructed of two stories: I filled the upper story with combs of large cells and the lower with combs of small cells. These two stories were separated from one another with a sort of division or diaphragm which left on each side a sufficient space for the passage of the workers from the one story to the other, but too narrow for the queen. I stocked this hive with a good number of bees, and confined in the upper story a very prolific female that had just lately finished her great laying of male eggs. Therefore, this female had only worker eggs to lay; she was compelled to deposit them in large cells, since there were none of the other sort about her. You will divine, sir the aim which I proposed in thus disposing matters. My reasoning was very simple. If the queen lays worker eggs in the large cells and if the workers are charged with transporting them when misplaced, they would not fail to take advantage of the liberty allowed them to pass from one story to the other; they would seek the eggs deposited in large cells and carry them to the lower story, containing the cells suitable for them. If, on the contrary, they left the worker eggs in the large cells, I should obtain certain proof that they are not entrusted with transporting them.

The result of this experiment excited my curiosity deeply. We watched the queen of this hive and her bees, for several days in succession, with sustained attention. During the first 24 hours, the queen obstinately refused to lay a single egg in the large cells which surrounded her; she examined them one after another, but passed on without insinuating her belly within any of them: she seemed restless, distressed; she traversed the combs in all directions; the weight of her eggs appeared to burden her, but she persisted in withholding them rather than deposit them in the cells of unsuitable diameter. Her bees, however, did not cease to pay her homage and treat her as a mother. I even saw, with pleasure, that when she approached the edges of the partition which separated the two stories, she gnawed them to try to enlarge the passage; the workers also labored with their teeth, and made efforts to enlarge the entrance to her prison, but ineffectually. On the second day, the queen could no longer retain her eggs, they escaped in spite of her; she dropped them at random. Yet we found 8 or 10 of them in cells, but they had disappeared the following day. We then conceived that the bees had transported them into the lower cells, we sought them with the greatest care; but I can assure you that there was not a single one there. On the 3rd day the queen again laid a few eggs, which disappeared as the first. We again sought them in the small cells but they were not there.

They Sometimes Eat the Eggs

The fact is that the workers eat them, and that is what deceived the former observers who claim that they transport them. They noted the disappearance of the misplaced eggs from the cells, and without further investigation asserted that the bees place them elsewhere; they take them indeed, but not to transfer them; they eat them.

Thus Nature has not entrusted the bees with the care of placing the eggs in appropriate cells; but she has given the females themselves enough instinct to know the nature of the egg which they are about to lay and to place it in a suitable cell. Mr. de Réaumur had already observed this, and in this my observations agree with his. It is therefore certain that, in the natural state, when fecundation had been timely and the queen has not suffered from any circumstance, she does not err in the choice of the different cells in which she is to deposit her eggs: she does not fail to lay those of workers in the small cells and those of males in the large cells.—I am speaking here, Sir, of what happens in natural conditions.—This distinction is important, for we do not find the same unerring instinct, in the behavior of females whose mating has been too long delayed; they make no selection of cells in which they are to lay. This fact is so true, that I often made mistakes on the kinds of eggs that they were laying; when I saw them lay indistinctively in both small and large cells, I thought that the eggs laid in the small cells were worker eggs: I was thus very much surprised at the time of their transformation into nymphs, to see them close up the cells with convex cappings, exactly similar to those that they place upon the cells of males: they were, in fact, males; those that were born in large cells became large drones.—I warn those who wish to repeat my experiments upon queens laying only male eggs, that they must expect to see those queens deposit drone eggs in worker cells.

Eggs Producing Males are Sometimes Laid in Royal Cells

Moreover, here is a curious observation: These same females, whose fecundation has been delayed, sometimes lay drone eggs in royal cells. When I give the history of swarms, I shall show, that, in a natural condition, when the queens begin their great laying of male eggs, the workers construct numerous royal cells: there is probably a secret relation between the production of those eggs and the formation of those royal cells: it is a law of nature from which the bees never derogate. It is not surprising, therefore, that cells of this sort or constructed in hives governed by queens laying drone eggs only. Neither is it singular that those queens should deposit in the royal cells the eggs of the only kind that they are able to lay, for in general their instinct seems altered. But what I cannot comprehend is that the bees take the same care of male eggs deposited in royal cells, as of the eggs that would become queens; they give them a more abundant food, they build up the cells as if containing a royal worm; they work upon them, in fact with such regularity that we have been frequently deceived, ourselves. More than once we opened one of these cells, after they had sealed them, in the persuasion of finding royal nymphs, but it was always a drone nymph that was lodged there. Here the instincts of the workers appear defective. In the natural state, they distinguish the worms of males from those of common bees, since they never fail to give a particular cover to the drone cells. Why then do they no longer distinguish the drone worms, when they are placed in royal cells? This fact deserved much attention. I am convinced that, in order to understand the laws of the instinct of animals we must carefully observe the cases where this instinct appears to err. (See 1st note of the 12th letter.)

Perhaps in beginning this letter, Sir, I should have given an abstract of the observations which other naturalists have made previously, on queens laying only male eggs; but I shall here repair that omission.—In a work entitled, *Histoire de la reine des abeilles*, translated from German by Blassière, there is printed a letter which Mr. Schirach wrote you in date of April 15, 1771, in which he speaks of several of his hives, the brood of which changed into drones. You remember sir, that he ascribed this accident to some unknown vice in the ovaries of the queen in these hives; but he was far from suspecting that retarded fecundation caused this vice of the ovaries. He justly felicitated himself on having discovered a method of preventing the dwindling of hives in this case; this was very simple, it consisted in removing the queen that laid male eggs only, and substituting another whose ovaries where not vitiated. But to make this substitution, it was necessary to procure queen-bees at will, and the discovery of this secret was Mr. Schirach's. I will speak of it in the following letter. You see by this detail that all the experiments of the German naturalist tended to preservation of the hives whose queens laid only male eggs and that he did not attempt to discover the cause of the vice in their ovaries.

Males Tolerated in Hives With Drone Laying Queens

Mr. de Réaumur also says a word, somewhere, concerning a hive in which he had found many more drones than workers, but he advances no conjecture upon this fact; he adds only, as a remarkable circumstance, that the males were tolerated in that until spring of the following year. It is true that bees governed by a queen laying only drone eggs, or by a virgin, preserve their drones several months after they have been massacred in the other hives. I cannot ascribe a reason for this, but it is a fact that I have witnessed many times during the long course of observations that I undertook upon queens with retarded impregnation. In general, it appeared that as long as a queen lays male eggs, her bees do not destroy the drones that live in the hive in the insect form.

Accept, sir, the acknowledgment of my respect etc.

Pregny, August 24, 1791

Larvae of Workers Converted to Queens

Sir, When you were induced, in the edition of your works, to give an account of Schirach's beautiful experiments on the conversion of common bees' worms into royal ones, you invited naturalists to repeat them. Indeed, I therefore hasten to inform you that all of my researches established its truth. During the 10 years that I have been studying bees, I repeated Schirach's experiment so many times, with such uniform success, that I cannot raise the least doubt. Therefore, I consider as a positive fact, that when bees lose their queen, and still have in their hive some worker's worms, they enlarge several of the cells in which they are located, feed them, not only with a different kind of food, but in greater amount, and that the worms reared in this manner, instead of changing to common bees, become real queens. I beg my readers to think over the explanation which you have given of so new a fact, and the philosophical consequences, that you deduced from it. *Contemplation de la Nature,* par. XI, chap. XVII.

I will limit myself, in this letter, with giving you some details upon the shape of the royal cells which the bees build around the worms destined for the royal state. I will terminate by discussing a few points upon which my observations differ from those of Mr. Schirach.

Operations of the Bees After Loss of Queen

When bees lose their queen, they perceive it very quickly and in a few hours undertake the necessary work to repair their loss.

They first select the young worker worms, which are to receive the proper care to convert them into queens, and at once begin to enlarge the cells in which they are lodged. Their mode of proceeding is curious. In order to make it most intelligible, I will describe their work upon a single cell, which will apply to all those that contain worms intended for queens. After having selected a worker worm, they sacrifice three of the contiguous cells; taking away the worms and the pap and build around this one a cylindrical enclosure; its cell thus becomes a perfect tube, with rhomboidal base, for they do not tamper with the pieces of this base; if they damaged it they would uncover the three corresponding cells on the opposite side of the comb, and therefore would sacrifice the worms that inhabit them, which is unnecessary and which Nature has not permitted. They therefore leave the rhomboidal base and are content with raising a cylindrical tube around the worm, which is thus placed horizontally, like the other cells of the comb. But this habitation is adapted to the intended royal worm for only the three first days of its existence; it requires a different situation for the days, which constitute so small a portion of the duration of its existence, it must live in a cell of nearly pyramidal form, the base of which is at the top and the point at the bottom. It seems that the workers are aware of this, for after the worm has completed its third day, they prepare the place to be occupied by its new lodging, gnawing away some of the cells located below the cylindrical tube, they mercilessly sacrifice the worms that are in them, and use the wax which they have just gnawed away to construct a new pyramidal tube which they solder at right angles to the first, working it downwards. The diameter of this pyramid decreases insensibly from its base, which is wide, down to the point. During the two days that the worm inhabits it, there is constantly a bee with her head more or less inserted in the cell: when a worker leaves another takes her place. They lengthen the cell as fast as the worm grows; they bring food, which they place before its mouth and around its body in a sort of band around it. The worm, which can only move in a spiral direction, turns incessantly to take the food before its head; it insensibly descends and at length arrives near the mouth of the cell: it is at this time that it must transform into a nymph. The care of the bees is no longer necessary: they close its cradle with an appropriate substance, and in proper time it undergoes its two metamorphoses.

Schirach's Method Equally Successful With Worms From a Few Hours to Three Days Old

Schirach holds that bees never select other than *3 day old worms*, to give them the "royal education": I have ascertained on the contrary, that this operation succeeds as well on worms aged only *2 days*. Permit me to relate at full length the evidence which I have acquired of this: it will demonstrate, at the same time, both the reality of the conversion of worker worms into queens, and the little influence which their age has upon the success of the operation.

In a hive deprived of its queen, I caused to be placed some pieces of combs containing worker eggs and already hatched worms of the same kind. The same day, the bees enlarged several of the worm cells, and changed them to royal cells, giving to the worms in them a thick bed of jelly. We then removed 5 of the worms placed in those cells, and Burnens substituted for them 5 worker worms which we had witnessed hatching from the egg 48 hours previously. Our bees did not appear aware of this exchange: they fed the new worms as well as those selected by themselves; they continued enlarging the cells in which they were placed, and closed them at the usual time; they then incubated these 5 cells during 7 days at the end of which time we took them away to preserve alive the queens which would be produced from them. Two of these queens emerged almost at the same moment; they were of large size and well formed in every respect. The three other cells having passed the term without any queen emerging, we opened them to ascertain their condition; we found a dead queen in nymph state in one of them, the other two were empty, the worms in them had spun their silk cocoons but had died before getting to the nymph state, and showed only a dried up skin. I can conceive nothing more conclusive than this experiment: it demonstrates that bees have the power of converting the worms of workers into queens, since they suc-ceeded in procuring them by operating on worms of workers which we ourselves had selected: it is equally demonstrated that, for the success of the process, it is not necessary that the worms be three days old, since those which we entrusted to the bees were only two days old.

Nor is this all: bees can convert into queens, worms still younger. The following experiment taught me that, when they have lost their queen, they destine worms only a few hours old to replace her. A hive in my possession, deprived of female, had not had any eggs or worms for a long time: I gave them a queen of the greatest fecundity; she soon began to lay in the worker cells; I kept her in the hive a little less than 3 days, and removed her before any of her eggs were hatched: the following day, that is the fourth day, Burnens counted 50 small workers, the oldest of which were hardly 24 hours old. However, several of them were already destined for queens, which was proved by the bees depositing around them a much greater provision of jelly than is supplied to common worms. The following day, the worms being nearly 40 hours old, the bees had enlarged their cradles; they had converted their hexagonal cells into cylindrical cells of the greatest capacity; they still labored at them the following days and closed them off on the fifth day from the hatching of the worms. Seven days after the sealing of the first of these royal cells, we saw a queen of the largest size emerge from it. This queen rushed towards the other royal cells and endeavored to destroy the nymphs or worms that were in them. I shall narrate the effects of her fury, in another letter.

You see Sir, from these details, that Mr. Schirach had not yet sufficiently varied his experiments, when he asserted that, in order to become converted into queens, the worms of the workers should be 3 days old. It is undoubted that the operation is equally successful, not only with worms 2 days old, but even with those that are only a few hours old.

Twofold Means of Making Queens

After having made the researches which I have just described, to verify Mr. Schirach's discovery, I desired to ascertain whether, as this observer claims, the only means which the bees have of procuring a queen is to give the common worms a certain kind of food and rear them in larger cells. You have not forgotten that Mr. de Réaumur had very different ideas upon this:

> "The mother must lay and does lay eggs from which bees fit to be mothers must in their turn proceed. She does so and we will show that workers know what she is to do. The bees, to which mothers are so precious, seem to take a great interest in the

eggs which are to supply them, and consider them as very important: They construct particular cells in which they are to be
deposited, etc. When a royal cell is only just begun, it has the
shape of a cup, or more precisely of an acorn cup, from which the
acorn had dropped. etc., etc."

Mr. de Réaumur did not suspect the possibility of the
conversion of a common worm into a queen, but he conceived
that the mother bee laid a particular species of eggs in the
royal cells, from which came worms that should be queens in
their turn. On the contrary, according to Mr. Schirach, bees
always having the possibility of procuring a queen by rearing
worker worms 3 days old in a particular manner, it would be
unnecessary for females to have the faculty of laying royal
eggs; such prodigality of means did not appear to him consistent with Nature's laws: therefore he asserts in proper
terms that the mother bee does not lay royal eggs in cells
prepared to that end: he considers the royal cells only as
common ones, enlarged by the bees at the moment when the
included form is destined to become a queen; and he adds that
in any case, the royal cell would be too deep for the belly of the
mother to reach its bottom to deposit an egg.

I admit that Mr. de Réaumur does not say anywhere that
he had seen the queen lay in the royal cell; however he had no
doubt of this, and after all my observations I see that he had
guessed correctly. It is quite certain that, at certain times of
the year, the bees prepare royal cells, that the queens lay in
them, and that from these eggs worms hatch which become
queens.

Mr. Schirach's objection concerning the length of the royal cells proves nothing: the queen does not wait until they are
finished, to lay in them; she deposits her eggs in them when
they are only sketched and have the shape of an acorn cup.
This naturalist, dazzled by the brilliancy of his discovery, did not
see the whole truth; he was the first to perceive the resource
which Nature granted to the bees, for repairing the loss of their
queen, and too soon persuaded himself that she had provided
no other means for the birth of females. His error arose in not
observing the bees in sufficiently narrow hives. Had had used

hives such as mine he would have found a confirmation of the opinion of Mr. de Réaumur, in every one that he opened in the spring. In that season, which is the season of swarms, hives in good condition are governed by a prolific queen. One finds in such hives royal cells of a different shape from those which the bees build around worker eggs, which they destine to become queens. They are large cells, attached to the comb by a pedicle, and hanging vertically like stalactites; such, in a word, as Mr. de Réaumur described. The females do not wait, to lay in them, until they are at full size; we have surprised several depositing the egg, when the cell was only as an acorn cup; the workers never lengthen them until the egg has been laid in them; they enlarge them as fast as the worm grows, and close them when it is about to transform into a royal nymph. It is then true that, in spring, the queen deposits, in the royal cells previously prepared, eggs from which insects of her own sort will hatch. Nature has thus provided a twofold means for the multiplication and conservation of the species of bees.

I have the honor, etc.

5ᵀᴴ Letter—Worker Bees Laying Fertile Eggs

Experiments Proving That There Are Sometimes in the Hives, Worker Bees Which Lay Fertile Eggs.

Pregny, August 25, 1791

Sir, The singular discovery of Mr. Riem, concerning the existence of fertile workers appeared very doubtful to you. Note: See Contemplations de la Nature New edition, in-4. Part XI, page 265.

You have suspected that the eggs, ascribed to workers by this naturalist, were really laid by small queens, which had been mistaken for workers on account of their small size. However you did not state decisively that Mr. Riem was mistaken; and in the letter which you did me the honor of addressing to me, you invited me to seek, through new experiments, whether there are truly in the hives worker bees capable of laying fertile eggs. I have made those experiments, Sir, with great care; you will judge of the degree of confidence which they merit.

On the 5ᵗʰ of August 1788, we found eggs and worms of drones in two of my hives, which had both been deprived of queens for some time. We saw there also the first rudiments of several royal cells, appended like stalactites at the edges of the combs. In those cells were some male eggs. As I was perfectly certain that there was no queen of the large size among the bees of these two hives, it was evident that the eggs that were there, the number of which increased every day, had been laid, either by queens of the small size, or by fertile workers. I had reason to believe that it was actually common bees that laid them; for we often observed bees of the latter kind introducing the posterior part of their body into the cells, assuming the same attitude as the queen when she is about to lay. But notwithstanding all our efforts, we had never been able to seize one in this position to examine her more closely; and we did not wish to assert anything until we had been able to hold in our fingers one of the bees that had been laying. We therefore continued our observations with the same assiduity, hoping that, by some fortunate hazard or in a moment of dexterity, we could secure one of those bees. For more than a month, all our endeavors failed.

Burnens then proposed to me to make upon those two hives an operation which requires so much courage and patience that I had not dared mention it to him, although the same plan had occurred to me. He proposed to examine, separately, all the bees in these hives, to discover whether some small queen had not insinuated herself among them, which had escaped our first researches. This experiment was very important, for if we did not find any small queens, we would acquire the demonstrative evidence that the eggs whose origin we were seeking had been laid by simple workers.

To accomplish with all possible exactness an operation of this nature, immersing the bees was not sufficient. You know, Sir, that the contact of water stiffens their exterior parts, that it alters to a certain point the shape of their organs; and as the small queens much resemble the workers, the slightest alteration in their shape would not have permitted us to distinguish with sufficient precision, to which species those that were immersed belonged. Therefore, it was necessary, to take each bee, one at a time, in the hives, alive, in spite of their anger, and observe their specific character with the greatest care. This is what Burnens undertook and executed with inconceivable dexterity. He spent 11 days in this operation, and during the entire time scarcely allowed himself any other relaxation than that required for relief of his eyes. He took in his hands every one of the bees that composed these two hives, examined carefully their proboscis, their posterior legs, their sting; he found none that did not possess the characters of the common bee; that is to say, the little basket on the posterior legs, the long tongue and the straight sting.   Having previously prepared glass cases containing combs, he placed each bee into one of them after having examined her: needless to say that he kept them confined; this precaution was indispensable, for the experiment was not yet ended; it was not sufficient to make sure that they were worker bees, it was also necessary to see whether any of them would lay eggs. So we inspected, for several days, the combs which we had given them, and shortly noticed newly laid eggs from which drone worms hatched in due time.

Burnens had held between his fingers the bees that produced them, and as he was positive that he had handled only common bees, it was demonstrated that there are, sometimes in the hives fertile workers.

After having verified Mr. Riem's discovery by so decisive an Experiment, we replaced all the bees that we had examined, into very thin glass hives; these hives which were only an inch-and-a-half thick could contain but a single row of combs; they were thus very favorable for observations. We no longer doubted that, by persisting in watching our bees, we should surprise one of the fertile ones in the act of laying, and seize her. We desired to dissect her, compare the state of her ovaries with those of queens, and take note of the difference. At length, on the 8th of September, we had the good fortune to succeed.

A bee was noticed in a cell in the position of a laying female; we did not give her time to leave the cell; we promptly opened the hive and seized that bee; she had all the external characteristics of common bees; the only difference we could recognize, and a very slight one, was that her belly was smaller and more slender than those of the other workers. We dissected her and found her ovaries smaller, more fragile, composed of less number of oviducts than the ovaries of queens; the filaments which contained the eggs were exceedingly fine and exhibited slight swellings at equal distances. We counted 11 eggs of sensible size, some of which appeared ready to be laid. This ovary was double, like that of a queen.

On the 9th of September, we seized another fertile worker, the instant she laid, and dissected her. Her ovary was still less developed than that of the preceding one, we counted only 4 eggs that had reached maturity. Burnens extracted one of these eggs from the oviduct which held it, and succeeded in fixing it by an end on a strip of glass: we may say in passing that this indicates that it is in the oviducts themselves that the eggs are coated with the viscous liquid with which they come to light and not in their passage under the spherical sac, as Swammerdam believed.

During the remainder of this month, we found still in the same hives 10 fertile workers, which we also dissected. We distinguished easily the ovaries in most of those bees; in a few, however, we found no trace of them; the oviducts of the latter were apparently but imperfectly developed, and more skill than we had yet acquired in dissecting was necessary for their discovery.

Fertile workers never lay eggs of common bees; they lay only drone eggs. Mr. Riem had already observed this singular fact, and in this regard, all my observations confirm his own. I shall only add to what he says that fertile workers are not absolutely indifferent in the choice of the cells for depositing their eggs. They always prefer to lay them in the large ones, and lay in small cells only when they do not find any of the larger diameter; but they have this in common with queens whose fecundation has been retarded that they also lay eggs in royal cells.

When speaking, in my third letter, of those females that lay only drone eggs, I recorded my surprise that bees bestow such care upon those deposited in royal cells, the assiduity with which they feed the worms which hatch from them, and the sealing under which they enclose them when nearing the term of their growth; but I do not know, Sir, why I forgot to tell you that, after having sealed those cells, the workers braid (guilloche) them and incubate them until after the last transformation of the males which they contain. Their treatment of the royal cells in which fertile workers have laid eggs of drones, is very different; they begin, indeed, by bestowing every care upon the eggs and the worms that inhabit them; they close the cells in suitable time; but they never fail to destroy them 3 days after having sealed them.

After having successfully finished these experiments, I had still to discover the cause of the development of the sexual organs of fertile workers. Mr. Riem did not engage in this interesting problem, and at first I feared that I might have no other guide to its solution than my conjectures. However, after long reflection, I perceived, in the connection of the facts of which this letter gives the details, a light to indicate the progress to be followed in this new research.

All Common Bees are Originally Females
Since the beautiful discoveries of Mr. Schirach, it is beyond all doubt that the common bees are originally of the female sex; Nature has given them the germs of ovaries; but she has permitted their expansion only in the particular case where those bees receive, in their worm form, a special food. So we must examine, especially, whether our fertile workers have received this special food, in the worm state.

All my experiments convinced me that bees capable of laying are born only in hives that have lost their queen. In such case, they prepare a large quantity of royal jelly, to feed the worms destined to replace her. Therefore, if fertile workers are born only in these circumstances, it is evident that they appear only in the hives whose bees prepare royal jelly. It was upon this circumstance, Sir, that I bent all my attention. It induced me to suspect that when bees give the royal treatment to certain worms, they, by accident or by a particular instinct the principle of which I do not know, drop some small particles of royal jelly into the cells next to those containing the worms intended for queens. The worms of workers that have accidentally received small doses of so active an aliment, must be more or less influenced by it: their ovaries must acquire some sort of development; but this development will be imperfect. Why? Because the royal food has been administered only in small doses, and besides, the worms in question, having lived in cells of the smaller diameter, their parts could not enlarge beyond ordinary proportions. The bees born from those worms will therefore have the size and all exterior characters of simple workers; but they will have in addition the faculty of laying a few eggs, solely from the effect of the small portion of jelly mixed with their other food.

In order to judge of the correctness of this explanation, it was necessary to follow the fertile workers from their birth, to investigate whether the cells in which they are raised are constantly in the vicinity of the royal cells, and whether the pap fed to them is mixed with particles of the royal jelly. Unfortunately this part of the experiment is very difficult to perform. When pure the royal jelly is recognized by its tarish and pungent taste, but when mixed with some other substance, its savor is imperfectly distinguished. I therefore confined myself to the examination of the location of the cells in which fertile workers are born. As this is important, allow me to describe one of my experiments in detail.

In June 1790, I observed that the bees in one of my thinnest hives had lost their queen for several days, and that they had no means of replacing her, since they had no worker's worms. I gave them a small piece of comb every cell of which contained a worm of this sort. As early as the following day, the bees lengthened several of those cells, to the shape of royal cells, around the worms which they intended for queens. They also bestowed some care upon the worms in the adjoining cells. Four days afterwards, all the royal cells were sealed, and with much gratification we counted 19 small cells which had also been perfected and were sealed with a flat capping. In these were the worms which had not received the royal treatment; but as they had grown in the vicinity of the worms destined for replacing the queen, it was very interesting for me to observe what would become of them. It was necessary to watch the moment of their last transformation. In order not to miss it, I removed those 19 cells and placed them into a grated box which was introduced among the bees; I also removed the royal cells; for it was very important that the queens that were to come should not disturb or complicate the results of my experiment. Another precaution was here required: it was to be feared that the bees, being deprived of the fruit of their labor, and the object of their hope, should become discouraged; therefore I supplied them with another piece of comb containing worker brood, expecting to remove this new brood without mercy, when the time came. This plan succeeded marvelously;

the bees, while bestowing their care upon these latter worms, forgot those which I had removed.

When the time arrived of the last transformation of my 19 cells, I caused the grated box in which they were enclosed to be examined each day, several times, and at length found six bees exactly similar to common bees. The worms in the remaining 13 cells perished without metamorphosis.

I removed from my hive the last piece of brood which had been placed there to prevent the discouragement of the workers; I put aside the queens born from the royal cells, and after having painted the thorax of my six bees red, after having amputated their right antenna, I placed them all 6 in the hive, where they were well received.

You readily conceive my object, Sir, in this course of operations. I know that there was no queen of either large or small size among my bees: if, then in the continuation of the observation, I should find newly laid eggs in the combs, how very likely that they had been laid by one or the other of my 6 bees. But to attain absolute certainty, it was necessary to take them in the act of laying, and some ineffaceable mark was required to distinguish them.

This arrangement was fully successful. Indeed we soon perceived eggs in the hive; their number increased daily; the worms that hatched from them were all of the drones sort; but a long interval elapsed before we could catch the bees that laid them. At length, by dint of assiduity and perseverance, we perceived one introducing her posterior part into a cell; we opened the hive and caught this bee; we saw the egg that she had deposited; and in examining her we recognized readily, by the remnant of red upon her thorax and the privation of the right antenna, that she was one of the 5 reared under the vermicular state in the vicinity of the royal cells.

I no longer doubted the correctness of my conjecture; I do not know, however, Sir, whether this demonstration will appear as rigorous to you as it does to myself; but here is my reasoning: If it is certain that the fertile workers are always born in the vicinity of royal cells, it is no less certain that this vicinity is, in itself, an indifferent circumstance; for the size and shape of those cells can have no effect upon the worms in the surrounding cells; there must be something more to this: We know that the bees bring to the royal cells a particular food; we also know that the influence of this pap is very powerful upon the ovaries; that it alone can develop this germ; we must necessarily suppose that the worms placed in the adjacent cells have had a portion of this food. This is what they gain by vicinity to the royal cells; the numerous bees going to the latter pass over them, stop and drop some portion of jelly destined for the royal worms. I believe that this reasoning is consistent with the principles of sound logic.

Receiving the Royal Food While Larvae Expands Their Ovaries

I so often repeated the experiment just described, and I have weighed all the circumstances with so much care, that I succeed in producing fertile workers in my hives, whenever I please. The method is simple. I remove the queen from a hive; the bees undertake to replace her at once, by enlarging several cells, containing the brood of workers, and giving royal jelly to the worms in them; they also let fall small doses of this pap upon the worms located in adjacent cells, and this food causes a certain development in their ovaries. Fertile workers are always produced in hives where the bees labor to replace their queen; but it is very rare to find them, because they are attacked and destroyed by the young queens reared in the royal cells. In order to save them, we must remove their enemies; we must take away the royal cells before the worms located in them have undergone their last transformation. Then the fertile workers, finding no rivals in the hive at the time of their birth, will be well received there, and if we take the trouble to mark them with some distinctive sign, we will see them, a few days afterwards, laying male eggs. Thus, the whole secret of the process consists in removing the royal cells at the proper time; that is as soon as they are sealed and before the young queens have left them. Note: I have often seen queen-bees, at the moment of their birth, begin by attacking the royal cells and afterwards the common cells adjoining. When I first observed this fact, I had not yet observed fertile workers, and I could not understand the motive of the fury of the queens against these common cells; but now I conceive that they distinguish the sort of bees enclosed in them, and that they must have against them the same instinct of jealousy, or the same feeling of aversion, as against the nymphs of queens proper.

I shall add but a word to this long letter. There is nothing very surprising in the birth of fertile workers, when one has mediated upon the consequences of Schirach's beautiful discovery. But why do these bees lay eggs of males only? I conceive that they lay a small number because their ovaries have had but an imperfect development; but I cannot distinguish why all their eggs are of the male sort. I do not understand any better of what use they are in the hives; and I have not hitherto made any experiments on the mode of their fecundation.

Accept, Sir, the assurance of my respect, etc.

6ᵀᴴ Letter—On the Combats of Queens, Massacre of Males, etc

...and on what Happens in a Hive When a Strange Queen Is Substituted for the Natural One.

Pregny, August 28, 1791

Sir, Mr. de Réaumur had not witnessed everything relative to these industrious insects, when he composed his history of bees. Several observers, and particularly those of Lusatia discovered a number of important facts that had escaped him; and I, in my turn, made diverse observations which he did not foresee; however, and it is a very remarkable thing, not only all that he expressly declares he saw has been verified by succeeding naturalists, but even all his conjectures have been found just; the German observers, Messrs. Schirach, Hattorf, Riem, sometimes contradict him in their memoirs; but I can assure you that, when they combat the experiments of Mr. de Réaumur, it is they are almost always mistaken; of which I can cite several examples. The one which I will mention today will give me the occasion of detailing some interesting facts.

Mr. de Réaumur observed that when a supernumerary queen is either born or supplied to a hive, one of the two soon perishes: he had not actually witnessed the combat in which she falls, but he conjectured that there is a mutual attack and that the empire remains to the stronger or the more fortunate. On the other hand, Schirach, and after him Riem, hold that the worker bees assail the stranger queens and kill them with their stings. I do not comprehend by what hazard they were able to make this observation; for, as they could at most only perceive the commencement of hostilities: bees move fast when they fight; they run in every direction, glide between the combs thus concealing their movements from the observer. For my part, Sir, though using the most favorable hives, I have never seen any combat between the queens and the workers; but often between the queens themselves.

Mutual Enmity of Queens

I had one hive in particular containing at the same time 5 or 6 royal cells, each inclosing a nymph; the oldest of them first accomplished her transformation. Scarcely ten minutes from the time of her leaving her cradle, she visited the other closed royal cells; she threw herself with fury upon the first: by dint of labor she succeeded in opening the tip, we saw her tearing the silk of the cocoon with her teeth; but probably her efforts did not succeed to her satisfaction, for she abandoned this end of the royal cell and began at the other extremity, in which she manage to make a larger aperture; when it was large enough she turned to introduce her belly into it; she made several motions until she succeeded in striking her rival with a deadly sting. Then she quitted the cell, and the bees which had been spectators of her labor, enlarged the breach that she had made and drew out the body of a dead queen scarcely out of its envelope of a nymph.

Meanwhile, the victorious attacked another royal cell and made in it also a large opening, but she did attempt to introduce her extremity into it; this second cell did not contain an already developed queen, ready to emerge from her shell; it contained but a royal nymph: it is therefore apparent that, under this shape, the nymphs of queens inspire their rivals with less furor; but they do not escape death any better, for whenever a royal cell has been opened before its time, the bees extract its contents, under whatever form, worm, nymph or queen; so after the victorious queen left this second cell, the workers enlarged the opening which she had effected and extracted the enclosed nymph; lastly the young queen attacked a third cell but did not succeed in opening it: she labored languidly appearing fatigued by her first efforts. At that time we needed queens for some particular Experiment, so we resolved to carry away the other royal cells which had not yet been attacked, to shelter them from her anger.

We next wished to see what would happen if two queens emerged from their cells at the same time and in what manner one of them would perish. We made upon this subject an observation which I find in my journal in date of May 15, 1790.

Queens Instincts Prevent Simultaneous Death

Two queens emerged from their cells, on that day, almost at the same moment, in one of our thin hives. As soon as they perceived each other they rushed upon one another, with the appearance of great anger, and placed themselves in such position that the antennae of each were caught in the teeth of their rival; their heads, corselets and bellies were opposed to each other, they had but to bend the posterior extremity of their bodies to pierce one another with their stings and both die in the combat. But it appears that Nature has not ordained that both combatants perish in the duel, but rather that when they find themselves in the position just described (that is belly to belly), they recede at once with the greatest precipitation. Thus, when the two rivals felt that their posterior parts were about to meet, they disengaged themselves and each ran away. You will observe, Sir, that I repeated this observation very often; it leaves no doubt, and it appears that in such a case, one may penetrate the intention of Nature.

There must be but one queen in a hive; therefore it is necessary, if by chance a second one is born or appears, that one of the two should be put to death. This could not be permitted to the workers because, in a republic composed of so many individuals, a simultaneous consent cannot be supposed to exist, it would frequently happen that a group of bees would pounce upon one of the females, while a second group would massacre the other, and the hive would be deprived of a queen. Therefore it is necessary that the queens themselves be entrusted with the destruction of their rivals. But as, in these combats, Nature demands only one victim, she has wisely provided that, at the moment when, from their position, both combatants might lose their lives, both should be so greatly alarmed, that they think only of flight, without using their stings.

I know that we run the risk of erring, when minutely seeking the final causes of the most trifling facts but in this, the aim and means appeared so clear that I have ventured to advance this conjecture. You will judge better than I, Sir, whether it is well founded; let me return to my digression.

A few minutes after our two queens separated, their fear ceased, and they again sought each other; soon they noticed one another and we saw them rush together: they again seized each other as before and placed themselves in the same position: the result was the same; as soon as their bellies met, they disengaged themselves and fled. During all this time the workers were much agitated and the tumult appeared to increase when the adversaries separated; at two different times, we saw them stop the queens in their flight, seize their legs and hold them prisoners for more than a minute. Lastly, in a third attack, the more rabid or stronger of the queens darted upon her rival when the latter did not see her; she seized her with her teeth at the base of the wing; then rose above her and brought the extremity of her belly upon the last rings of her enemy, which she readily pierced with her sting; quitting hold of the wing which she held, she withdrew her sting; the vanquished queen fell, dragged herself languidly, quickly lost her strength and soon expired. This observation proves that virgin queens engage in single combats. We next wished to discover whether fertile queens or mothers entertained against each other the same animosity.

The Common Bees Seem to Promote Their Combats

On the 22nd of July, we selected for this observation, a thin hive whose queen was very fertile, and as we were curious to learn whether she would destroy the royal cells, as virgin queens do, we placed 3 of these closed cells in the center of her comb. As soon as she perceived them, she rushed upon the group which they formed, pierced them at the base, and did not leave them until the nymphs in them were exposed. The workers which hitherto, had been spectators of this destruction, now came to remove the nymphs, they avidly took the pap which remained at the bottom of the cells, and sucked also the fluid from the abdomen of the nymphs, and finally destroyed the cells from which they had been drawn.

We next introduced into this hive a very prolific queen, whose corselet we had painted to distinguish her from the reigning queen: a circle of bees quickly formed around this stranger, but their intention was not to welcome or caress her, for the insensibly so accumulated around her and surrounded her so closely, that in a minute she lost her liberty and found herself a prisoner. It is a remarkable circumstance here, that at the same time, other workers collected around the reigning queen and restrained all her motions: we saw the instant when she was about to be confined like the stranger. It would seem that the bees foresaw the combat in which the two queens were about to engage, and they were impatient to behold the issue of it; for they retained them prisoners only when they appeared to withdraw from each other, and if one of the two, less restrained in her motions seemed desirous of approaching her rival, all the bees forming those clusters gave way to allow them full liberty for the attack; but returned and enclosed them again if the queens appeared disposed to run.

We have very often witnessed this fact: but it presents so new and extraordinary a trait in the policy of bees, that it must be seen again a thousand times to dare assert it positively. I would recommend, Sir, that the naturalists attentively watch the combats of queens and particularly the role played by the workers. Do they seek to accelerate the combat? Do they excite the fury of the combatants by some secret means? How is it that although accustomed to bestow care upon their own queen, there are circumstances in which they stop her when she prepares to avoid an impending danger?

A long series of observations would be necessary to solve these problems. It is a vast field for experiments, the result of which would be infinitely curious. Pardon my frequent digressions; this subject is deeply philosophical but your genius would be required, Sir, to handle and present it: I will proceed with the description of the combat of our queens.

The cluster of bees that surrounded the reigning queen having permitted her to move slightly, she appeared to advance towards that part of the comb where her rival stood; all the bees then receded before her; gradually the multitude of workers that separated the two adversaries dispersed; until only two remained, who also departed and allowed the two queens to see one another: at that instant the reigning queen rushed upon the stranger, seized her with her teeth at the base

of the wings, and succeeded in fixing her against the comb
without any possibility of resistance or motion; next she curved
her belly and pierced with a deadly stroke this unhappy victim
of our curiosity.

Lastly, to exhaust every combination, we still had to discover whether there would be a combat between two queens
one of which would be fertile and the other virgin, and what
would be the circumstances and the issue.

We had a glass hive, whose queen was a virgin 24 days
old; we introduced into it a very prolific queen, putting her on
the opposite side of the comb, that we might have time to see
how the workers would receive her: she was soon surrounded
with bees who confined her. However she was confined but a
moment; as she was pressed with the necessity of laying, she
dropped her eggs and we could not see what became of them;
the bees certainly did not place them in cells, for on inspection
we found none. The group surrounding this queen having
dispersed a little, she advanced towards the edge of the comb
and soon found herself very near the virgin queen. At first
sight, they rushed on one another; the virgin queen got on the
back of her rival, and gave her several stings in the belly, which
struck only the scaly part and did her no harm; and the combatants parted: a few minutes after they returned to the
charge; this time the fecundated queen mounted on the back
of her rival, but she vainly sought to pierce her, the sting did
not enter the flesh; the virgin queen disengaged herself and
fled; she succeeded yet to escape from another attack, in
which the fertile queen had the advantage of position. These
two rivals appeared of equal strength, and it was difficult to
foresee to which side victory would incline, until at last, by
successful hazard, the virgin mortally wounded the stranger,
and she expired at that moment.

The stroke had penetrated so deeply that she was at first
unable to withdraw her sting and was drawn down by the fall of
her enemy. We saw her make many efforts to disengage her
spear: she succeeded only by turning on the extremity of her
belly as on a pivot. It is probably that the barbs of the sting

were bent by this motion, and lying spirally around the stem, thus came out of the wound that they had made.

I believe, Sir, that these observations will no longer leave you any doubts upon the conjecture of our celebrated Réaumur. It is certain that if several queens are introduced into a hive, one alone will preserve the empire, the others will perish from her attacks, but the workers will at no time attempt to use their stings against the foreign queen. I conceive what has misled Messrs. Schirach and Riem; but to explain it, I must relate at considerable length a new trait in the policy of bees.

In the natural state of hives, several queens may be found, born in royal cells constructed by the bees; they will remain there until a swarm has formed, or until a combat between those queens decides to which the throne shall appertain; but excepting this case, there never can be supernumerary queens, and if an observer wishes to introduce one, he can accomplish it only by force, that is by opening the hive. In a word, in the natural state, a foreign queen can never insinuate herself there, for the following reasons.

A Guard is Constantly at the Entrance of the Hive

Bees place and preserve a sufficient guard, night and day, at the entrance of their habitation: those vigilant sentinels examine all that present themselves, and as if distrusting their eyes, they touch, with their flexible antennae, every individual endeavoring to penetrate the hive, and the various substances put within their reach, which, to be said in passing, leaves but little doubt of the antennae being the organ of feeling. If a stranger queen appears, the guards seize her on the instant; to prevent her from entering, they lay hold of her legs or her wings with their teeth, and crowd so closely around her that she cannot move; gradually other bees come from the interior of the hive and join this cluster, making it still more compact; all their heads are turned towards the center where the queen is enclosed, and they cling with so much eagerness, that the ball formed by them may be taken up and carried about a few moments without their perceiving it; it is utterly impossible that a foreign queen, so closely enveloped and confined, be able to penetrate in the hive. If the bees retain her too long imprisoned, she perishes, her death probably caused by hunger, or deprivation of air: it is very certain at least that she is not stung: in only one single instance did we see the stings of bees turned towards a queen thus imprisoned and it was through our fault; moved by her situation, we endeavored to remove her from the center of the ball that surrounded her; the bees became enraged at once, darted their stings and a few strokes killed her. It is so certain that those stings were not intended for her that several workers were themselves killed; and it was certainly not their intention to kill one another. Had we not interfered, they would have been content with confining the queen and would not have massacred her.

To return to Mr. Riem, it was in a similar circumstance that he saw the workers eagerly pursuing a queen; he thought that they designed to pierce her with their stings, and concluded that the common bees were entrusted with the destruction of supernumerary queens.

After having ascertained that in no case do the workers kill supernumerary queens with their stings, we were curious to learn how a strange queen would be received in a hive deprived of the reigning one; to elucidate this point, we made a multitude of experiments the details of which would too much lengthen this letter; I shall only relate the principal results.

What Ensues When Bees Lose Their Queen
When we remove the queen from a hive, the bees do not perceive it at first; they do not interrupt their labors, they care for their young; they do all the ordinary operations, with the same tranquility; but after a few hours, they become agitated; all appears in tumult in their hive; a singular hum is heard; they leave their young, run over the surface of the combs with impetuosity and appear in a delirium; they evidently discover that the queen is no longer among them. But how do they perceive it? How do the bees on the surface of one comb know that the queen is not on the next comb?

While speaking of another trait in the history of our bees, you have yourself, Sir, proposed these same questions; I am assuredly not yet in position to answer them, but I have collected a few facts which may facilitate the discovery of this mystery by the naturalist.

I do not doubt that this agitation arises from the knowledge they have of the loss of their queen; for as soon as she is returned to them, calm is restored instantly among them, and what is very singular is that they recognize her; this expression, Sir, must be accepted strictly. The substitution of another queen does not produce the same effect, if she is introduced in the hive within the first 12 hours after removed of the reigning queen. In such case the agitation continues, and the bees treat the stranger just as they do when the presence of their own queen leaves nothing for them to desire; they seize her, envelope her all around, and keep her a long time captive in an impenetrable cluster; usually she dies, either from hunger or deprivation of air.

Effects of Introducing a Stranger Queen

When 18 hours elapse before the strange queen is substituted for the reigning queen removed, she is first treated in the same manner, but the bees that surround her are sooner weary; the ball which they form around her becomes less compact; gradually they disperse and the queen is at last liberated; we see her walk with weak and languishing steps: sometimes she dies within a few minutes. We have seen queens escape in good health from an imprisonment of 17 hours, and end with reigning in the hives where they had been so ill-received at first.

But if we wait 24 or 30 hours, to substitute a strange queen for the removed queen, she will be well received and will reign from the moment of her introduction in the hive.

Note: I speak here of the good reception given after an interregnum of 24 hours, by the bees to a strange queen substituted for their natural queen; but as this word reception is rather vague, it is proper to enter into some details to determine the sense which I give it.—On the 15th of August of this year, bees had been deprived of queen for 24 hours, and in order to repair their loss, had already commenced the construction of 12 royal cells of the kind described in one of the preceding letters.—At the time when I placed this strange female upon the comb, the bees near her touched her with their antennae, passed their trunks over all parts of her body, and gave her honey; then they made way for others that treated her in exactly the same way. All those bees vibrated their wings at the same time and ranges in a circle around their sovereign. Hence resulted a sort of agitation which gradually communicated to the workers situated on the same side of the comb, and induced them to come and see, in their turn, what was happening. They soon arrived, broke through the circle formed by the first, touched the queen with their antennae gave her some honey, and after this little ceremony they retired without disorder, without tumult, as if experiencing some very agreeable sensation.—the queen had not yet left the spot where I had put her, but after a quarter-hour she began to walk. The bees, far from opposing her motion, opened the circle in the direction which she took, followed her, and stood in a line about her. She was oppressed with the need of laying and dropped her eggs. Lastly, after an abode of 4 hours, she began to deposit male eggs in the large cells that she met.

While these events passed on the surface of the comb where I had placed the queen, all was perfectly quiet on the opposite side: it appeared as if the workers there were unconscious of the arrival of a queen in their hive; they worked with great activity upon the royal cells as if ignorant that they no longer needed them; they cared for the royal worms, brought jelly to them, etc. But at length, the new queen passed to their side; she was received by them with the same eagerness that she had experienced from their companions on the first side of the comb; they stood in line, gave her honey, touched her with their antennae; and what proves better that they treated her as a mother was their immediate desisting from work at the royal cells; they removed the royal worms and ate the pap which they had accumulated around them. From this moment the queen was recognized by all her people, and behaved in her new habitation as she would have done in her native hive.

These details appear to give a fairly correct idea of the manner in which the bees welcome a strange queen, when they have had time to forget their own. They treat her exactly as if she was their natural queen, except that, in the first instant there may be more warmth, or if I dare so express, more demonstrations. I am conscious of the impropriety of these expressions, but Mr. de Réaumur has in some manner consecrated them: he does not hesitate to say that the bees give their queen care, respect and homage, and from his example, these same expressions have escaped most authors who have spoken about bees.

An absence of 24 or 30 hours is thus sufficient to cause the bees to forget their first queen. I abstain from conjectures.

Massacre of the Males

This letter being filled only with descriptions of combats and lugubrious scenes: I should give you in closing the account of some more pleasing and interesting fact relative to their industry. However to avoid returning to duels and massacres, I shall here subjoin my observation upon the carnage of the males.

You remember, Sir, that all the observers of bees agree in saying that, at a certain period of the year, the workers expel and kill the drones. Mr. de Réaumur speaks of these executions as a horrible slaughter, indeed he does not assert expressly that he has witnessed it; but what we have see is so consistent with his statement, that there is no doubt of his having seen the details of this massacre.

It is usually in the months of July and August that the bees get rid of the drones. Then we see them chase them and pursue them to the inner parts of the hives, where they collect in numbers; and as at the same time we find a great many drone bodies on the ground in front of the hives, it does not appear doubtful that the workers, after having expelled them, kill them with their stings. However, we do not see the sting used upon them, on the surface on the combs; they are content with pursuing them and driving them away. You say this yourself, Sir, in the new notes which you added to the *Contemplation de la Nature* (note 5, Chapter XXVI, part XI), and you seem disposed to think that the drones, reduced to retire in a corner of the hive, perish there from hunger. This conjecture is very probably. Still it might be possible that the carnage took place in the bottom of the hive and had been unobserved, because that part is dark and escaped the observer's eye.

To appreciate the justice of this suspicion, we conceived the idea of having the stand which supports the hive made of glass, and placing ourselves under it, to see what passed on the scene. We constructed a glazed table, upon which we placed 6 hives, stocked with swarms of the previous year, and lying under it, we sought to discover how the drones lost their lives. This invention succeeded admirably. On the 4th of July 1787, we saw the workers massacre the drones in 6 swarms at the same hour and with the same peculiarities. The glazed table was covered with bees that appeared full of animation, rushing upon the drones as they came to the bottom of the hive; they seized them by the antennae, by the legs, or the wings; and after having dragged them about, or so to speak, quartered them, they pierced them with their stings, directed between the rings of the belly; the moment when this formidable weapon reached them was always that of their death; they stretched their wings and expired. However, as if the workers had not considered them as dead as they appeared to us, they would again strike them, so deeply that they had much trouble in withdrawing their stings, and had to turn round upon themselves, to succeed in withdrawing them.

On the next day, we resumed the same position, to observe these same hives, and witnessed new scenes of carnage. During 3 hours, we saw our furious bees destroy the males. They had massacred all their own on the previous evening; but on that day they attacked the drones driven from the neighboring hives that took refuge in their home. We saw them also tear from the cells a few remaining larvae of males; they greedily sucked all of the fluid from the abdomen, and then carried them out. The following days no drones appeared in those hives.

These two observations seem to be decisive, Sir; it is incontestable that nature has charged the workers with the killing of the males at certain times of the year. But by what means does she excite their fury against them? This also is one of those questions which I will not attempt to answer.

It Never Ensues in Hives Deprived of Queens
However, I have made an observation which may lead some day to the solution of the problem. The bees never kill the males in the hives deprived of queens; on the contrary they find there a safe asylum, while a horrible massacre prevails in other places; they are tolerated and fed, and a great many are see, even in January. They are also preserved in the hives

which, without a queen properly so called, have among them some individuals of that sort of bees that lay eggs of males, and in those whose *half fertile* queens, if I may so express it, engender only drones. Therefore, the massacre takes place only in hives whose queens are completely fertile, and it never begins until the season of swarms is past.

I have the honor of being etc.

7ᵀᴴ LETTER—RECEPTION OF STRANGE QUEENS

Continuation of the Experiments on the Reception of a Stranger Queen: Observations of Mr. de Réaumur Upon This Subject.

Pregny, August 30, 1791

Sir, I have often told you how much I admired Mr. de Réaumur's memoirs upon bees. I am glad to repeat that, if I have made any progress in the art of observing, I am indebted for it to the profound study of the works of this excellent naturalist. In general his authority is so powerful that I can hardly trust my own experiments when the results are different from those obtained by him. So, when I find myself in opposition to the historian of bees, I repeat my experiences, vary the processes, examine with the utmost caution all the circumstances that might mislead me, and never interrupt my labors until I have acquired the moral certainty of not being mistaken. With the help of these precautions, I have recognized the correctness of Mr. de Réaumur's eyes, and I have a thousand times seen, that if certain experiments seemed to combat them, it was from incorrect execution. Yet, I must except some cases, in which my results have been constantly different from his. Those exposed in my previous letter, on the manner in which the bees receive a strange queen in place of their accustomed one, are of that number.

After having removed the queen of a hive, if I at once substituted a strange one, the usurper was ill-received; they surrounded her, balled her, and often ended by smothering her. I could succeed only, in making them adopt a new queen, by waiting 20 to 24 hours, to introduce her. At the end of that time, they appeared to have forgotten their own queen, and received with respect any female put in her place. Mr. de Réaumur says, on the contrary, that if we remove the queen from the bees and give them another at once, she will be well received. To prove this, he gives the details of an Experiment, that one should read in his own work (Quarto edition, tome V, page 258); I will give only an extract from it: he induced four or five hundred bees to leave their hive and enter a glass box, in which he had fixed a small piece of comb towards the top; at first they were much agitated; to quiet them he tried to offer them a new queen. From that time the tumult ceased, and the foreign queen was received with due respect.

I do not contest the result of this Experiment, but in my opinion it does not warrant the conclusion drawn by Mr. de Réaumur: the apparatus employed removed the bees too far from their natural situation, to enable him to judge of their instinct and dispositions. In other circumstances, he has himself seen that bees reduced to small numbers lose their industry, their activity, and imperfectly continue their ordinary labors. Thus their instinct is modified by each operation that reduced them to too small a number. To render such an experiment truly conclusive, it should then be made in a populous hive, removing from that hive her native queen, and immediately substituting a stranger; I am persuaded that in such a case, Mr. de Réaumur would have seen the bees imprison the queen, ball her for 15 or 18 hours at least, and often end by suffocating her. He would not have witnessed a favorable reception of a strange queen, until he had waited 24 hours before introducing her in the hive, after the removal of the native queen. No variation took place in the result of my experiments in this regard: their number and the attention with which they were made make me presume that they merit your confidence.

A Plurality of Queens is Never Tolerated

In another passage of the Memoir already quoted (page 267) Mr. de Réaumur affirms that the bees having a queen with which they are pleased are nevertheless disposed to give the best possible reception to a strange female seeking refuge among them. I have proved that the workers never use their stings against any queen, but this is far from a welcome to a stranger queen; they retain her within their ranks, they press her in their ranks and appear to give her freedom only when she prepares to combat the reigning queen. But this observation can be made only in our thinnest hives. Those of Mr. de

Réaumur had at least 2 parallel combs; and through this disposition he could not see some very important circumstances
which influence the conduct of the workers when they are given
several females. He mistook for caresses the circles which they
form at first around a strange queen; and if the queen advanced a little between the combs, it was impossible for him to
see that those rings, which were always contracting, ended in
the restraint of the female enclosed within them. Had he used
thinner hives, he would have seen that what he supposed to be
the signs of a welcome was but the prelude of a real imprisonment.

I am reluctant to say that Mr. de Réaumur was mistaken;
but I cannot admit with him that in certain occasions the bees
tolerate in their hives a plurality of females. The experiment
upon which he bases this ascertain cannot be considered
decisive. In the month of December he introduced a strange
queen in a glass hive placed in his cabinet, and confined her
there. The bees could carry nothing out, the stranger was well
received; her presence awakened the workers from their torpidness, into which they did not relapse. She excited no carnage, the number of dead bees on the bottom board did not
sensibly increase, and no dead queens were found. In order to
draw from this observation any consequence favorable to the
plurality of queens, it was necessary to ascertain whether the
hive still had its native queen, when the new queen was introduced; the author neglected this precaution; it is very probable
that the hive which he mentions had lost its queen, since the
bees were languid, and the presence of a stranger restored
their activity.

I hope, Sir, that you will pardon this slight criticism. Far
from seeking faults in the works of our celebrated Réaumur, I
had the greatest pleasure when my observations agreed with
his, and more especially when my experiments justified his
conjectures. But it was necessary to point out the cases in
which the imperfection of his hives led him into error and to
explain from what reasons, I did not see certain facts in the
same manner that he did. I desire especially to merit your

confidence and I am aware that I need the greatest efforts when I must combat the historian of the bees.

I confide in your judgment, Sir, and ask you to accept the assurances of my respect, etc.

8ᵀᴴ Letter—Is the Queen Bee Ovipa-rous? Spinning of Cocoons, Sizes of Cells and Bees

Pregny, September 4 1791

Sir, I shall gather together in this letter several isolated observations, relative to diverse points of history of bees in which you desired me to engage. You desired me to seek whether the queen is really oviparous. Mr. de Réaumur has not decided this question, he even says that he never saw a worm hatch; he only affirms that worms are found in cells where eggs were deposited three days previously. You understand, sir, that in order to seize the moment when the worm emerges from the egg, we must not confine ourselves to observations within the hive; for the continual motion of the bees does not permit us to see precisely what passes at the bottom of the cells. The eggs must be taken out, placed upon a strip of glass under the microscope, and every change which they undergo attentively watched.

There is still one other precaution to take: as a certain degree of heat is necessary for them to hatch, if the eggs were too soon deprived of it, they would wither and perish. The only method to succeed in seeing the worm come out, consists therefore in watching the queen while she lays, marking the eggs which she has just deposited so as to recognize them, and remove them from the hive to place them upon a strip of glass, only an hour or two before the three days elapse. Thus the worms will certainly hatch, for they will have enjoyed the necessary heat as long as possible. Such is the course which I followed. Here is the result.

In the month of August we removed a few cells, contain-ing eggs laid three days previously; we cut down the walls of all those cells and placed upon a glass slide the pyramidal bottom on which the eggs were fixed. Slight motions of curing and of straightening were soon perceptible in one of the eggs; at first the lens did not show us any external organization on the surface of the egg; the worm was entirely concealed by its pellicle: we placed it then upon the focus of a very powerful lens; but while we were preparing this apparatus, the worm bust the imprisoning membrane, and cast off a part of its envelope; we saw it torn and crumpled on some parts of its body and more particularly upon its last rings; the worm, by lively action, curved and straightened itself alternately and occupied 20 minutes in concluding the casting of its skin; its lively exertions ceased then, it lay down, bent its body in a curve and seemed to take a needed rest. This worm proceeded from an egg laid in a worker cell and would have become a worker.

The Queen Bee is Oviparous

We next directed our attention upon the moment when a male worm was to hatch. We exposed it to the sun on the glass slide, and with the help of a good lens we discovered 9 rings of the worm under the transparent pellicle of the egg; this membrane was still entire; the worm was completely motion-less: we distinguished the two longitudinal lines of the trache-ae, and many of their ramifications. We did not lose sight of the egg a single instant and this time noticed the first motions of the worm. The large end curved and straightened alternate-ly and almost touched the base upon which its point was fixed. These efforts burst the membrane first at the upper part to-wards the head, then on the back, and afterwards in all the parts successively. The crumpled pellicle remained in lumps on different parts of the body, then fell off. So it is positive that the queen is oviparous.

Some observers state that the workers care for the eggs laid by the queen before the worms hatch, and it is true that, at any time that we examine the hive, we always see workers with their head and thorax inserted in the cells containing eggs and remaining motionless in that position for several minutes. It is impossible to see what they do because their body con-ceals the interior of the cell. But it is easy to ascertain that, when they assume this attitude, they are not caring for the eggs. If we enclose the eggs in a grated box at the moment when the queen has laid them, and deposit them in a strong hive so they may have the necessary degree of heat, they hatch at the usual time, just as if they had been left in the cells. So they have no need of particular care from the bees to hatch them.

Bees Seem Occasionally to Repose

I have reason to believe that, when the workers enter the cells and remain there 15 or 20 minutes, it is only to repose from their flight and their labors. My observations on this subject are very definite. You know, sir, that bees sometimes construct cells of irregular shape against the panes of the hive; these cells glazed on one side are very convenient to the observer, since all that passes within them is exposed. I have often seen bees enter such cells when nothing could attract them there; they were finished cells and yet contained neither eggs nor honey. Therefore the workers came thither only to enjoy some instants of rest. Indeed, they would remain for 15 or 20 minutes in them so motionless, that one might have thought them dead, had not the dilation of their rings showed that they were breathing. This need of repose is not special with the workers, the queens also sometimes, enter the big male cells and remain long motionless. This attitude prevents the bees from paying full homage to them; yet, even in these circumstances, the workers do not fail to circle around them and to brush the part of their belly which remains uncovered.

The drones do not enter the cells, when they wish to rest, but they cluster against one another on the combs, and sometimes remain in this position for 18 or 20 hours, without the slightest motion.

As it is important, in several experiments, to know exactly the length of time that the three sorts of worms exist, before assuming their ultimate shape, I shall here subjoin my particular observations on this subject.

Interval Between Production of the Egg and the Perfect State of Bees

Worms of worker.

Three days in the egg state, five days in the worm state, at the end of which time the bees close its cell with a wax covering; the worm then begins to spin its silk cocoon, in which operation 36 hours are consumed. Three days later, it metamorphoses into a nymph and spend seven days and a half in this form Note: all other translations say six days for this but Dadant appears correct as the French copies I can find say "sept jours & demi sous cette forme".—Transcriber; so it reaches its last state, that of a bee, on the 20th day of its life, counting from the moment the egg was laid. Note: 20 days is 1 day shorter than is the currently believed development time but may be explained by natural cells which Huber had vs. enlarged cells; or differences in genetics.— Transcriber.

The royal worm.

The royal worm also passes 3 days in the egg, and 5 as a worm: after these 8 days, the bees close its cell and it begins at once to spin its cocoon which operation occupies 24 hours. It remains in complete repose during the 10th and 11th day and even during the 16 hours of the 12th. Then it transforms into a nymph and spends 4 days and a third in this stage. Thus it is in the 16th day of its life that it reaches the state of perfect queen.

The male worm.

Three days in the egg, six and a half as worm: it changes into a winged insect only the 24th day after the laying of the egg.

Although the worms of bees are apod, they are not condemned to absolute immobility in their cells: they advance in a spiral. This motion, so slow during the first 3 days that it can hardly be perceived, afterwards becomes more evident: I have seen them perform two complete revolutions in an hour and three quarters. When the end of their metamorphosis approaches, they are only two lines (11/64th in. or 4mm) from the orifice of the cell. The position which they assume is always the same; they are bent in an arc. It follows that, in the horizontal cells, such as those of the workers or of drones, the larvae are perpendicular to the horizon; on the contrary, in the royal cells, the worms are placed horizontally. It might be thought that the difference of position has great influence on the increment of the various larvae, yet it has none. By reversing combs containing common cells of brood, I brought the worms to a horizontal position, but they did not suffer in their development. I have also turned the royal cells so that their worms were placed vertically and their growth was neither less speedy nor less perfect.

Mode of Spinning the Cocoon

I have paid a great deal of attention to the manner in which the worms spin the silk of their cocoons, and I witnessed in this matter, new and interesting peculiarities. The worms of workers and of males spin complete cocoons in their cells, that is, closed at both ends and surrounding the whole body; the royal worms, on the other hand, spin only incomplete cocoons, that is, they are open at the posterior part and envelope only the head, thorax and first ring of the abdomen. The discovery of this difference in the shape of the cocoon, which may at first seem too minute, gave me extreme pleasure, as it evidently shows the admirable art with which nature connects the various traits of the industry of bees.

That of the Queen is Open at One End

You remember, Sir, the proofs which I have given you of the mutual aversion of queens, of their combats, and of the animosity with which they seek to destroy one another. When there are several royal nymphs in a hive, the first one trans-formed into a queen attacks the others and pierces them with her sting. But she could not succeed in this, if they were enveloped in a complete cocoon. Why? Because the silk that the worms weave is so strong that the cocoon is of close tissue, and the sting could not penetrate through it or if it did, the queen could not withdraw it, because the barbs would be retained by the meshes of the cocoon, and she would thus perish, a victim of her own fury. Thus, that she may destroy her rivals, it is necessary that their posterior parts be uncov-ered; the royal nymphs must therefore weave incomplete cocoons; take note, please, that it is the last rings which must remain uncovered, for they are the only part which the sting can penetrate; the head and the thorax are covered with scaly plates which it cannot pierce.

Hitherto, Sir, Observers have called for our admiration of nature, in her care for the multiplication and preservation of the species, but in the facts which I relate, we must admire also her precautions in exposing certain individuals to a mortal danger.

The details which I have just entered clearly indicate the final cause of the opening which the royal worms leave in their cocoons, but they do not show us whether it is in obedience to a particular instinct that they do so or whether widening of their cells prevents them from stretching the treads in the upper part. This question interested me very much. The only way to decide it was to observe the worms while they spin, which could not be done through their opaque cells: it occurred to me to dislodge them and introduce them into glass tubes, which I had caused to be blown in exact imitation of the different kinds of cells. The most difficult part was to draw them from the habitations and place them into these new domiciles. Burnens performed this operation with much address; he opened in my hives several sealed royal cells; selecting the time when we knew that they were about to begin their cocoons, he took them out cautiously, and introduced one in each of my glass cells, without doing them any harm.

We soon saw them prepare their work: they began by stretching the anterior part of their body in a straight line, leaving their posterior part curved, thus forming an arc of which the longitudinal sides of the cell were tangents, and afforded two points of support. Being sufficiently supported in this position, their head was next brought to the different parts of the cell which it could reach, and carpeted the surface with thick silk. We noticed that they did not stretch their threads from one wall to the other, which they could not do, because being obliged to sustain themselves by keeping their posterior rings curved; the free and movable part of their body was not long enough to admit of their mouth fixing threads upon diametrically opposite sides. You have not forgotten, Sir, that the royal cells are in the shape of a pyramid, the base of which is broad, with a long and thin point. Those cells are placed vertically in the hives, with their base at the top and point below.

In this position, you will conceive, the royal worm can sustain itself only when the curve of its posterior part secures two points of support, and it cannot obtain this support unless it rests upon the lower part or near the point. Thus if it wanted to ascend towards the wide end, to spin a thread, it could not reach both walls, because they are too far apart. It could not touch one side with its tip, the other with its back, consequently it would tumble down. I made positively sure of this by placing a few royal worms in glass cells that were too large, and the diameter of which was greater towards the point than in ordinary cells: there they were unable to sustain themselves.

These first experiments prevented the supposition of a particular instinct in royal worms. They proved that, if they spin incomplete cocoons, it is because they are compelled to do so by the form of their cells. However I desired to have a still more direct proof. I placed worms of the same kind in cylindrical glass cells, or portions of glass tubes resembling common cells, and I had the pleasure of seeing these worms spin complete cocoons, as the worms of workers do.

Lastly I placed common worms in very wide cells and they left their cocoon open. It thus demonstrated that the royal worms and the worker worms have exactly the same instinct, the same industry, or in other words, when placed in similar circumstances, they conduct themselves in the same manner. I will add here that the royal worms, artificially lodged in cells of such a shape that they are able to spin complete cocoon, undergo all their metamorphoses equally well. The obligation which nature has imposed upon them, to leave their cocoon open, is not necessary to their development, it has no other object that that of exposing them to the danger of death under the strokes of their natural enemy: a very new and truly singular observation.

Experiments on the Effects of Cell Size

In order to complete the history of the worms of bees, I must relate the experiments that I have made on the influence which the size of the cells has upon them. It is to you, Sir, that

I am indebted, for the suggestion of the experiments needed upon this interesting subject.

As we often find in the hives males that are smaller than usual, and also sometimes queens of a smaller size than they should be, it was desirable to determine in general to what degree the cells in which bees have passed the first period of their existence has influence upon their size. With this view, you advised me to remove from a hive all the combs composed of common cells, leaving only those composed of large cells. It was evident that if the eggs of common bees, which the queen laid in those cells, would produce workers of a larger size, we should conclude that the size of the cells had a decided influence on that of the bees.

The first time I made this experiment it was unsuccessful because moths having invaded the hive discouraged my bees: but I repeated it and the result was remarkable.

I removed from one of my finest glazed hives all the combs composed of common cells, leaving only those composed of drone cells, and in order to have no vacant room in it, I added more combs of the same kind. It was in June, the season most favorable to bees. I expected those bees to quickly repair the damage produced in their hive by this operation, that they would work upon the breaches made and fasten the new comb to the old; but I was much surprised to see that they did not begin the work. I observed them for several days, in the hope that they would resume activity. But this hope was disappointed. Indeed they did not fail in their respect to their queen, but except in this their behavior was quite different from what it is usually: they remained clustered on the combs without exciting any sensible heat; a thermometer placed amount them rose only to 22° Réaumur (= 81° F = 27.5° C) though it was at 20° Réaumur (= 77° F = 25° C) in the open air. In a word they appeared to be in the greatest discouragement.

The queen herself, though very fertile, and though she must have been oppressed with the need of laying, hesitated a long time, before depositing any eggs in the large cells; she dropped them rather than lay them in the unsuitable cells.

However, on the second day we found six which had been deposited regularly. Three days after, the worms had hatched and we followed their history. The bees commenced to feed them they did not appear very eager at this work, yet I was in hopes that they would continue to care for them. I was mistaken, for on the following day all the worms disappeared and the cells were empty. Dismal silence reigned in the hive, only a few bees took wing, those that returned had no pellets on their legs: all was cold and inanimate. To promote a little motion, I supplied the hive with a comb of small cells, full of male brood of all ages. The bees, which had obstinately refused to work in wax for 12 days, did not unite this comb to their own; however their industry was wakened in a manner that I had not foreseen; they removed all the brood from this comb, cleaned out the cells and made them ready to receive new eggs.

Queen laying multiple eggs

I do not know whether they expected their queen to lay in them, but if they did, they were not disappointed: from this moment the female no longer dropped her eggs; she came to this new comb and laid such a number of eggs that we found 5 or 6 together in several of the cells. I then removed all the combs of large cells to put small cells in their place and this operation restored their complete activity.

The circumstances of this experiment seem worthy of attention; they prove first that Nature has not left the queen the choice of the eggs which she is to lay; it is ordained that at certain times of the year the female should lay male eggs; she is not permitted to invert this order. You have seen, Sir, in the third letter, that another fact led me to the same consequence, and as this was very important, I was delighted to see it confirmed by a new observation. I repeat therefore that the eggs are not indiscriminately mixed in the ovaries of the queen, but arranged so that, at a certain season, she can lay only a certain kind. So it would be vain at the time of the year when the queen should lay the eggs of workers, to attempt forcing her to lay drone eggs by filling her hive with large cells; for by the experiment just described we see that she prefers to drop her worker eggs haphazard, rather than place them in unsuitable cells, and that she will not lay male eggs. I do not yield to the pleasure of granting this queen discernment or foresight, for I perceive a sort of inconsistency in her conduct. If she refused to lay the eggs of workers in large cells because Nature taught her that their size I not proportioned to the size or need of the common worms; why did she not learn also that she should not lay several eggs in the same cell? It appeared much easier to rear a single worker worm in one large cell than several of the same kind in a small cell. The supposed discernment of the queen is not very much enlightened. The most prominent feature of industry here appears in the common bees of this hive. When I gave them a comb of small cells filled with male brood, their activity was awakened; but instead of caring for this brood, as they would have done in other circumstances, they destroyed these worms and nymphs, and cleaned out the cells, so the queen, oppressed with the need of laying be enabled to deposit her eggs. Could we allow them either reason or sentiment, this would be an interesting proof of their affection for her.

The experiment here detailed at length, not having fulfilled my object in determining the influence of the size of the cells upon that of the worms, I devised another which was more successful.

I selected a comb of large cells containing eggs and worms of males. I caused all of these worms to be removed from their pap, and Burnens substituted worms one day old, taken from worker cells, then gave this comb to be cared for to the bees that had a queen. The bees did not abandon these substituted worms; they sealed the cells with an almost flat capping very different from that which they place on the cells of males, which shows that, although these worms were in large cells, they were well aware that they were not drone worms. This comb remained in the hive for eight days from the time the cells were sealed. I then had it removed to examine the nymphs which it contained. They were worker nymphs, in a more or less advanced state; but as to size and shape they were exactly similar to those that make their growth in the smaller cells. I concluded that the worker worms do not acquire greater size in large than in small cells. Although I made this experiment only once, it appears decisive. Nature which has intended the workers to grow in cells of a certain dimension, undoubtedly ordained that they should receive in them the full development of their organs: a greater space would be useless to them; and they do not reach greater size in spacious cells than in those that are intended for them. If there were cells, in the combs, of a smaller size than common cells, and if the queen should lay worker eggs in them, it is probable that the bees reared in them would attain a less size than ordinary workers, because they would be cramped in those cells, but it does not ensue that a large cell should give them an extraordinary size.

The effect produced on the size of drones by the diameter of the cells which their worms inhabit may serve as a rule to judge of what must happen to worker worms in similar circumstances. The large male cells have all the space required for full extension of their organs. Thus, even if we reared drones in still larger cells, they would grow no larger than ordinary drones. We have the proof of this in those that are produced by queens whose fecundation has been retarded. You will remember, Sir, that these queens sometimes lay drone eggs in royal cells: the drones reared in such cells, much more spacious than those provided for them by nature, are no larger than ordinary males. Thus it is correct to say that whatever be the size of the cells in which bees are reared, they will not acquire a larger size than is proper to their kind, but if they grow in smaller cells than those intended for them, as their growth will then be checked they will not attain the usual size. Note: Huber did not have access to foundation, let alone different sizes of foundation, so he only had drone sized cells to use in his experiments. Baudoux did research on this same concept by using foundation that was stretched to increase the cell size and proved that cell size does control the size of the resulting worker. The result of Baudoux's research is the 5.4mm cell size on our standard foundation today.—Transcriber.

I had proof of this in the following experiment: I had a comb composed of drone cells and another of worker cells, both occupied with drone worms. Burnens took worms from the small cells and placed them in the large cells on the bed of jelly which had been prepared for them: in return he introduced into the small cells worms which had hatched in the larger ones, and gave both to the care of a hive whose queens laid only male eggs. The bees were not disquieted by this displacement, they took equal care of the worms and when they reached the time of metamorphosis, they gave to both kinds of cells the convex covering which they usually place upon the cells of males. Eight days afterwards we removed these combs and found, as I had expected, large drone nymphs in the large cells and small males in the small ones.

You pointed out to me, Sir, another Experiment, which I made with great care, but which met with an unexpected obstacle. To appreciate the degree of influence of royal food upon the development of worms, you desired me to remove a little of this pap with the end of a pencil and to feed it to a larva of workers in a common cell. Twice I attempted this operation without success, and I am certain that it can never succeed, for the following reason:

When the bees have a queen and we put in their charge worms in cells in which we have placed royal jelly, they promptly remove those worms and greedily eat the pap upon which they were placed. When on the contrary, they are deprived of a queen, they change the common cells containing these worms into royal cells of the largest size; then the worms which were to be only common bees are infallibly converted into queens.

But there is another situation in which we can judge of the influence of the royal jelly, administered to worms in common cells. I described these details to you at length in my letter upon the existence of fertile workers. You have not forgotten, Sir, that these workers owe the development of their sexual organs to particles of royal jelly with which they were fed while in the worm shape. For want of new observations more directly upon this subject, I refer you to the experiments described in my 5th letter.

Accept the assurance of my respect, etc.

9TH LETTER—ON THE FORMATION OF SWARMS

Pregny September 6, 1791

Sir, I can add a few facts to the information which Mr. de Réaumur has given us on the formation of swarms.

In his history of bees, this celebrated naturalist says that it is always or almost always a young queen that heads a swarm; but he did not assert the fact positively; he had some doubts and here are his own words:

> "Is it very certain as we have supposed until now, in coincidence with all who have treated of bees, that the colony is uniformly headed by a young mother? May not the old mother become disgusted with her habitation? Or may she not be impelled by peculiar circumstances to abandon all her possessions to the young female? It would be in my power to solve this question otherwise than by probabilities, had not mishaps destroyed the bees of hives whose queens I had marked with a red spot on the corselet."

These expressions seem to indicate that Mr. de Réaumur suspected that the old queens sometimes head the swarms. From the following details, you will see, Sir, that his conjectures were fully justified.

The same hive may cast several swarms, in the course of spring and the fine season. The old queen is always at the head of the first colony that goes; the others are conducted by the young queens. Such is the fact which I shall prove in this letter; it is accompanied with remarkable circumstances, which I shall not neglect.

But before beginning this account, I must repeat that which I have stated many times, that one must use leaf or flat hives to see what belongs to the industry and instinct of the bees. When we allow them to build several parallel combs, we can no longer observe what passes constantly between them; or if we wish to see what they have built we must dislodge them by water or smoke, a violent proceeding which leaves nothing in natural conditions, disturbs the instinct of the bees, and exposed the observer to mistaking simple accidents for permanent laws.

The Old Queen Always Conducts the First Swarm

I now proceed to the experiments proving that an old queen always conducts the first swarm.

I had a glass hive composed of 3 parallel combs, placed in frames closed like the leaves of a book: the hive was fairly well peopled, and abundantly supplied with honey and comb with brood of all ages. I removed its queen on the 5th of May 1788: on the 6th I transferred to it all the bees of another hive, with a fertile queen at least a year old. They entered readily and without fight and were generally well received. The old inhabitants of the hive, which since the removal of their queen had begun 12 royal cells, also gave the fertile queen a good reception; they offered honey to her, and made regular circles around her; however there was a little agitation in the evening, but confined to the surface of the comb upon which we had put the queen and which she had not quitted. All remained perfectly quiet on the other side.

On the morning of the 7th, the bees had destroyed their 12 royal cells. Order continued to reign in the hive; the queen laid alternately male eggs in the large cells and worker eggs in the small ones.

Towards the 12th we found our bees busy building 22 royal cells of the kind described by Mr. de Réaumur, that is, the bases not in the plane of the comb, but suspended by pedicles of different length, like stalactites, on the edge of the passages made by the bees through the combs. They resembled the cup of an acorn, and the longest were not to exceed two and half lines (13/64th inch or about 1/5 inch or 5mm) from the bottom to the orifice.

On the 13th, the queen's belly appeared to us to be more slender than when she was introduced in the hive: but she still laid some eggs, both in the worker and male cells. We also surprised her this day, at the moment when she was laying in one of the royal cells: she first dislodged the worker employed there, by pushing her away with her head; then after having examined the bottom, she introduced her belly into it, by supporting herself with her anterior legs on one of the adjoining cells.

On the 15th, the queen appeared still more slender; the bees continued to care for the royal cells, which were unequally advanced: some to 3 or 4 lines. (1/4 to 1/3 inch or 6 to 8 mm) while others were already an inch in length (25mm); thus proving that the queen had not laid in all those cells on the same date.

On the 19th, when we least expected it, the hive swarmed; we were warned of it only by the noise which it made in the air: we hastened to collect it and placed it in a prepared hive; though we had overlooked the circumstances of its departure, the particular object of this experiment was fulfilled, for on examination of all the bees of the swarm, we became convinced that it had been led by the old queen, the one which we had introduced on the 6th of the month, which we had made easy to recognize by the deprivation of one of her antennae. Observe that there was no other queen in this colony. In the hive which she had left we found 7 royal cells, closed on the end but open on the side and entirely empty. Eleven more were sealed and some others newly begun; but there was no queen left in the hive.

The new swarm next became the object of our attention: we observed it during the rest of the year, during the winter and the following spring, and in April, we had the satisfaction to see another swarm issue, with this same queen that had conducted one in the previous month of May, of which I have just spoken.

You see, Sir, that this experiment is positive. We used an old queen, placed her in the hive at the time of her laying of drone eggs: we saw the bees accept her, and at that time begin the building of royal cells. The queen laid in one of those cells under our eyes, and lastly left this hive with a swarm.

But Never Before Depositing Eggs in the Royal Cells

We repeated this observation several times with equal success. Thus it appears incontestable that it is always the old queen that leads the first swarm out of the hive; but she leaves it only after having deposited eggs in the royal cells from which young queens will hatch after her departure. The bees prepare these cells only when they see the queen laying male eggs, and this is attended by a remarkable fact, namely, that after termination of this laying her belly is notably diminished; she can fly more easily, whereas, previous to the laying of male eggs, her belly is so heavy that she can hardly drag it along. Therefore it is necessary that she should lay them, to be able to undertake a journey which sometimes may be very long.

But this single condition is not sufficient; it is also necessary that the bees be very numerous in the hive; they should be superabundant, and it may be said that they are aware of it, for if the hive is scantily peopled, they will not build any royal cells at the time of the laying of male eggs, which is the only period when the old queen is able to conduct a colony. We acquired the proof of this in an experiment made on a very large scale.

On the 3rd of May 1788, we divided in two each of 18 hives whose queens were about a year old; so each portion of those hives had but half of the bees that were there before the division: 18 of those half hives were thus without queens; but in the space of 10 or 15 days, the bees made up this loss and secured new females: the other 18 had very fertile queens. They soon began to lay male eggs, but the bees, seeing themselves in small number, did not construct any royal cells and none of the hives swarmed. Therefore, if the hive containing the old queen is not very populous, she remains in it until the subsequent spring; and if the population is then sufficient, the bees will construct royal cells, as soon as the queen begins her laying of male eggs; she will deposit eggs in them and will issue at the head of a colony, before the birth of any young queens.

Such is, Sir, an abridged abstract of my information upon swarms, led by old queens; excuse the lengthy details upon which I am about to enter, on the history of royal cells which remain in the hive after the departure of the queen. Everything relative to this part of the history of bees was hitherto very obscure; a long course of observations, protracted during several years, was necessary to partly remove the veil concealing these mysteries; it is true that I was indemnified by the pleasure of seeing my experiences reciprocally confirmed; but owing to the assiduity which they required, these researches were very laborious.

Having established, in 1788 and 1789, that queens a year old conducted the first swarms and that they left in the hive worms or nymphs which were to transform into queens in their turn, I undertook, in 1790, to profit by the goodness of spring, to observe all that relates to these young queens; I shall now extract the principal experiments from my Journals.

On the 14th of May, we introduced bees from 2 straw hives into a very thin, large glass hive, giving them only one queen born in the preceding year, and which had already commenced laying drone eggs in her native hive.

We introduced her on the 15th; she was very prolific; she was well received and quickly commenced to lay in small and large cells alternately.

On the 20th, we found the foundations of 16 royal cells: they were all on the edges of the passages which the bees establish in the thickness of the combs in order to pass from one side to the other; they were shaped like stalactites.

On the 27th, 10 of these cells were much enlarged, though unequal, and none had the length which bees give them when the worms are hatched.

On the 28th, previous to which the queen had not ceased laying, her belly was much reduced, but she began to exhibit agitation. Her motions soon become more lively; yet she still examined the cells as when she wants to lay in them: sometimes introducing into one the half of her belly, then withdrawing it brusquely. At other times introducing it no deeper, she would lay an egg, placed irregularly; not fastened by one of its points to the bottom of the cell, but laid upon the center of one of the panes of the hexagon. The queen produced no distinct sound in her course, and we heard nothing different from the ordinary humming of the bees; she would pass over the body of those that were in her way; sometimes if she stopped the bees that met her stopped also, as if to consider her; they would advance brusquely toward her, strike her with their heads and climb on her back; she would then start, carrying several thus upon her; none gave her any honey, but she took some herself out of the open cells on her way; they no longer hedged around her or surround her with regular circles. The first bees that were aroused by her motions followed her running, and excited, in passing, those that were still quiet upon the combs. The path followed by the queen was noticeable, after her passage, by the agitation created, which was no longer quelled. She had soon visited every part of the hive and caused general excitement; if any places still remained tranquil, those that were agitated would arrive and communicate the excitement. The queen no longer laid in the cells, she dropped her eggs: the bees no longer cared for the young; they ran through the hive in every direction; even those returning from the field, before the agitation reached its height, no sooner entered the hive than they participated in these tumultuous motions, and neglecting to rid themselves of the pollen pellets which they carried upon their legs, ran about blindly. At last, in another moment, all the bees rushed to the entrance of the hive and the queen with them.

As it was very important for me to see the formation of new swarms in this hive and that for that reason I wished it to remain very populous, I caused the queen to be removed at the time when she came out, so that the bees might not fly too far but would return. In fact after losing their female, they did return to the hive. To increase the population still more, I added another swarm which had issued from a straw hive on the same morning and whose queen was also removed.

Although all the facts here related were very positive and apparently not susceptible of any error, I wished to duplicate them; I was especially anxious to discover whether the old queens always follow a similar course. So I decided to place in this hive a year-old queen, hitherto observed by me, and which had just begun to lay the eggs of males. She was introduced on the 29th. On the same day, we discovered that one of the royal cells, that the previous queen had left behind, was larger than the others; and, from its length we supposed that the included worm was 2 days old. So the egg from which it had come must have been laid on the 24th and the worm had hatched on the 27th. On the 30th, the new queen laid many eggs, alternately in large and small cells. On that day and the two following, the bees enlarged several cells into royal cells, but unevenly, which proved that they contained larvae of different ages.

On the 1st of June one of them was sealed, on the 2nd, another. The bees also commenced several new ones. Everything was still perfectly quiet in the hive at 11 o'clock in the morning; but at mid-day, the queen changed from the utmost quiet to a very marked agitation, which insensibly was communicated to the workers in every part of their dwelling. Within a few minutes, they crowded towards the entrances and left the hive along with the queen; they settled upon the limb of a neighboring tree; I caused the queen to be sought and removed, so that the bees, deprived of her, should return to the hive, which they did. Their first care seemed to seek for their female; they were still very much excited, but at 3 o'clock all was quiet and in order.

On the 3rd they resumed their ordinary labors; they cared for the young, worked within the open royal cells and also gave some attention to those that were closed: they made waved wax work on them (guilloche), not by applying wax bands upon them but by removing some of it from the surface; this braiding is almost imperceptible near the point of the cell; it becomes deeper above, and the workers excavate it still more to the big end of the pyramid. The cell once closed thus becomes thinner, so much so that in the last hours that precede the metamorphosis of the queen into a nymph, one may see its motions through the thin coat of wax upon which the braiding is founded, provided the cells are held between the eye and sunlight. It is quite remarkable that, in making the cells thinner from the time when they are closed, the bees regulate this labor, so that it terminates only when the nymph is ready to undergo its last metamorphosis: upon the 7th day, the cocoon is almost complete unwaxed, if I may use this word; it is at this part that the head and thorax of the queen are located. This leaves to her but the trouble to cut the silk of which it is woven. Very probably this labor is intended to promote the evaporation of the superabundant fluids of the royal nymph, and the bees grade it proportionally with the age and condition of the nymph. I undertook some direct experiments upon this matter but they are not yet completed. On the same 3rd of June, our bees closed a third royal cell, 24 hours after closing the second. The following days the same operation was performed on several other cells.

Every moment of the 7th, we expected the queen to leave the royal cell which had been sealed on May 30. On the preceding evening, her period of 7 days had elapsed. The waving upon the cell was so deep that we could perceive in part what passed within; we could discern that the silk of the cocoon was cut circularly, a line and a half (1/8 inch or 3 mm) from the point, but as the bees were unwilling that she should quit the cell they had sealed the cover to it with some particles of wax.

Singular Effect of a Sound Emitted by Perfect Queens
What seemed most singular was that this female in her prison emitted a very distinct sound or clacking: it was still more distinct in the evening and was composed of several notes on the same tone, in rapid succession.

On the 8th, we heard the same sound from the second cell. Several bees kept guard around each royal cell.

On the 9th, the first cell opened. The young queen that emerged was lively, slender, of brown color; we then understood why the bees retain the females captive in their cells, beyond term; it is that they may be able to fly, the instant they are liberated. The new queen occupied all our attention: whenever she approached the royal cells, the bees on guard pulled her, bit her and chased her away; they seemed very irritated against her and she enjoyed tranquility only when at considerable distance from any royal cell. This performance was frequently repeated during the day; she piped twice: we saw her doing so, standing with her thorax against a comb, her wings crossed on her back, in motion, but without being unfolded or farther opened. Whatever might have caused her to assume this attitude, the bees seemed affected by it and remained motionless.

The hive presented the same appearance on the following day. Twenty-three royal cells still remained assiduously guarded by a great many bees. Whenever the queen approached, the guards became agitated, surrounded her, bit her, mobbed her and usually drove her away; sometimes, in those circumstances, she piped, assuming the attitude already described, and from that moment the bees remained motionless.

The queen confined in cell № 2, which she had not yet left, was heard piping at different times. We also saw accidentally how the bees fed her. By attentive examination, we noticed a small aperture in the end of the capping which she had cut, and out of which she might have emerged, had not the workers covered it with wax to retain her still longer. She alternately thrust and withdrew her tongue through this slit: the bees at first did not notice it, but at length one of them saw it and applied her own proboscis on that of the captive queen, then gave way to others also approaching her with honey. When she was satiated, she withdrew her trunk and the bees again closed the opening with wax.

This same day, between midday and one o'clock, the queen became extremely agitated. The royal cells had multiplied very much; she could go nowhere without finding one, and as soon as she approached she was ill treated; she fled elsewhere, but obtained no better reception. Her travels agitated the bees; they remained for a long time in great confusion; then they precipitately rushed to the entrance of the hive, issued and settled upon a tree in the garden. It singularly happened that the queen could not follow them and head the swarm herself. She had attempted to pass between two royal cells before the bees had abandoned them and was so confined and bitten as to be unable to move. We removed her and placed her in a separate hive, prepared for a particular experiment: the bees that had swarmed and that had gathered upon a branch soon perceived that their queen was not with them and returned to the hive of their own accord. Such is an account of the second colony (swarm) of this hive.

We were extremely desirous of ascertaining what would become of the other royal cells: 4 of the sealed ones contained fully developed queens, which might have emerged had not the bees prevented them. They were not opened during the moments previous to the agitation of the swarm nor at the time of the issue.

On the 11th, none of these queens was at yet liberated: that of № 2 must have ended her transformation on the 8th; so she had been a prisoner for 3 days; and her confinement lasted longer than that of № 1, which had caused the formation of the swarm. We did not divine the cause of this difference in their captivity.

Multiple queens in a swarm

On the 12th, this queen was at length liberated, we found her in the hive; she was treated exactly as her predecessor; the bees left her quiet when away from the royal cells, and tormented her cruelly when she approached them. We watched this queen for a long time, but not foreseeing that she would lead out a colony on the same day, we left the hive for a few hours. Returning at noon, we were very much surprised to find it almost deserted; during our absence it had thrown a prodigious swarm, which was still clustered, in a thick bunch, on the branch of a neighboring pear tree. We also saw, with astonishment that 3rd cell open, its cap sill hanging as by a hinge. In all probability the captive queen profited by the disorder that preceded the issue of the swarm, to escape. We had no doubt then that both queens were in the swarm; we found them both and removed them, so that the bees might return to the hive, which they did, immediately.

While we were occupied in this operation, the captive queen № 4 left her prison, and the bees found her upon their return. They were at first very much agitated, but calmed towards evening and resumed their ordinary labors; they kept strict guard around the royal cells, and took great care to repulse the queen whenever she attempted to approach them; there were still 18 closed cells to guard.

At 10 in the evening, the queen of № 4 was liberated, so there were two living queens now in the hive; they first tried to fight, but succeeded in disengaging themselves from each other; during the night they fought several times without result: on the following day, the 13th we witnessed the death of one of them which fell by the wounds of her enemy. The details of this duel were entirely similar to those that I gave elsewhere on the "combats of queens".

The victorious queen now gave us a very singular spectacle. She approached a royal cell and took this moment to pipe and place herself in the posture which strikes the bees motionless. We thought, for a few minutes that taking advantage of the dread she caused to the workers on guard, she would succeed in opening it and killing the young female in it; so she prepared to mount on the cell; but in so doing she stopped her piping and abandoned the attitude which paralyzes the bees; instantly the guards of the cell regained courage; and by tormenting and biting the queen, drove her away.

On the 14th, the queen emerged from the cell № 6; and at 11 o'clock the hive threw a swarm with all the disorder previously described: the agitation was even so considerable that an insufficient number of bees remained to guard the royal cells, and several of the imprisoned queens made their escape. There were 3 of them in the cluster of the swarm, and three others remained in the hive. We removed those that had led the colony, so as to compel the bees to return.

They returned to the hive, resumed their post around the royal cells and maltreated the queens that tried to approach them.

In the night of the 14th to the 15th, there was a duel in which one queen fell; we found her dead the next morning before the hive; but there still remained 3, as one had hatched during the night. On the morning of the 15th, we witnessed a duel between 2 of these queens; and only two were left free at one time: they were both exceedingly excited, either with the desire of fighting, or by the treatment of the bees when they came near the royal cells: their agitation quickly communicated to the bees of the hive, and at noon they impetuously departed with the two females. This was the 4th swarm that had left the hive from May 30th to June 15th. It cast still another on the 16th, of which I shall not give account, as it showed nothing new.

Unfortunately we lost this last swarm, which was very strong; the bees flew out of sight and could not be found. The hive remained now very thinly inhabited; only a few bees that had not participated in the agitation at the time of the swarming remained, together with those that returned from the field after the departure of the swarm. The royal cells thereafter were slenderly guarded; the queens escaped from them, several fights ensued, until the throne remained with the successful one.

In spite of her victories, from the 16th to the 19th she was indifferently treated by the bees for during those 3 days she preserved her virginity. At length she went forth to seek the males, returned with all the external signs of fecundation and was thenceforth treated with every mark of respect: she laid her first eggs 46 hours after fecundation.

Behold, Sir, a simple and faithful account of my observations on the formation of swarms. In order to render this account more clear, I have not interrupted it with the detail of several particular experiments which I made at the same time, with the intention of elucidating several obscure points. If you will permit, this shall be the subject of future letters. Although my statements are lengthy, I still hope to interest you.

Accept, Sir, the assurances of my respect.

P.S. In reading over this letter, Sir, I find that I have failed to anticipate an objection which might embarrass my readers, and to which I must reply. Since I returned the bees to the hive from each of the 5 swarms that had issued, it is not surprising that this hive was continually stoked so sufficiently that each colony was numerous; but in the natural state, things do no happen in this way; the bees composing a swarm do not return to the hive which they have left, and it will be asked what resource of population enables an ordinary hive to cast 3 or 5 swarms without being too much weakened.

I do not wish to lessen the difficulty; I have said that the agitation which precedes swarming is often so considerable, that most of the bees quit the hive; and it is then difficult to comprehend how, in 3 or 4 days afterwards, this hive may be able to send out another fairly strong colony.

But take notice that, when she leaves the hive, the old queen leaves there a prodigious quantity of worker brood. These soon transform into bees and sometimes the population is almost as large after the first swarm has been cast as before it left. Thus the hive is perfectly capable of furnishing another colony without being too much impaired. The 3rd and 4th swarms weaken it more sensibly; but the number of remaining inhabitants is nearly always large enough to continue the labors without interruption, and these losses are soon replaced by the great fecundity of the queens. You will remember that they lay above a hundred eggs per day.

If, in some cases, the agitation is so great that all the bees participate in it and leave the hive, the desertion lasts but for an instant: the swarms depart during the finest moments of the day, at the time when the bees are gathering honey through the country; those that are thus busy at the diverse harvests take no part in the agitation of the cast; when they return to the hive they quietly resume the labor, and their number is not small, for, when the weather is fine, at least a third of the bees are in the field at one time.

Even in the embarrassing case of so great an agitation that all the bees desert the hive, it does not follow that all those that try to leave become members of the new colony. When this delirious agitation seizes them, they rush and accumulate all at one time towards the entrances and become heated in such a manner that they perspire copiously; the bees nearest the bottom supporting the weight of all the others, seem drenched; their wings become moist; they are incapable of flight; and even when able to escape, they do not go farther than the bottom board, and soon reenter.

The newly hatched bees do not leave with the swarm, still feeble, they could not sustain themselves in that flight. Here, then are many recruits to people this habitation which we thought deserted.

10ᵀᴴ Letter—On the Formation of Swarms Continued

Pregny, Sept. 8ᵗʰ 1791.

In order to have more regularity in the continuation of the *history of swarms,* I believe, Sir, that it is proper to recapitulate, in a few words, the principle facts of the preceding letter, and to give upon each of them the developments resulting from several new experiments which I have not yet mentioned.

1ˢᵗ: *Both drone and queen rearing occur in April and May*

If, on the return of spring, we examine a well peopled hive, governed by a fertile queen, we shall see her lay, in April and May, a prodigious number of eggs of males; and the workers will choose this time to build several royal cells of the kind described by Mr. de Réaumur.

Such is the result of several long continued observations, between which there has never been the slightest variation, and I do not hesitate to announce it to you as a demonstrated fact; but I must add a necessary explanation.

Before a queen begins her great laying of male eggs she must be 11 months old, when younger she lays only worker eggs. A queen hatched in spring will perhaps lay 50 or 60 male eggs, altogether, during the course of the summer, but before she begins her great laying of drone eggs, which should be of one or two thousand, she must have completed her 11ᵗʰ month. In the course of our experiments, which more or less disturbed the natural sequence of things, it often happened that the queen did not attain this age until October; and from that time began laying male eggs; the workers also selected that time to build royal cells, as if they were induced to it by some emanation from them. Note: The laying of drone eggs by a young queen in October is a very unusual incident and we wonder whether Huber noticed such a thing more than once. It appears to us to have been an exception probably from the failing of this queen.—Translator. No swarm resulted, for in the autumn the requisite circumstances are absolutely wanting; but it is no less evident that there is a secret relation between the laying of the eggs of males and the construction of royal cells.

This laying usually continues 30 days. On the 20th or 21st day, from its beginning, the bees lay the foundation of several royal cells; they sometimes build 16 or 20, we have seen as many as 27. As soon as they are 2 or 3 lines in depth (1/6th in.=4 mm 3 lines=¼ in.=6 mm) the queen lays in them eggs of her own sort, but does not lay them all the same day: in order that the hive may throw several swarms, it is important that the young females that are to conduct them be not all born at the same time; it seems as if the queen knew it in advance, for she takes care to allow at least a day between the laying of each egg deposited in these cells. Here is the evidence: the bees know that the cells must be sealed at the time when the worms in them are about to transform into nymphs; they close these cells at different dates; so it is evident that the worms in them are not precisely of the same age.

The queen's belly is extremely distended, before she begins to lay drone eggs, but it decreases sensibly as she advances, in this laying, and when it is terminated, her belly is very slender: she then finds herself in a state to undertake a journey which circumstances may prolong: therefore this condition was necessary; and as everything harmonized in the laws of nature, the time of birth of the males corresponds with that of the females which they are to fecundate.

2nd: The 1st swarm cast by a hive in the spring is always conducted by the old queen

When the larvae hatched from the eggs, laid by the queen in the royal cells are ready to transform to nymphs, this queen leaves the hive leading a swarm with her: it is a constant rule that the first swarm cast by a hive in the spring is always conducted by the old queen.

I think I can divine the reason of it: in order that at no time there be a plurality of females in the hive, Nature has inspired the queens with a mutual hate for one another: they cannot meet without seeking to fight and destroy each other. When nearly of equal age, the chance of combat is equal between them and chance decides to which the throne shall belong; but if one combatant be older than the others, she is stronger, and the advantage will be with her; she will destroy her rivals successively as they are born. Thus if the old queen did not leave the hive before the young ones emerge from the royal cells, she would destroy them all at the time of their last transformation: the hive could not swarm and the species would perish. In order to preserve the race, it was necessary that the old queen should conduct the first swarm. But what is the secret means employed by Nature to induce her to depart? I do not know.

In our country it is very rare, though not without example, for the swarm led by an old queen to become populous enough, in the space of three weeks to give a new colony, which the same queen conducts also; and it may happen as follows:

Nature has not willed that she should quit the first hive before completing her laying of male eggs; it was necessary that she should be freed of them that she might become lighter; besides, if her first occupation, when entering a new domicile, was the laying of more males, she might perish by age or accident before laying those of workers; the bees then would have no means of replacing her and the colony would perish.

All of these matters have been anticipated with infinite wisdom. The first action of a swarm is to build worker cells: they work upon them with much ardor and as the ovaries of the queen have been disposed with admirable foresight, the first eggs that she lays in her new habitation are worker eggs. This laying ordinarily continues 10 or 11 days; and during that time the bees build some combs with large cells. It appears as if they knew that she would lay drone eggs also: indeed, she again deposits some, though in much smaller number than the first time; yet enough to encourage the bees to construct royal cells. Now, if in these circumstances the weather remains favorable, it is not impossible that a second colony may be formed, which will be led by the old queen, 3 weeks after her having headed the first swarm. But I repeat it, this fact is rare in our climate: I now return to the history of the hive from which the queen has led the first colony.

3rd: The Instinct of Bees is Affected During the Period of Swarming

As soon as the old queen has conducted the first swarm, the bees remaining in the hive take particular care of the royal cells, guard them severely, and permit the young queens reared in them to emerge only successively, at an interval of several days from each other.

In my previous letter, Sir, I gave you the details and proofs of this fact: I shall add some reflections. During the period of swarming, the instinct of the bees seems to receive a particular modification. At any other time, when they have lost their queen, they design several workers' worms to replace her, prolong and enlarge the cells of these worms, give them food more abundant and of a more pungent taste; and by these cares they cause to grow into queens worms that would have been only common bees naturally. We have seen them build at one time 27 royal cells of this sort, but when they are sealed the bees no longer endeavor to preserve the young females in them from the attacks of their enemies. One of them will perhaps leave her cradle first, and will assail all the other royal cells successively, which she will tear open should several queens hatch at the same time, they will seek each other, will fight, there will be several victims, and the throne will remain with the victorious female. Far from opposing such duels, the bees appear rather to excite the combatants.

It is quite different in the time of swarms. The royal cells then constructed are of a different shape from the former; they are built like stalactites; when just outlined they fairly resemble the cup of an acorn. As soon as the young queens reared in them are ready for their last transformation the bees assiduously guard them. The female from the first egg laid by the old queen hatches at last; the workers treat her first with indifference; soon she yields to the instinct which urges her to destroy her rivals; she seeks the cells where they are enclosed; but no sooner does she approach, than the bees pinch her, pull her, chase her and compel her to withdraw; and the royal cells being numerous, scarcely can she find in the hive a place to rest. Ceaselessly tormented with the desire of attacking the other queens, and ceaselessly repelled, she becomes agitated, she hastily traverses the different groups of workers to which she communicates her agitation. At this instant we see numbers of bees rush towards the entrances of the hive; they fly out with their young queen and go seek another home elsewhere. After their departure, the remaining workers liberate another queen, which they treat with the same indifference as the first, chasing her away from the royal cells, and which, perpetually harassed in her way, becomes agitated, departs, carrying another swarm along with her. This scene is repeated three or four times during the spring, in a well peopled hive. At last, the number of bees becomes so greatly reduced that they can no longer preserve a strict watch over the royal cells; several young females emerge at the same time from their prison, they seek each other, fight, and the victorious queen of all these duels thereafter reigns peaceably over the republic.

The longest intervals we have observed between the departures of each natural swarm, were between 7 and 9 days. This is the time that usually elapses between the first colony led out by the old queen, and the swarm conducted by the young liberated females; the interval is shorter between the second and the third; and the fourth sometimes departs the day after the third. In hives left to themselves, 15 to 18 days are sufficient for the casting of 4 swarms, if the weather is favorable, as I am about to explain.

We never see a swarm form except on a fine day, or to speak more exactly, at the time of the day when the sun shines and the air is calm. We have observed in a hive all the precursors of swarming, disorder, agitation; but a cloud passed before the sun, and calm was restored in the hive; the bees thought no longer of leaving. An hour afterwards, the sun having again appeared, the tumult was renewed, it grew rapidly and the swarm left.

Bees in general seem much alarmed at the prospect of bad weather. When they range about the fields, the passage of a cloud before the sun induces them to return precipitately, and

I am inclined to believe that it is the sudden diminution of the light which disquiets them, for if the sky is uniformly cloudy, and there are no alterations of clearness and obscurity, they go to the field for their ordinary collections and even the first drops of a light rain do not make them return in great precipitation.

I have no doubt that the necessity of a fine day for the casting of a swarm is one of the reasons which induced nature to give the bees the means of protracting the captivity of their young queens in the royal cells. I will not conceal the fact that they sometimes appear to use this privilege in an arbitrary manner; however the confinement of the queens is always longer when bad weather lasts for several days together. Here the final object cannot be mistaken. Were the young females at liberty to leave their cradles, as soon as they completed their last development, there would be a plurality of queens in the hives during the bad days, and consequently combats and victims: the bad weather might continue until all the queens reached the term of their development and attained their liberty. After the fights, one alone, victorious over the others, would remain in possession of the throne, and the hive, which naturally should produce several swarms, could not give a single one: the multiplication of the species would thus be left to the chance of rain or fine weather, instead of which it is rendered independent of either by the wise disposition of Nature. By allowing a single female to escape at one time, the formation of swarms is ensured. This explanation appears so simple that I think it superfluous to insist up upon it.

But I should mention another important circumstance resulting from the captivity of queens in the royal cells; it is that they are able to fly and leave as soon as the bees free them, and by this means they are capable of profiting of the first moment of sunshine to lead away a colony.

You know, Sir, that none of the bees, whether workers or drones are able to fly before a day or two after leaving the cell, they are still weak, whitish, their organs are infirm; at least 24 or 30 hours are required before the acquisition of perfect strength, and the development of their faculties. It would be the same with the females, where not their confinement protracted beyond the period of transformation, but we see them emerge strong, brown, full grown and in better condition for flying than they will be at any other time of their life. I have elsewhere mentioned the constraint employed by the bees to retain the females in captivity; with a band of wax they solder the cappings of the cells to the sides. I have also explained how they feed them, so will not repeat these details here.

Queens are Liberated From Their Cells According to Their Age

Another remarkable fact is that the females are set at liberty according to their age. We marked all the royal cells with numbers at the time when they were sealed by the workers; and we chose this period because it exactly indicated the age of the queens. We noticed that the oldest one was always liberated first, the one immediately younger was next, and so on; none of the females was freed from prison before the elder ones.

The Bees Probably Judge of This by the Sound

I have asked myself, a hundred times, how do bees distinguish so accurately the age of their captives? I should do better to answer this question, like so many others, by a simple avowal of my ignorance; however, Sir, permit me to offer a conjecture. You know that I have not abused, as some authors do, the right of giving myself up to hypothesis. May not the pipings or sound emitted by the young queens, in their cells, be one of the means employed by Nature to inform the bees in the age of their queens? It is certain that the female whose cell was closed first, pipes first also. The queen in the cell closed next pipes sooner than the others, and so on to the end. As their captivity may last 8 or 10 days, it is still possible that the bees may forget which queen piped first, but it is also possible that the queens diversify their song, increasing it as they become older, and the bees may distinguish these variations. We have been able, ourselves to recognize differences in the piping, either in the succession of notes, or in the intensity of the piping; there are probably still more imperceptible variations, which escape our organs, but which those of the workers may recognize.

That which gives weight to this conjecture is the fact that the queens reared by the method discovered by Schirach are entirely mute; and the workers never form any guard around their cells, (supersedure cells—Translator) of their transformation: when they have undergone it, they permit them to fight to the death until one has been victorious over all the rest. Why? Because then the sole object is to replace the lost queen; so, provided that among the worms reared as queens, a single one succeeds, the fate of the others is uninteresting to the bees; whereas, at the time of swarms, it is necessary to rear a succession of queens, for conducting the diverse colonies; and to ensure the safety of these queens, they must be preserved from the consequences of the mutual hate which animates them against each other. That is evident cause of all the precautions that bees, instructed by Nature, take during the period of swarming; that is the explanation of the captivity of the females; and in order that the duration of this captivity be measured upon the age of the queens, it was requisite for them to have some means of distinguishing the time when they should be liberated. This means consists in the piping which they emit, and the variations which they are able to give it.

In spite of all my researches, I have been unable to discover the situation of the organ which serves in producing this sound. I have undertaken a new course of experiments upon this subject, but they are still unfinished.

There is still another problem to be solved: why is it that the queens reared by Mr. Schirach's method are mute, while those bred in swarming time have the faculty of emitting a certain sound? What is the physical cause of this difference?

I thought at first that it must be ascribed to the period of their life when the worms that are to become queens receive the royal pap. At the time of swarms, the royal worms receive the royal food, from the moment of leaving the egg: on the contrary, those intended for queens, by Mr. Schirach's method, receive it only on the second or third day of their existence. It appeared to me that this circumstance was quite influential upon the different parts of the organs, and especially on the vocal organs; but experiments have destroyed this conjecture.

I caused to be constructed glass tubes in exact imitation of royal cells, to observe the manner of metamorphosis of those worms into nymphs, and of the nymphs into queens. In my eighth letter, I described the observations which I here recall. We introduced into one of these artificial cells the nymph of a worm reared for a queen according to Mr. Schirach's method. We performed this operation 24 hours before the time when it was to undergo its last transformation, and we replaced the glass cell into the hive, that they nymph might have the necessary degree of heat. On the following day, we had the pleasure of seeing it divest itself of its' cast-skin and assume its ultimate form; she could not escape from her prison, but we had contrived a small aperture, so that she might thrust out her trunk, that the bees might feed her. I expected her to be complete mute; but she emitted sounds similar to those described elsewhere; therefore my conjecture was erroneous.

I next supposed that the queen, being restrained in her motions and in her desire for liberty, this constraint induced her to emit these sounds. From this new point of view, the queens, whether reared by the Schirach method or the other, should be equally capable of piping, but to be induced to it, they must be under restraint. But those produced from worker worms are not under restraint in a single moment of their life, in a natural condition; and if they do not pipe, it is not because they are deprived the voice organ, it is because nothing impels them to pipe: on the other hand, those that are born at the time of swarming are induced to it by the captivity in which the bees keep them. I give little weight to this conjecture, Sir, and though I state it here, it is less to claim merit than to put other observers in the way of discovering a better conjecture.

Neither will I claim the credit of having discovered the piping of the queen. Ancient authors mentioned it; upon this matter, Mr. de Réaumur cites a work published in Latin in 1671 under the title of *Monarchia Feminina*, by Charles Butler (See Réaumur, Vol. V. *inquarto,* pages 232 and 615).

He gives a short abstract of the observations of this naturalist, who we can easily see, had embellished or rather disguised the truth, by mixing with it the most absurd fancies; but it is nevertheless evident that Butler had heard the real piping of queens, and did not confound it with the confused hum frequently heard in the hives.

4th: *Young Queens Conducting Swarms are Virgins*
When young queens leave the hive, leading a swarm, they are still in the virgin state.

The day following the settling in their new abode is usually that in which they go in quest of the males; that time is commonly the fifth day of their life as queens; for they spend 2 or 3 days in captivity, one at freedom in the native before issuing, and the fifth in their new domicile; the queens reared from worker worms, by the Lusatian method, also spend 5 days in the hive before flying for fecundation. The ones as well as the others, are treated with indifference by the bees, as long as they retain their virginity; but as soon as they return with the external signs of fecundation, they are welcomed by their subjects with most willing respect. However 46 hours elapse after fecundation before they begin to lay. The old queens, that lead the first swarm in spring, do not need further commerce with the males to preserve their fecundity. A single mating is therefore sufficient to impregnate all the eggs which they will lay for two years at least.

I have the honor of being, etc.

11ᵀᴴ Letter—On the Formation of Swarms Continued

Pregny, September 10, 1791

Sir, I have collected, in the two preceding letters, my principal observations upon swarms, those most frequently repeated, and of which the constantly uniform results left to me no apprehension of error. I have drawn what appeared to be the most immediate consequences, and in all the theoretical part, I have carefully avoided advancing beyond facts. What remains to be mentioned today is more conjectural, but you will find there the relation of several experiments which I believe interesting.

The Conduct of Bees to Old Queens is Peculiar

I have shown that the principal motive of the departure of young females at the time of swarming is their insuperable antipathy to each other; I have repeatedly stated that they cannot gratify their aversion because the workers, with the utmost care, prevent them from attacking the royal cells. This perpetual contrariness to their actions at length gives them a visible inquietude, a degree of agitation that induces them to depart: all the young females are successively treated in the same way in hives that are to swarm. But the bees behave very differently towards the old queen destined to conduct the first swarm; always accustomed to respect fertile queens, they do not forget what they owe to her; they allow her the greatest liberty in all her motions; they permit her to approach the royal cells, and even if she attempts to destroy them, the bees do not object. She executes her wishes without obstacle, and her flight cannot be ascribed, like that of the young females, to the opposition she meets; therefore, in the preceding letters I candidly confessed myself ignorant of the motive of her departure.

However, on more mature reflection, it did not appear to me that this fact affords so strong an objection against the general rule as I had at first conceived. It is very certain, at least, that the old queens, as well as the young ones, entertain the greatest aversion towards the individuals of their own sex. I had the proof of it in the great number of royal cells that I saw them destroy. You will remember, Sir, that in the detail of my first observation on the departure of the old queen, I mentioned 7 royal cells opened on the side and destroyed by this queen. When the weather is rainy for several days in succession, they destroy them all, in which case there is no swarm, as too often happens in our country, where the springs are ordinarily rainy. Queens never attack those cells where there is only an egg or a very young worm in them; but they begin to fear them when the worm is about to transform into a nymph or when it has already undergone this transformation.

The presence of royal cells containing nymphs or worms near the change into nymphs, inspires old queens with the utmost horror or aversion, but there remains to be explained why, being free to destroy them, they do not always do so. On this I am limited to conjectures. It may be that the great number of royal cells in a hive at one time, and the labor required to open them all, creates in the old queens an insuperable terror; they commence indeed with attacking their rivals, but incapable of succeeding promptly, their disquiet increases and changes to a terrible agitation. If, at this time, the weather is favorable, they are naturally disposed to depart.

It may readily be understood that the workers, accustomed to their queen, whose presence is for them a real necessity, crowd after her in her departure, and the formation of the first swarm creates no difficulty in this respect.

What induces the bees to follow the young queens?
But undoubtedly you will ask, Sir, what motive can induce the bees to follow the young queens from the hive, when they treat them so badly, and in their most amicable moments testify perfect indifference towards them. It is probably to escape the heat to which the hive is then exposed. The extreme agitation of the young females, before the cast, induces them to run back and forth on the combs; they pass through the groups of bees, shock them, bewilder them, and impart their delirium to them, and this tumultuous disorder raises the temperature to an insupportable degree. We several times

proved it by the thermometer. In a populous hive, in the spring it is usually between 27° and 29° Réaumur (90° to 97° F or 32° to 36° C), but during the tumult which precedes swarming it rises above the 32° Réaumur (104° F or 40° C), and this is intolerable to bees; when exposed to it, they rush precipitately towards the entrances and depart. In general, they cannot endure a sudden increase of heat; they leave their domicile when they feel it, neither do those returning from the field enter when the temperature is extraordinary.

Through direct experiments I have ascertained that the impetuous courses of the queen over the combs really excite the bees, and this is how I ascertained it. I desired to avoid a complication of causes; it was especially important to learn whether, outside of the time of swarming, the agitation of a queen would be transmitted to the bees. I took two virgin females, over five days old, and susceptible of fecundation. I put them in separate glass hives, sufficiently populous; after having introduced them, I closed the openings so that the air had free circulation but the bees could not escape. I prepared to observe these hives at every moment of the day when weather invites both males and queens to take flight for fecundation: the following day the weather was variable, none of the males issued from my apiary, and the bees were tranquil; but the next day, towards 11 o'clock, the sun shining, my two imprisoned queens began to run about, seeking an exit in all parts of their domicile, and finding none, traveled over the combs with most evident symptoms of disquiet and agitation; soon the bees participated in this disorder; I saw them crowd to the bottom of the hives where the entrances are situated; unable to escape, they ascended with equal rapidity, and ran blindly over the cells until 4 in the afternoon. This is about the hour when the sun, declining on the horizon, recalls the males to their hives: queens requiring fecundation never remain later abroad; so the two females which I observed became calmer and in short time, tranquility was restored. This proceeding was repeated several days in succession, with perfectly similar symptoms, and I became convinced that the agitation of bees, at the time of the casting of swarms, has nothing singular, but that the hives are always in great tumult when the queen herself is agitated.

Swarm queens are all different ages, yet emergency queens are all the same age

I have but one more fact to mention, Sir; I have already stated that when the bees have lost their female, they give to simple worker worms the royal education, and that, according to the discovery of Mr. Schirach, they usually repair the loss in 10 days. In this case, there is no swarming; all the young females emerge from their cells at about the same time, and after a cruel war, the empire remains to the most fortunate one.

I comprehend well that the principal intention of Nature is to replace the lost queen; but since the bees are at liberty, for this operation, to select eggs or worms of workers during the first 3 days of their life, why do they give royal treatment only to worms of equal age, which are to undergo their last metamorphosis at about the same time? Since they are able, at the time of swarming, to retain the young females in captivity within their cells for more or less time, why do they allow the queens, that are reared by the Schirach method, to escape all at once? By prolonging their captivity more or less, they could fulfill two most important objects, in repairing the loss of their females, and securing a succession of queens to conduct several swarms.

I first supposed that this difference in conduct proceeded from the different circumstances in which they find themselves. They are induced to make all dispositions relative to swarming only when in great numbers, and when they have a queen occupied with her great laying of male eggs; whereas, when they have lost their female, they no longer find drone eggs in the combs to influence their instinct; they are in a certain degree, disquiet and discouraged.

Therefore after removing a queen, I contrived to render all the other circumstances as similar as possible to those in which the bees find themselves when they prepare to cast a swarm. I increased excessively the population of the hive, by introducing into it a great number of workers; I supplied them with several combs containing male brood in all stages. Their first occupation was to construct royal cells after Schirach's methods, and to rear worker larvae with royal food: they also began the building of several cells in stalactite shape; as if urged to it by the presence of male brood; but they did not complete them, for there was no queen among them to deposit eggs in them. Lastly I gave them several sealed royal cells, taken indifferently from hives preparing to swarm; but all these precautions were useless. My bees were occupied only with replacing their lost queen, they gave no particular care to the royal cells which I had entrusted to them; the queens in them emerged at the usual time without having been confined a single instant, they fought several combats, and there were no swarms.

Recurring to subtleties, we might perhaps point out the cause or the aim of this apparent oddity; but the more we admire the wise dispositions of the author of nature, in the laws which He had prescribed to the industry of animals, the greater reserve we need in admitting any supposition adverse to this beautiful system, the more we must distrust the facility of imagination with which, by embellishing the facts, we seek to explain them.

In general, the naturalists who have long observed the animals, and those especially who have selected the insects for the favorite object of their studies, have too readily ascribed to them our sentiments, our passions and even our views. Yielding to admiration, disgusted perhaps with the contempt generally shown in speaking of insects, they have conceived themselves obliged to justify the consumption of time which they bestowed upon them, and have embellished the different traits of the industry of these minute animals with all the colors supplied by an exalted imagination. Even our celebrated Réaumur is not altogether exempt from reproach on this score: in depicting the history of bees, he often ascribes to them combined intentions, love, foresight and other faculties of too elevated an order. I think I perceive that, although he formed for himself very correct ideas of their operations, he would have been pleased if his reader admitted that they are sensible of their own interest. He is a painter who, by happy prejudice, flatters the original whose features he depicts. On the other hand, the illustrious Buffon unjustly considers bees as pure automatons. It was reserved for you, Sir, to restore the theory of animal industry towards more philosophical principles, and to show that those of their actions which have a moral appearance depend on the association of *purely sensible ideas.* It is not my intention here to penetrate such depths or insist upon the details.

But as the ensemble of the facts relative to the formation of swarms presents perhaps more subjects of admiration than any other part of the history of bees, I believe it proper to point out in a few words the simplicity of means by which wise nature directs the instinct of these insects. It could not grant to them the least portion of intelligence; it left to them, therefore, no precaution to take, no combination to follow, no foresight to exercise, no knowledge to acquire. But after molding their *sensorium* in conformity with the diverse operations with which they were charged, it was through the impulse of pleasure that it directed their execution. It therefore preordained all the circumstances relative to the succession of their different labors and to each of these it united an agreeable sensation. Note: It has since been ascertained that it is most probably the "agreeable sensation" here mentioned which impels the queen to lay mostly the eggs of workers, which are fecundated as they pass by the spermatheca. It is only when she is fatigued by the continuous recurrence of this agreeable sensation that she rests herself by laying unfertilized or drone eggs which evidently pass out without effort on her part. It is to be regretted that Huber did not know of parthenogenesis when he wrote the above.—Translator. Thus when bees construct their cells, when they care for the worms, when they collect provisions, we must seek there neither method, nor affection, nor foresight; we must consider, as the determining cause, only the pleasure of a sweet sensation, attached to each of these functions. I address a philosopher, and as these are his own opinions applied to new facts, I believe my language will be understood; but I beg my readers to read and meditate upon those of your works which treat of the industry of animals. Let me add but this: that the attraction of pleasure is not the sole impulse that prompts them; there is another principle, the prodigious influence of which at least is regard to bees, was not yet know; that is the sentiment of aversion which all the females feel against each other, at all times, a sentiment whose existence is so well demonstrated by my observations, and which explains a multitude of important facts in the theory of swarms.

12ᵀᴴ Letter—Queens Laying Drone Eggs, Queens Deprived of Their Antennae

Pregny, September 12, 1791

Sir, in relating to you in the third letter, my first observations upon queens that lay only the eggs of drones, I have shown that they deposit these eggs indifferently, in cells of all dimensions, and even in royal cells: I said also that the common bees give, to the worms from the drone eggs laid in royal cells, the same care as if they were actually to be transformed into queens; and I added that in the instance, the instinct of workers appeared to be at fault.

Note: I have ascertained through new observations, that bees recognize the larvae of drones, as well when the eggs producing them have been laid in royal cells, by queens whose fecundations has been retarded, as when they have been deposited in common cells.

It has not been forgotten that the royal cells are shaped like a pear, the large end of which is at the top; or in the shape of an inverted pyramid, the axis of which is about vertical, and the length of 15 or 16 lines (about 1 ¼ in. or 32 mm). It is known also that queens lay in those cells when they are but outlined, when they fairly resemble the cup of an acorn.

The bees give the same shape and dimensions, at first, to the cells which serve as cradles for males; but when their larvae are about to be transformed, it is easy to perceive that they have not taken them for royal worms; for instead of closing their cells in pointed form, as they invariably do when containing larvae of the latter sort, they widen them at the end, and after adding a cylindrical tube, they close them with a convex capping, differing in nothing from those which they are accustomed to put on the cells of males; but as this tube is of the same capacity as the hexagon cells of the smallest diameter, the larvae which the bees thus cause to descend into this part of the cell, and which are to undergo there their last metamorphosis, become drones of the smaller size. The total length of these extraordinary cells is 20 to 22 lines (1 2/3 to 1 5/6 in. 42 to 47 mm).

Yet, the bees do not always add a cylinder to a pyramidal cell; they are then content with enlarging a little their lower part, and the larvae which make their growth there may become large drones. I am ignorant of the cause of the differences sometimes observed in the shape of these cells; but it appears very certain to me that the bees never are deceived in them, giving us in this occasion a great proof of the instinct with which they are endowed. Nature, which has entrusted the bees with the rearing of their young, and with the care of providing them with aliments proper to their age, or even to their sex, must have taught them how to recognize them. There is so little resemblance between adult males and workers, that some difference must also exist between the larvae of both kinds; doubtless the workers distinguish it, though it has escaped our notice.

Indeed it is very singular that the bees knowing the worms of males so well, when the eggs from which they are produced are laid in small cells, and never failing to give them a convex capping at the time of their transformation into nymphs, should no longer recognize the worms of this sort, when the eggs from which they hatch are laid in royal cells, and treat them as if they were to become queens. This irregularity depends upon something which I cannot fathom.

In revising what I had the honor to write you upon this subject, I realized that there was still an interesting experiment wanting to complete the history of queens that lay only the eggs of drones; it was to investigate whether those females themselves could distinguish that the eggs which they lay in royal cells are not of the female sort: I had already observed that they do not try to destroy these cells when sealed, and I thence concluded that, in general, the presence of royal cells in their hive does not inspire in them the same aversion as it does to the females whose fecundation has not been delayed: but to ascertain the fact more positively, it was necessary to examine how the presence of a cell containing a royal nymph would affect a queen that had never laid any other than drone eggs.

This experiment was easy; I made it on the 4th of September of this year, upon one of my hives which had been deprived of its natural queen, for some time. The bees of this hive had not failed to construct several royal cells to replace their female. I chose this moment to give them a queen whose fecundation had been retarded to the 28th day, and which laid none but the eggs of males; at the same time, I removed all the royal cells, except one that had been sealed 5 days: a single cell remaining was sufficient to show the impression it would make on the strange queen just placed among the bees. If she endeavored to destroy it, it would be, to my mind, a proof that she foresaw the birth of a dangerous rival. Please, Sir, to excuse this use of the term *foresee,* which I recognize as improper, but it avoids a long circumlocution. If, on the contrary, she did not attack it, I would thence conclude that the delay of fecundation, which deprived her of the faculty of laying worker eggs, had also impaired her instinct: and that is what came to pass: this queen passed over the royal cell several times, that day and the next, without seeming to distinguish it from the rest; she laid very quietly in the surrounding cells; and notwithstanding the cares constantly bestowed by the bees upon this cell; she did not appear for an instant to suspect the peril with which she was threatened by the royal nymph there included. Besides, the workers treated their new queen as well as they would have treated any other female: they lavished honey and *respects* upon her, and formed around her those regular circles which one would be tempted to consider as the expression of homage.

Retarded Impregnation Affects the Instinct of Queens

Thus, independent of the disorder which the delay of fecundation causes in the sexual organs of the queens, it certainly imparts their instinct; they no longer entertain aversion or jealousy against those of their own sex in the nymph state; they no longer seek to destroy them in their cradles.

My reader will be surprised that these queens, whose fecundation has been retarded, and whose fecundity is so useless to the bees, nevertheless should be so welcome and should become as dear to them as the females that lay eggs of both kinds; but I remember observing a fact more astonishing still. I saw workers bestow every attention on their queen though sterile, and after her death treat her dead body as they had treated her when alive, and long prefer this inanimate body to the most fertile queens that I offered them. This sentiment, which assumes the appearance of so lively an affection, is probably the effect of some agreeable sensation communicated by the queen to the bees, independent of their fertility. The queens which lay only male eggs doubtless excite the same sensation in workers.

While recalling this last observation, I remembered a statement of Swammerdam: this celebrated author stated, somewhere, that when a queen is blind sterile, or mutilated, she ceases to lay and the workers of the hive no longer gather any crop or do any work, as if they knew that in such a case, it is useless to labor; but in advancing this fact, he does not cite the experiments which caused him to discover it; those made by myself have given me some very curious results.

I several times amputated the four wings of queens, and after this mutilation, not only did they continue to lay, but the workers showed them no less consideration than before. Swammerdam therefore has no foundation for saying that mutilated queens cease to lay; indeed in his ignorance of the necessity of fecundation outside of the hive, it is possible that he cut the wings off virgin queens, and that they, becoming incapable of flight, remained barren from their inability to seek the males in the air. The amputation of their wings does not render them sterile, if they were fecundated before losing them.

We frequently cut off one of the antennae to recognize a queen more readily, and this was not prejudicial, either to her fecundity or her instinct, nor to the attention paid to her by the bees; it is true that, as one antenna still remained, the mutilation was imperfect, and this experiment decided nothing.

But the amputation of both antennae produced most singular results. On the 5th of September of this year, I caused to be cut off both of the antennae of that same queen which laid only male eggs, and replaced her in the hive immediately after the operation: from that time, there was great alteration in her manner. We saw her travel over the combs with extraordinary vivacity; scarcely had the workers time to separate and recede before her: she dropped her eggs haphazard, without thinking of depositing them in any cells. As the hive was not very populous, a part of it was without combs; it was there she repaired; she remained long motionless and appeared to avoid the bees; however a few workers followed her in this solitude, and treated her with most evident respect, seldom did she ask for honey; but when she did she directed her trunk only with an uncertain groping, sometimes upon the legs and sometimes upon the heads of the workers, and when it reached their mouths it was by chance. At other times she returned upon the combs, then quitted them to run upon the glass sides of the hive, and in all her various motions she still dropped her eggs. At other times she appeared tormented with the desire of leaving her habitation rushing towards the entrance, she entered the glass tube adapted to it, but the external orifice of this tube being too small for her passage, after useless efforts she returned; notwithstanding these symptoms of delirium the bees did not cease to render her the same attention as they ever pay to their queens, but she received it with indifference. All the symptoms just described appeared to me as the effect of the amputation of the antennae; however, her organization having already suffered from retarded fecundation and as I had observed a sort of weakening in her instinct, the two causes might possibly concur in operating the same effect. To distinguish what particularly belonged to the deprivation of the antennae it was necessary to repeat the experiment upon a queen otherwise well organized, and capable of laying both kinds of eggs.

Amputation of the Antennae Produces Singular Effects

This was done on the 6th of September; I amputated the antennae of a female which I had been observing for several months, and which, gifted with great fecundity, had already laid a great number of eggs of workers and males. I placed her afterwards in the same hive where the queen of the preceding experiment still remained, and she exhibited precisely the same signs of agitation and delirium which I think useless to repeat: I shall only add that, in order to better judge of the effect produced by the privation of the antennae upon the industry and instinct of queen bees, I observed attentively how these two mutilated queens treated each other: you have not forgotten, Sir, the fierceness in the combat of two queens, when they possess all their organs: so it was very interesting to learn whether they would experience the same reciprocal aversion, after losing their antennae. We watched these a long time; they met several times in their courses, and did not exhibit the slightest sign of malevolence. This last fact is, in my opinion, the most complete proof of the change operated in their instinct.

Another very remarkable circumstance, which the experiment just related gave me occasion to observe, was the good reception which the bees gave this second stranger queen, while they still preserved the first. After having so often seen the signs of discontent occasioned by a plurality of queens in their hives, after having witnessed the clusters which they form around supernumerary queens to confine them, I could not expect them to render the same care to this second mutilated queen as they had given the first. Was it not that, after the loss of their antennae, these queens no longer retained any characteristics serving to distinguish one from the other?

I should be more inclined to admit this conjecture, that when I introduced into this hive a third fertile queen who had retained her antennae, she was exceedingly badly received. The bees seized her, bit her, surrounded her so closely that she could hardly breathe or move. Therefore, if they treat equally well two females, deprived of their antennae, in the same hive; it is probably, because they experience the same sensation from both, and have no longer means of distinguishing them from each other.

From all this I conclude that the antennae are not a frivolous ornament for insects; to all appearances they are the organs of touch or smell; but I cannot decide which of these two senses resides in them; it is not impossible that they be organized in such a manner as to fulfill both functions at once.

As in the course of this Experiment, the two mutilated females constantly desired to escape from their hives. I wished to see what either of them would do, if set at liberty and whether the bees would accompany her in her flight: therefore, I removed from the hive the first queen introduced, and also the third leaving the fertile mutilated one, and I enlarged the glass tube of the entrance, so that she might pass out.

During the same day, this queen left her habitation; at first she took flight, but as her belly was still full of eggs, she seemed too heavy, could not sustain her flight, fell down and did not attempt it again. No workers accompanied her. But why did they abandon her at her departure, after having given her so much attention, while she lived among them? You know, Sir, that queens governing a weak swarm are sometimes discouraged, and leave their hive, leading away all their little population with them.

Similarly also sterile queens, and those whose homes are ravaged by the moths, depart and are followed by all their bees. Why then, in the experiment which I relate here, did the workers allow their mutilated queen to depart alone?

I shall answer this question by only a conjecture. It appears that bees are induced to quit their hive by the increase of heat occasioned by the agitation of their queen and the tumultuous disorder which she communicates to them. But the mutilated queens, notwithstanding their delirium, do not excite the workers because in their travel they seek especially the uninhabited parts and the glass panes of the hive; they strike some groups of bees in passing; but the shock is similar to that of any other body that produces only a local and instantaneous emotion; the agitation resulting from it is not communicated from one to another like that occasioned by the hurry of a queen which, in the natural state, wishes to abandon her hive and lead out a swarm: there is no augmented heat and consequently no cause to render the hive insupportable to the bees.

This conjecture, which fairly explains why bees persist in remaining in the hive, after the departure of their mutilated queen, does not account for the motive inducing the queen herself to depart. Her instinct is changed; this is all that I perceive; I see nothing more. It is very fortunate for the hive, however, that she should leave it promptly; for, since the bees do not cease caring for her, as long as she remained they would not think of securing another; and if she delayed her flight, it would be impossible for them to replace her; since the worms of workers would have passed the term at which they are convertible into royal worms, and the hive would never serve to replace her, for not being deposited in the cells, they wither and produce nothing.

One more remark upon females that lay only male eggs. Mr. Schirach thought that one branch of their double ovary suffered some alteration; he appears to have supposed the one of these branches contains only male eggs, while the other has none but worker eggs, and as he ascribed to some disease the incapacity of certain queens to lay worker eggs, his hypothesis was fairly plausible. In fact, if the eggs of males and those of workers are indiscriminately mixed in both branches of the ovary, it appears at first sight, that any cause acting upon this organ should equally affect the two kinds of eggs. If, on the contrary, one branch is solely occupied with eggs of drones and the other with worker eggs only, we may conceive that one of these branches may be diseased and the other intact. This conjecture, however presumable, is confuted by observation. We lately dissected several queens that laid only drone eggs and we found both branches of their ovaries equally developed, equally sound, if I may use this expression. The only difference which we noticed was that in these ovaries the eggs did not appear as close together as they are in the ovaries of queens which lay eggs of both sorts.

I have the honor to be etc.

13ᵀᴴ LETTER—ECONOMICAL VIEWS ON BEES

Pregny, October 1ˢᵗ 1791

Advantage of the Leaf Hive

Sir, I shall talk to you in this letter upon the advantages presented by hives of new construction which I have used, and which I have called *book hives* or *leaf hives,* for the promotion of the *economical science* of bees.

I will not relate the different methods hitherto employed to compel bees to yield to us a share of their honey and of their wax; they were all cruel and ill-understood.

It appears evident that when we cultivate bees to share the product of their harvests, we must endeavor to multiply them as much as the nature of the country permits, and consequently spare their lives at the time we plunder them. Therefore it is an absurd proceeding to sacrifice whole colonies to take the riches which they contain. The inhabitants of our districts, who follow no other methods, annually lose enormous numbers of hives, and as our springs are generally unfavorable to swarms, the loss is irreparable. I know well that they will not adopt my method at first: they are too much attached to their prejudices and their old customs; but the naturalists and the enlightened cultivators will be sensible of the utility of the process which I indicate, and if they put it to use, I hope their example will contribute to extend and perfect the culture of bees.

It is not more difficult to lodge a natural swarm in a leaf hive than in any other of a different shape. However there is a precaution essential to success which I must not omit. Though bees are indifferent to the position of their combs and their greater or less size, they are obliged to construct them perpendicular to the horizon and parallel. Therefore if they were left entirely to themselves, in establishing them in one of my new hives, they would often construct several small combs, parallel to each other indeed, but perpendicular to the plane of the frames or *leaves:* at other times they would fasten them on the joint of two of these frames, and by this disposition nullify the advantages that I claim to derive from the shape of my hives, since they could not be opened at will, without cutting the combs. We must therefore lay out the direction upon which they must build them; the cultivator himself must place the foundations of their edifice, and the method is very simple; it is sufficient that a portion of comb be fastened securely in the upper part of a few of the frames of which a hive is composed: you may be assured that the bees will lengthen this comb and in prosecution of their work will follow precisely the direction indicated.

Volume 1 Plate I Fig 3—Leaf Hive, open.

It Renders the Bees Tractable

Therefore you will never have any obstacle to overcome in opening the hive; no stings to dread, for that is also one of the singular and valuable properties of such construction, it renders the bees *tractable.* I appeal to you, Sir, in witness of this fact; in your presence I have opened all the frames of one of my most populous hives and you were much surprised at the tranquility of the bees. I desire no other proof of my assertion; but I must repeat it, for in the last analysis it is in the facility of opening those hives at pleasure that all the advantages depend for the perfecting of the economic science of beekeeping.

Leaf Hive with cover.

It is not necessary to add here that, when I say that I can render the bees *tractable,* I do not claim the silly presence of *domesticating* them, for this causes the vague idea of *charlatanism,* and I do not wish to expose myself to such reproach: I ascribe their tranquility, when their home is opened, to the manner in which they are affected by the sudden introduction of light; they appear rather to testify fear than anger; we see a great number withdraw, enter the cells head first, as if to conceal themselves; and my conjecture is confirmed by their being less tractable in the night or after sunset that in the day time.

Thus, we must select the time when the sun is still above the horizon, to open the hives, and do it with care. We must avoid opening the hive too brusquely; in separating the combs we must act slowly, taking care to wound none of the bees: when they are too much clustered upon the combs we must brush them softly with a feather, (A broom made of vegetable fiber, asparagus tops, grass, etc., is much less apt to anger them than a feather—Translator) and, above all things, not breathe upon them; the air which we exhale appears to anger them: the nature of this air evidently possesses some irritating quality; for if we use bellows to blow upon them, they are rather inclined to escape than to sting.

Convenient for Forming Artificial Swarms

Let me return to the detail of the advantages of *leaf* hives. I shall remark first that they are very convenient for forming *artificial* swarms. In the history of *natural* swarms, I have shown how many favorable circumstances were requisite for their success. I knew by experience that they very often fail in our climate; and even when a hive is disposed to swarm, it often happens that the swarm is lost, either because the instant of its departure has not been foreseen, because it rose out of sight, or because it settled in inaccessible places. Thus, instructing the cultivators, in the forming of artificial swarms, is doing them a real service, and the shape of my hives renders this operation very easy. This demands some explanations.

Since according to Schirach's discovery, bees which have lost their queen can procure another, provided there be worker brood in their combs not over 3 days old, it results that we can produce queens at will in a hive, by remove the reigning one. Therefore, if a sufficiently populous hive be divided in two, one half will retain the queen, and the other half will not be long in procuring one; but for the success of this operation we must choose a propitious moment, and this choice is easy and sure only in *leaf* hives: they are the only hives in which we can see whether the population is sufficient to admit of division, whether the brood is of proper age, whether males are born or ready to emerge to impregnate the young queen at her birth, etc.

Volume 1 Plate I Fig 2—Leaf Hive, with dividers in to make an artificial swarm.

Supposing the concurrence of all these conditions, the following is the process to be pursued. Separate the leaf hive through the middle without any jar. Between the two halves insert two empty leaves fitting exactly against the others, each of them closed with a box partition on the side where they fit against each other. You will then seek which of the two halves contains the reigning queen and mark it to avoid error. If by chance she remains in the division having the most brood, she is to be transferred into the one having less, in order to give the bees the greater chances of procuring another female. The two halves must now be connected with one another by a small cord tightly drawn around them, and care must be taken that they occupy the same stand in the apiary as before the operation. The opening which served as an entrance, up to this time, now becomes useless, it must be closed; but as each have hive must have an entrance and as they must be as far apart as possible, a new opening must be made at the bottom of each of the outside frames, that is to say, the 1st and the 12th (see Plate I). However these entrances must not be both opened on the same day: the bees that are deprived of queen must be confined in their half for 24 hours, and the door must be opened only enough to admit of the access of air. Without this precaution, they would soon emerge to seek their queen in the apiary and would not fail to find her in the other division, they would enter it in great number, until too few remained to perform the necessary labors: while this accident will not ensue, if they be confined for 24 hours, since that interval of time is sufficient to make them forget their queen.

When all the circumstances are favorable, the bees of the division which is deprived of queen will begin on the same day their labor to procure another, and their loss will be repaired 10 or 15 days after the operation. The young female they have reared soon afterwards issues to seek males, returns home fertilized and at the end of two days commences the laying of worker eggs. Nothing more is wanting to the bees of this half-hive and the success of the artificial swarm is assured.

It is to Mr. Schirach that we are indebted for this ingenious method of forming swarms. In the description which he gives, he holds that by producing young queens, in the early days of spring, precious swarms might be procured, which certainly would be advantageous in several circumstances: but unfortunately this is impossible: this observer believed that queens were fertile of themselves; consequently he imagined that, after they were artificially produced, they would lay and give birth to numerous posterity. But this is an error; the females require the concourse of the males to become fertile, and if they do not find any within a few days after their birth, their laying, as I have proved, is completely disarranged. Therefore if we made an artificial swarm before the usual time when the males are born, the young female would discourage the bees through her sterility or, should they remain faithful to her, awaiting the time of her fecundation, as she could not receive the approaches of the male before 3 or 4 weeks she would lay eggs producing drones only, and the hive would equally perish. Thus the natural order must not be disarranged; but on the contrary, we must wait, to divide the hives, until they contain drones born or near birth.

Besides, if Schirach succeeded in obtaining artificial swarms, notwithstanding the great inconvenience of the hives which he used, it was owing to much skill and continuous assiduity. He had formed some pupils; these in their turn had communicated to others the method of forming swarms. There are people now in Saxony who traverse the country practicing this operation; but those conversant with the matter can alone dare undertake it with common hives, whereas every cultivator can undertake it with leaf hives.

They May There be Forced to Work in Wax

They will find in this construction another very precious advantage; they will thus compel their bees to work in wax.

This leads me to what I believe is a new observation: while directing our admiration to the parallel position of the combs, which the bees build, the naturalists have overlooked another trait in their industry, namely the equal distance they uniformly preserve between them. Measure the interval between them you will find it usually of 4 lines (one-third inch or 8mm). One readily perceives that, were they too distant from one another, the bees would be greatly dispersed, unable to communicate their heat reciprocally and the brood could not receive sufficient warmth. If, on the contrary, they were too close, the bees could not travel freely between them, and the work of the hive would suffer. So they must be separated by a certain distance, always uniform, equally adapted to the service of the hive and the care of the worms. Nature, which taught bees so many things, instructed them in the regular preservation of this distance: it sometimes happens at the approach of winter that our bees lengthen the cells which are to contain honey, and thus contract the interval between the combs; but this particular labor is in preparation of a season when it is important to have great magazines, and during which, their activity being relaxed, it is no longer necessary for their communications to be so spacious and free. On the return of spring, the bees hasten to shorten the elongated cells, so they may become fit to receive the eggs which the queen must lay in them, and thus re-establish the suitable distance which nature has ordained.

Uniform Distance Between the Combs

This being premised, in order to compel the bees to work in wax, or which is the same thing to build new combs, it is only necessary to spread apart those already built, that they may construct others in the interval. Supposing that an artificial swarm is lodged in a leaf hive, composed of six frames, each of which contains a comb; if the young queen which governs this swarm is as prolific as she should be, her bees will be very active in their labors and disposed to make great collections of wax. To induce them towards it, an empty frame should be placed between two others, each containing a comb: as all these frames are of equal dimensions, and of the necessary width for containing a comb, it is evident that the bees, finding precisely the necessary space for constructing a new one in this empty frame will not fail to do so, because they are under the obligation of never leaving a space of more than 4 lines between them. Take notice, Sir, that without the need of guide for the direction to be followed, they certainly will build this new comb parallel to those already there, to preserve the law which requires an equal interval between them, throughout their entire surface.

If the hive is strong and the weather good, we may insert 3 empty frames between the old combs, one between the first and second, one between the third and fourth, and the last between the fifth and sixth. The bees will need 7 or 8 days to fill them and the hive will then contain 9 combs. Should the weather continue with a favorable temperature, one may introduce 3 more new frames, consequently in2 or 3 weeks the bees will have been forced to construct 6 new combs. The operation might be still further extended in warm climates, where the country presents perpetual bloom; but in our country I have reason to believe that the labor should not be forced further during the first year.

From these details you perceive, Sir, how preferable the leaf hives are to hives of any other form, and even to the ingenious ekes (or stories—Translator) of which Mr. Palteau gave a description, for by means of the latter, the bees cannot be compelled to work more in wax than they would if left to themselves; whereas they are obliged to do it by the alternating of empty frames. Secondly when they have constructed combs in these stories, they cannot be removed without deranging the bees, destroying considerable portions of the brood and in a word, without causing real disorder in the hive.

Besides mine have this advantage; that one may daily observe what passes, and judge of the most convenient moment to take from them a part of their crop. When we have all the combs before us, we distinguish easily those that contain only brood which we must preserve. We see how abundant the provisions are and what share of them we may take away.

I should too greatly lengthen this letter, were I to give you an account of all my observations of the time proper for inspecting hives, on the rules to be followed in the different seasons, and on the proportion to be observed in despoiling the bees of their wealth. It would require a separate work to develop the diverse details: I may someday engage in it. Meanwhile I shall be always disposed to communicate my method to the cultivators who may wish to follow it, and the directions of which a long practice has shown me the utility.

I shall add only that we run risk of absolute ruin for the hives, when we take from them too great a proportion of honey and wax. In my opinion the art of cultivating these insects consists in moderately using the right of sharing their crops, but to compensate this moderation every means must be employed to promote the multiplication of bees. Thus, for example, if we wish to procure, each year, a certain quantity of honey and wax, it will be better to seek it in a greater number of hives, manages with discretion than to plunder a few of a great proportion of their treasures.

It is certain that we injure greatly the multiplication of these industrious insects, when we rob them of several combs in a season unfavorable to the collection of wax, (Evidently Huber had not yet ascertained the origin of beeswax when he wrote this. His experiments upon the production of wax are given further— Translator) for the time occupied in replacing them is taken from that which should be consecrated to the care of the eggs and worms, and so the brood suffers. Besides we must always leave them a sufficient provision of honey for winter; for although they consume less during that season, they do consume, because they are not torpid, as some authors have asserted. Therefore, if they have not enough honey, they must be supplied with some; this requires a very exact measure.

Natural Heat of Bees

Note: They are so far from being torpid during the winter, that when the thermometer in the open air drops several degrees below zero R (Réaumur, $0°R=0°C=32°F$), it still stands at 24° to 35° R (86° to 88° F. or 30° to 44° C) in hives sufficiently populous. The bees then cluster together and move to preserve their heat.

Swammerdam was of the same opinion, and I will quote him: "The heat of the hive is so considerable, even in the middle of winter, that the honey dose not crystallize or assume a granulated consistency, unless the bees be in too small numbers; moreover when their queens are very fertile, they feed their young with honey, even in the middle of winter, caring for them, warming them and warming each other as well. I do not know whether there are any other insects that have this in common with bees, for hornets, wasps and bumble bees, as well as flies and butterflies, remain torpid during the whole of winter, without stirring or changing place."

Mr. de Réaumur found brood of all ages, in several hives, in January. The same thing happened to me, when the thermometer in them stood around 27° R (93° F or 34° C).

Since I am speaking of thermometric observations, made upon the hives I shall cursorily remark that Mr. Dubost of Bourg-en-Bresse, in a memoir otherwise worthy, asserts that worms cannot hatch below 32° R (104° F or 40° C). I have repeatedly made the experiment with very accurate thermometers and obtained a very different result. This degree is so little suitable that when the thermometer points to it, in the hive, the heat becomes intolerable to the bees, and they leave. I presume that Mr. Dubost was deceived by introducing his thermometer too suddenly in a cluster of bees, and the agitation causes among them, by this operation, forced the thermometer higher than it should naturally go. Had he kept it there a few moments, he would have seen it fall back to the 28^{tho} or 29^{tho} R (95° to 97° F or 35° or 36° C), for that is the ordinary temperature of hives in summer. In August this year, we saw the thermometer in the open air stand at 27½° F (94° F or 34° C) while at the same moment, in the most populous hives, it did not rise above the 30th° R (99° F or 37½ ° C). The bees had little motion and a great number of them rested on the supports of the apiary.

Distance to Which They Fly

I admit that in determining to what extent hives may be multiplied in a certain district, we should learn first how many this district can support and this is problem still unsolved: it depends on another problem the solution of which is not any better known, the determination of the greatest distance that bees ramble from their hives to gather their harvest. Different authors assert that they may wander several leagues from their home; but from the few observations that I have made, I believe this distance much exaggerated. It appeared to me that the radius of the circle they traverse does not exceed half a league (about 1 ½ miles or 2.4 Km). Since they return to their hive with the greatest speed, when a cloud passes before the sun, it is probably that they do not go very far. Nature, which has inspired them with such terror for a storm and even for rain, evidently does not permit them to stray at distances which expose them too long to the injuries of the weather. I endeavored to ascertain this more positively, by transporting to various distances from the apiary, and in all sorts of directions, bees with the corselet painted, that we might recognize them on their return. None ever returned which had been carried 25 or 30 minutes from their domicile, while those transported a less distance readily found their way back. I do not report this Experiment, Sir, as decisive. Though in ordinary conditions, bees do not fly above half a league, it is quite possible that they go much farther when the vicinity of their homes does not provide them with any flowers. For a conclusive experiment on this subject it would be necessary to make it in vast arid or sandy plains, separated by a known distance from a blooming country.

Thus this question appears undecided; but without pronouncing on the number of hives that a district can maintain, I shall remark that certain kinds of vegetable productions are much more favorable than others to bees. For example, more hives may be kept in a country where buckwheat is cultivated than in a district of vineyards or wheat.

Here, Sir, I terminate the account of my observations on bees. Though I had the good fortune to make some interesting discoveries, I am far from considering my labor finished; there are still several problems to solve on the history of these insects. The experiments which I project may throw some light on them. I shall have much greater hopes of success, if you, Sir, will continue to give me your advice and directions. Accept the homage of my respect and my gratitude.

FRANCIS HUBER

End of First Volume.

VOLUME II

PREFACE

Twenty years have elapsed since the publication of the first volume of this work; however, I have not remained idle. But before bringing to light new observations, I wanted time to verify the truths which I believe I established. I had hoped that better trained naturalists would desire to ascertain for themselves the correctness of the results obtained by me, and I thought that, by repeating my experiments, they might ascertain facts which escaped my notice. But no other attempt has since then been made to penetrate further into the history of those insects, and yet it is far from exhausted.

Although I was deceived in this expectation, I flatter myself with having obtained the confidence of my readers, my observations appear to have given light on several phenomena that had not yet been explained; the authors of several works upon the economy of bees have commented upon them; most of the cultivators have adopted entirely, as the basis of their practice, the principles which I discovered; and the naturalists themselves have taken interest in my efforts to pierce the double veil which shrouds for me, the natural sciences. (Huber here alludes evidently to the fact that he was blind—Translator) Their assent should have emboldened me sooner to edit the facts contained in this second volume, had not the loss of several persons dear to me disturbed the quietude which such occupations require.

The profound, indulgent and amiable philosopher, whose benevolence encouraged me to come forward, in spite of the disadvantages of my position, Mr. Charles Bonnet, died, and discouragement took possession of me. Sciences lost, in losing him, one of the genii sent from heaven to make science lovable; who, by linking them with the most natural sentiments of man, and by giving to each the rank and degree of interest due to it, bound the heart as well as the mind, and charmed our imagination without misleading it through delusions.

I found in the friendship and enlightenment of Mr. Senebier, some relief for the privations imposed upon me. A continued correspondence with this great physiologist, while enlightening me upon the course to follow, revived my existence in some manner; but his death surrendered me to fresh sorrows. Lastly, I was also to be deprived of the use of those eyes which had taken the place of my own, of the skill and devotedness which I had had at my bidding during 15 years. Burnens, the faithful observer, whose services I will always gladly recall, was called back into the bosom of his own people and, being appreciated as he deserved to be, he become one of the first magistrates of a considerable district.

This last separation which was not the least painful one, since it deprived me of the means of diverting my mind from those which I had already suffered, was nevertheless softened by the satisfaction which I found in observing nature through the organs of the being who is the dearest to me, and with whom I could enter into more elevated considerations. (Huber's wife—Translator)

But that which most especially connected me again with natural history, was the taste my son manifested for this study. I communicated my observations to him: he expressed sorrow in leaving, buried in a notebook, work that would seem likely to interest naturalists: he noticed the concealed reluctance which I felt in classifying the materials gathered, and offered to edit them himself. I accepted his offer; the reader will not be astonished therefore, if this work is found to differ in its two component parts. The first volume contains my correspondence with Mr. Bonnet; the second presents a set of memoirs: in the one, we had limited ourselves to the simple exposé of facts; in the other the point was to describe difficult matters, and in order to diminish the dullness, we have sometimes freely made such comments as the subject suggested. Moreover, when giving my notes to my son, I also transmitted my ideas to him; we have blended our thoughts and our opinions; I felt the need of giving him possession of a subject in which I had acquired some experience.

This new book treats of the work properly speaking of the bees, or of their architecture, their respiration and their senses. The Memoirs which I caused to be inserted in periodical magazines, such as that on the origin of wax and on the sphinx atropos, have been established in their proper place. They have both undergone a few changes and the latter has been enriched with additional experiments. Lastly I am publishing upon the sex of worker-bees (a long debated question) a Memoir which, I trust, will no longer leave any doubt concerning Schirach's discovery.

I might have added several observations to those which I now give to the public; but they do not present a sufficient ensemble, and I prefer to wait until they may be accompanied with facts concerning them.

FOREWORD OF THE EDITOR

The Observations which I publish in the name of my father long exercised his patience and that of Burnens. It was not sufficient to follow with exactness the maneuvers of the bees, it was also requisite to perceive their connection, and understand the aim to which they pointed.

Another and perhaps greater difficulty was to clearly see complicated forms and secure a distinct idea of their combination. Models of clay, made with great skill, supplied that which speech could not explain.

In this way, my father secured, from the accounts given by Burnens, a fairly complete theory of the architecture of bees.

He conceived no doubts of the correctness of his observations, but in order to obtain new ideas, or the confirmation of facts already understood, he desired that I should revise them myself before they were published.

Therefore I procured hives similar to those that he had used, and it was with great enjoyment that I witnessed, in my turn, all the points of this astonishing industry; it was with equal pleasure that I was enabled to agree with the conscientious exactness of the observer in whom my father had placed his confidence, and I can add only a small number of details to those already recorded.

—Pierre Huber, son of Francis Huber

INTRODUCTION

No people, perhaps no nation has had as many historians as these republics of laborious insects, whose industry seems to be intended for us. There are periodical works solely relative to the culture of bees; associations have been founded, the object of which is to discuss the advantages of such or such method; the centuries have accumulated observations; but in spite of the progress of sciences, we are still ignorant concerning the constituents of beeswax; it is true that most of the authors to whom we are indebted for those numerous writings, gave us their uncertain opinions as precepts, sometimes their dreams as theories based upon experience; and, piling up the quotations, citing one another, they have contributed to the perpetuation of errors instead of dispelling them. But there are, fortunately, a few respectable authors as to talent and truthfulness, who, overstepping the common limits, sought, like true naturalists, to ascertain the laws which govern those colonies.

The bees have even attracted the attention of geometricians; those of antiquity already understand the purpose of the hexagon prisms of which they build their combs; but it was reserved for modern theories to appreciate the extent of the geometrical problem which those insects solve in the construction of the base of their cells. These bases, built in pyramids, offered, for speculation, one of the greatest philosophical subjects, to those who do not believe that everything may be explained by the supposition of blind necessity. Skilled mathematicians have found that, between all the forms that bees might select in an endless list of pyramids, they preferred that which offered the greatest advantages; for it is not to them, says Réaumur (the writer who knew nature best)

> "…it is not to them that the honor is due, it was ordained by an intelligence which sees the immensity of infinite things, and all their combinations, more clearly and more distinctly than it can be perceived by our modern Archimedes."

But without attributing to the workman the glory of invention, it must be granted, at least, that the execution of so complicated a plan could not be entrusted to stupid creatures, to gross animal machines. If their routine, that this regularity in the work is subject to exceptions, and that they are able to counterbalance their errors by additions or partial reductions, so that no inconvenience results for the whole: if we prove that there is no irregularity in their work without a purpose, we will appreciate the greatness of their task and the delicacy of their organization.

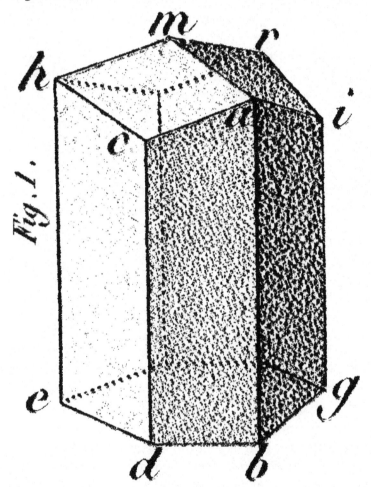

Volume 2 Plate I Fig 1—Configuration of one cell viewed standing on end.

In order to give a proper idea of the work of bees, let us assume an isolated cell placed with its opening downwards upon a horizontal plan; it thus represents a small six-sided prismatic column, surmounted with a capital in pyramid shape, depressed and obtuse, Volume 2 Plate 1, Fig. 1.

Volume 2 Plate I—Hive to Observe Comb Building.

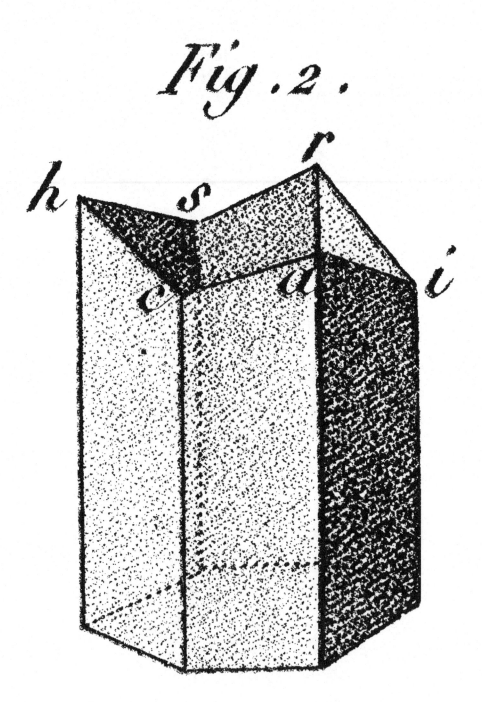

Volume 2 Plate I Fig 2—Same as Fig 1 but with "cap" (bottom of cell) removed.

The six faces of the hexagon, which appear at first sight as so many plates of wax, of rectangular shape, are cut at right angles at the orifice; but at the opposite extremity they are cut obliquely; so that their greater edges are not of equal length. Each plane is united to its neighbor by a smaller edge, the long edge of the one to the long edge of the other, and its short edge to the short edge of a third; the result is that, if we were to remove the capital, we would notice that the edge of the hexagon tube forms projections and recesses alternately, that is to say three projecting angles (h, a, r) and three recessive angles (e, i, s) fig. 2.

From the top of the three projecting angles, three edges proceed which meet opposite the center of the cell (am, hm, rm, fig 1); these divide the base into three parts and the spaces between them being filled to the edge of the recessive angles, they assume the shape of lozenges, or rhombs (achm, fig 1). Small scales of wax fill these spaces, so that each cell is composed of six panes in trapeze shape and three rhombs.

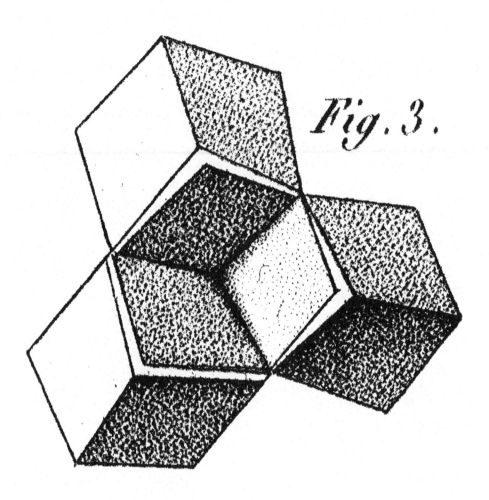

Volume 2 Plate I Fig 3—Showing the bottom of one cell is part of the bottoms of three opposing cells.

The combs of the bees, as we know, are composed of two rows of cells back to back, not singly however, but in part: each cell resting against three cells of the opposite side (figs. 3 and 4).

To fulfill these conditions, the bees need only to erect, upon the three edges which divide the base of each cell, similar panes to those of the cell itself, and which joining the other plates of similar shape, produce hexagon prisms. This is what we almost always see in the combs of bees: one may test it by piercing with a pin the three rhombs which form the base of a cell. When examining the opposite side of the comb we find that we have pierced the bottom of each of the three cells.

In addition to the economy of material which appears to ensue from this position of the cells we notice a still more positive advantage, that of contributing to the strength of the whole.

We wonder how such small insects have been led to follow so regular a plan; how the multitude of them can concur in such an arrangement, what means nature uses to direct them? Let us transcribe a few quotations that will make known to us the opinions of various naturalists upon this matter.

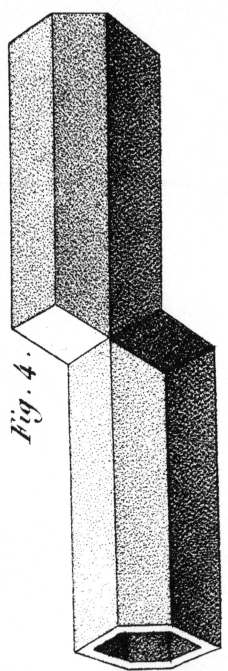

*Volume 2 Plate I Fig 4—Showing the bottom of one cell is
part of the bottoms of three opposing cells.*

A celebrated author, a painter rather than a faithful observer of nature, was not perplexed in the explanation of these marvels. He wrote:

"We must acknowledge, that taking the bees singly, they have less genius than the dog, the monkey or the greater number of animals: we must acknowledge that they have less docility, less fondness, less feeling, in fact less qualities relatively to our own; then we must acknowledge that their apparent intelligence is due to the union of their multitude; however this union itself does not presuppose any intelligence, for it is not with moral view that they unite, it is without their consent that they find themselves together: this association is only a physical union, ordained by nature, independent of any views, or any reasoning. The mother-bee produces ten thousand individuals at one time; if these ten thousand individuals were still more stupid than I believe them to be, they would still be compelled to organize themselves in some fashion, in order to continue their existence; as they work with equal ability, if they began by harming each other, they would at length be compelled to harm each other as little as possible; that is, to help each other, so they appear to have an understanding and to have similar aims; the observer will soon ascribe to them the intellect which they lack, he will try to explain each action; each motion will soon be given a motive, and from this will follow numberless reasonings marvels or monsters; for those ten thousand individuals which have been produced together, live together and have undergone their metamorphoses in similar time, cannot fail to do exactly the same thing, and with the least feeling will adopt some mode of living, of arrangement, of agreeing with each other, of occupying their home, coming back to it after having left it, etc., hence architecture, geometry, order foresight, love of country or of the republic, all based upon the admiration of the observer.

"Society in animals that appear to gather together freely and for convenience implies the experience of feeling, but the association of beasts which, like bees, are together without having planned it, does not imply anything; whatever may be the results, it is evident that they have not been anticipated, nor ordained, nor conceived by those that execute them, and that they proceed only from the universal mechanism and laws of motion established by the Creator. Place together, in the same room, ten thousand automatons animated with a living force, and all induced, through the perfect resemblance of their outer and inner being and by the conformity of their life, to do exactly the same thing in the same place, and a regular work will necessarily result: the relations of harmony, similitude, position, will be there, since they will depend upon the conformity of life: the relations of contiguity, of extent of shape will be present also since the space is limited and circumscribed; and if we admit the least degree of feeling in these automatons, even only such as is necessary for them to be conscious of their own existence, seek their own conservation, avoid noxious things, prepare useful things etc., their work will not only be regular, well proportioned, similar, equal, but it will also have symmetry, strength, convenience to the highest point of perfection, because, in making it, each of those ten thousand individuals has tried to place itself in the most commodious way, and because it has been compelled also to act and to place itself in the position least uncomfortable to others.

"Moreover, those cells of bees, those vaunted and admired hexagons furnish me one more arm against enthusiasm and admiration; that figure, though geometrical and regular as it appears, and is, in hypothesis, is but a mechanical and rather imperfect result often found in nature, noticeable even in its most crude productions; crystals and several other stones, several salts, etc., often assume this shape in their formation. We see the same hexagons in the second stomach of ruminants; we find them in seeds, in seed-capsules, in certain flowers, etc. Fill a vessel with peas or with some other cylindrical seed, and close it hermetically, after having filled with water all the spaces between those seeds; then boil the water and all the seeds will assume the six-sided shape. The reason of this is purely mechanical; each cylindrical seed, in swelling occupies a greater space in the space allowed; they necessarily become hexagonal by reciprocal compression; each bee seeks to occupy also a sufficient space, it is therefore necessary also, since their body is round that their cells be hexagonal through the same cause of reciprocal obstacles.

"We admit in the bees more intelligence, because their work is more regular: we say that they are more ingenious than wasps, hornets, &c, that are architects also, but whose structures are coarser and more irregular than those of bees; we blind ourselves to the fact, or perhaps we do not know, that the greater or less regularity depends solely upon the number and the shape, and not in the least upon the intelligence of those little beasts; the more numerous they are, the more forces act in like manner or in opposition to each other, and therefore the more mechanical constraint, the more forced regularity and apparent perfection will there be in their production"

One can readily recognize the author of this discourse through the arguments and the style which embellishes them; we shall leave to some more eloquent writer the task of refuting, Mr. Buffon. The two passages which we will now quote taken from the *Contemplation de la Nature.* (part XI, notes 9 and 11 of the XXVII° chapter, last edition), while answering in a direct manner the hypotheses of this author, we will give a correct idea of the progress in the history of bees through Maraldi and Réaumur, relative to the building of combs; it will serve at the same time to indicate their opinion on the origin of beeswax.

Note: Mr. Bonnet having written nothing in the text of the manner in which bees gather honey and wax, nor of their art in the construction of their beautiful works, this omission is supplemented in a note transcribed here.

"The jaws, the trunk and the six legs are the main instruments which have been given the bees to execute their different labors. The teeth are two little sharp scales, working horizontally, and not up and down like our own: the trunk, which the bee unfolds and stretches out at will does not act in the manner of a pump; I mean that the bee does not use it to suck; it is a sort of long tongue covered with hairs, and it is by licking in the flowers that it loads itself with liquid which is passed to the mouth to descend through the esophagus into the first stomach, which is its receptacle. One perceives that this liquid is honey; the bees are familiar with the little nectariferous glands, situated at the base of the calyx of flowers and containing this honey; after filling their honey sac with it, they go and disgorge it into cells; they fill them and thus store it away, closing the cells with a capping of wax. But there are other honey cells which they do not seal because they are store cells for the daily needs of the community.

"It is also upon the flowers that the bees gather the wax-producing material or raw wax; the dust of the stamens composes this material. The industrious bee dips into the interior of flowers that have the greatest abundance of this dust; the little hairs with which her body is covered become loaded with this dust; the worker plucks it off with brushes existing on her legs for this purpose, and forms with it two pellets that the legs of the second pair placed in basket-like cavities existing on the third pair of legs. Loaded with those two pellets of wax-forming material the diligent bee returns to the hive, and deposits them in cells provided for that purpose. These cells thus become wax-magazines and remain open; but the bee is not satisfied with thus unloading her burden: she enters into the cell, head first and spreads the two pellets, kneads them and deposits on them a little saccharine matter. If the labor which she has executed in gathering this harvest has fatigued her too much, another bee comes along and kneads the pellets and spreads them; for all the Helots of this little Sparta are equally aware of all that needs to be done in each particular case, and acquit themselves equally well of it. But it does not always happen that the bee has only to dip into the blossoms to gather this dust with her fleece; there are circumstances when the harvest is not so easy, and requires some dexterity on the part of the worker. Before its full ripeness, the dust is enclosed in capsules which botanists have named "the apex of the stamen." The worker which seeks pollen, from still closed capsules, is compelled to open those capsules and she does so with her mandibles, then she seizes the pollen grains with her first pair of legs: the articulations of the end of these legs act like hands; the grains are then passed to the second pair of legs which after depositing them within the baskets of the third pair, tamp them down by striking them several times; the slight moisture of the grains helps to hold them there also and to pack them together; the worker repeats the same maneuvers, completing the filling of the two baskets, and hastens to the hive with her plunder.

"This dust which the bees gather from the flowers, is not the same as the wax which they mold with so much industry, it is only the raw material, and this material requires a preparation and digestion in a particular stomach, in a second stomach. It is there that it becomes true beeswax; the bees then disgorge it through their mouth, in the shape of a pap or white foam, which hardens quickly in the air: while this dough is yet ductile, it assumes easily any shape which the bee may desire to give it, it is for her the same as clay for the potter.

"A great physicist, who studied deeply the geometric work of bees, thought that he could reduce it to its actual value by considering it as the simple result of a coarse mechanism; he thought that bees crowded against one another, naturally gave wax a hexagonal figure, and that it was with the bees' cells as with any balls of soft material which, pressed against each other, would assume the shape of dice. I am thankful to this physicist for his aloofness from the allurements of the marvelous; I should like to praise him upon the correctness of his comparison, but we will show that the work of the bees is far from simplicity of mechanism that he was pleased to imagine.

"The reader has not forgotten that the cells of bees are not simple hexagon tubes, these tubes have a pyramidal base, formed of 3 pieces in lozenges, or 3 rhombs, and it is with these that they form the foundation of the cells: on two outside faces of this rhomb they erect two of the walls of the cell; then they shape a second rhomb which they fasten to the first giving them the proper slope; on these exterior walls they erect two new walls of the hexagon; lastly they build the third rhomb and the two last walls: all this work is at first rather massive but must not remain this. The skilled workers perfect it, thin it down, polish it, straighten it; their jaws serve them as planes and files. A really fleshy tongue, fastened at the base of the jaws, also helps the work of the teeth. Many workers succeed each other in this labor; that which one has only sketched another finishes a little further, a third perfects it, etc. and although it has thus gone through so many hands, it appears as if made in a mold.

"We have just shown (in note 9), that each cells' base is pyramidal, and that the pyramid is formed of 3 equal and similar rhombs; the angles of these rhombs might vary infinitely; that is, the pyramid might be more or less pointed, more or less flat: the

savant Maraldi, who measured the angles of the rhombs with extreme precision, found that the large angles generally measured
109° and 28', while the small angles measured 70° 32'. Mr. de Réaumur, who meditated upon the processes of insects, ingeniously
surmises that the choice of these angles, between so many others,
was based upon the possible saving of wax, and that, of all cells
of equal capacity with pyramidal base, those that could be build
with the least quantity of materials were those whose dimensions
corresponded with these actual measurements. So, he requested a
skilled geometrician, Mr. Koenig, who know nothing of these
measurements, to determine by reckoning what should be the angles of a hexagon cell with pyramidal base, in order to require the
least possible material in its construction; for the solution of this
fine problem, this geometrician resorted to minute analysis, and
found that the angles of the large rhombs should be of 109° 26',
and the small ones 70° 24'; a surprising agreement between his solution and the actual measurements. Mr. Koenig demonstrated also that, in preferring a pyramidal best to a flat base, the bees save
the amount of wax which would be needed to build a flat base.

Note: Mr. Konig thought that bees should make the rhombs of
the cells 109° 16' and 70° 34' in order to use the least possible
quantity of wax (Réaumur Vol. V, Memoir VIII).

Mr. Cramer, formerly professor to whom Koenig had suggested
the same problem, found that these angles should be 109° 28½' and
70° 31½'. This result is the same as that secured by Father
Boscovisch, who notes that Maraldi had superficially given the angles
as 110° and 70°, and that those which he gave 109° 28' and 70° 32'
were of the dimensions necessary, in order that the angles of the
trapezium be equal, near the base (Me. Of the Royal Academy 1712).
In addition, Father Boscovisch indicates that all the angles which
form the plane of the cell are equal, and of 120°, and he assumes
that this equality of obliquity facilitates the building of the cell, which
might be a motive of preference, as well as the economy of it. He
demonstrates that bees do not by any means save the quantity of
wax that would be used in a flat base for the construction of each cell,
as Messrs. Koenig and Réaumur had believed.

Maclaurin writes that the difference between a cell with pyramidal base and a cell with flat base, that is to say, the economy that
bees secure, is equal to one-fourth of the six triangles, which would

have to be added to the trapeziums or faces of the cells, so they should become rectangles.

Mr. Lhuillier, a professor in Geneva, estimates that the bees save 1/51 of the total expense and demonstrates that it might be as much as 1/5 if the bees had no other requirements to fulfill; but he concludes that it is not greatly perceptible on each cell, although it might prove more perceptible on the entire comb because of mutual fitting in of the cells on the opposite sides of the comb (Memoir of the Royal Academy of Sciences of Berlin, 1781)

Lastly Mr. Le Sage demonstrates that, whatever be the obliquity of the rhombs, the capacity of the cell remains the same. The combs, he says are two cells deep, disposed in such a way that whatever we may take away or give to the front ones must be given or taken away from the rear ones, so that: 1° the entire comb would neither lose nor gain anything and also 2° the front ones would still be equal to the rear ones, owing to the symmetry with which they are reciprocally incased within each other.

"While following the reasoning of the historian of insects upon the geometric shape of the cells of bees and wasps, the illustrious Mairan (Jean Jacques d'Ortous de Mairan—Transcriber) expressed himself as follows:

Whether beasts think or not, it is positive that they conduct themselves in thousands of occasions as if they did think; the illusion in this matter, if it be an illusion, was well arranged for us. But without intending to touch upon this great question, and whatever be the cause let us for a moment surrender ourselves to appearances and use every day language.

'Geometricians, among whom we must number Mr. de Réaumur, have endeavored to make us appreciate all the art contained with the wax combs, and the paper wasps nests, so ingeniously laid out in tiers, sustained with columns, and these tiers or stories built in an infinity of sexangular cells. It was not without cause that the statement was made that this figure was the most convenient, if not the only convenient one, among all possible polygons, to fulfill the intentions that we must attribute to the bees and wasps that construct them. It is true that the regular hexagon is the necessary outcome of the apposition of round, soft and flexible bodies, when pressed against each other, and that it is apparently for that reason that we see it so often in nature, as for instance in the capsules of the seeds of certain plants, in the scales

of several animals, and sometimes in the particles of snow on account of the small spherical or circular bubbles of water which have flattened against each other in freezing; but there are so many other require-ments to fulfill in the building of the hexagonal cells of bees and wasps, and which are so beautifully fulfilled, that even if we should deny them a part of the honor to which they are entitled on this, it is hardly possible to deny that they have added much by choice and that they have skillfully taken advantage of this necessity imposed upon them by nature.' "

The writings of the naturalists, in whom I have the greatest confidence, are therefore not favorable to the opinion expressed by Mr. de Buffon, who attributes one of the marvels of nature to entirely mechanical combinations. Experience had already taught us that we cannot explain the work of bees through such gross means, and I soon became convinced through my own observations of the correctness of Mr. Bonnet in this regard.

My researched will doubtless bring numerous modifica-tions to the ideas held in his time upon the art with which these insects construct their combs; but I hope they may contribute to the support of a very different theory from that of the elo-quent historian of animals.

Note Well: **Skilled modern mathematicians have al-so exerted themselves upon the problem of the minimum amount of wax in the cells; but their conclusions are quite different from those of their predecessors. The note just quoted taken from the papers of Mr. G. L. Le Sage, of Geneva, indicates the progress made in this research.**

CHAPTER I: MY OPINIONS ON BEESWAX

Since the time of Réaumur and de Geer, whose works have inspired a general taste for entomology, observing minds have caused great steps to be made in science; all its branches are extended, and the history of bees, more than any other, has been enriched, in this interval.

Schirach and Riem opened a new road, and perhaps and perhaps we ourselves have contributed to clear it of the prejudice which clogged its progress, by establishing the facts announced, in a more rigorous manner.

Since then, some observations were published in different countries, but with so little development and in so inaccurate a manner as compared with what is now required of natural sciences, that they would sink in oblivion did we not endeavor to support them by facts that may strengthen them.

Naturalists have principally directed their attention to wax: several chemists have also attempted to analyze it, but there is so little accord in the results of these labors, as to prove the insufficient discussion of this subject, which requires new examination.

One opinion appeared well established, among those which we have quoted from the contemplation of nature, when Mr. Bonnet wrote that which he had accepted, after the best writers of his time, concerning the conversion of the dust of the stamens into beeswax. The reader must have perused with interest the details which he gave of the manner in which the bees harvest this substance, load themselves with it, store it, and preserve it; all of these facts had been scrupulously observed by Réaumur, Maraldi and several other savants, so that no doubts may be raised upon this point; it is also evident that this dust, taken by the bees from the flowers, is of real use to them, since they bring home such great quantities of it, but is this truly the elementary principle of beeswax?

Appearances favored this hypothesis; the bees supplying the cultivator with two precious substances, honey and beeswax, and each day gathering under his very eyes, the nectar of flowers and their fecundating dust, one might readily believe the latter substance to be crude wax.

Réaumur entertained some doubt, not upon the actual conversion, but upon the manner in which it took place; was wax formed from this dust itself or was the latter only one of the principal ingredients of it? After several experiments, quite simple but inconclusive, he inclined to the latter opinion, but he always expressed it with the reserve which is noticeable in friends of the truth; he thought to have made sure that the bees submitted pollen to a special elaboration, that it was converted into real beeswax in their stomach, and that this was disgorged from their mouth in the shape of a sort of pap. He had noticed, however, the very great difference existing between the fecundating dust and the beeswax itself, and several observations made by him should have caused him to dismiss this idea, had he drawn correct consequences from them.

Discovery of wax scales under the rings of the abdomen

Science had stopped at this point, when a Lusatian cultivator, whose name has not reached us, made a most important discovery. Mr. Willelmi, a relative of Schirach, who caused such great progress to be made in the history of bees, wrote to Mr. Bonnet, August 22nd, 1768:

> "Allow me, Sir, to write here an abridged account of some new discoveries that the Society (of Lusace) has made. We believed until the present that bees discharge wax through their mouth, but it has been noticed that they exude it through the rings which form the posterior part of their body. In order to ascertain it, one must draw the bee, with the point of a needle, from the cell in which she works, one will then notice by stretching her body slightly, that the wax with which she is loaded is to be found under her rings, in the shape of scales, etc." (*Histoire de la Mère Abeille*, by Blassière)

The author of this letter did not name the naturalist who made this beautiful observation; whoever he be, he deserved to be better known. However, this did not appear to Mr. Bonnet as established upon sufficient proof to make him relinquish the already accepted ideas, and persuaded by his influence, we did not investigate the basis of his opinion.

But several years afterwards, however, in 1793, we were greatly astonished to find small scales of material resembling beeswax, under the rings of some bees.

This discovery was of greatest interest in every respect; we displayed these scales of wax to several of our friends, and having exposed them to the flame of a candle, we found in them the characters of true beeswax.

However, John Hunter an Englishman of high repute, observing bees at the time when I did so myself, conceived some doubts which brought him the same results. He discovered the true wax receptacle under the belly of these insects, and gave the detail of his observations in a memoir inserted in the philosophical transactions, in 1792.

By raising the lower segments of the abdomen of bees, he found scales of a fusible material which he recognized as beeswax. He ascertained the difference existing between the pollen of the stamens and the material of which combs are built, and he attributed a new property to those pellets which bees bring home on their legs. This was a notable step forward, but Hunter was unable to witness the use made of these scales of wax which he assumed to be produced within the body of the bee, he could offer only conjectures upon the use of pollen. We carried our own observations further, and were able, not only to confirm his experiments, but also to give them greater development; thus those facts, announced in Germany, in England and in France, could not fail to secure the confidence of all naturalists.

It was under the inferior rings of the belly of the bees that we found the scales of wax; they were arranged in pairs under each segment, in small pockets of peculiar shape, and located on the right and left of the angular edge of the abdomen; none was found under the rings of the drones or of the queens, the structure of these parts being very different in these two classes; the workers alone therefore possess the faculty of secreting wax, to employ the expression of John

Hunter (see "Extract from the Memoir by John Hunter" following this chapter)

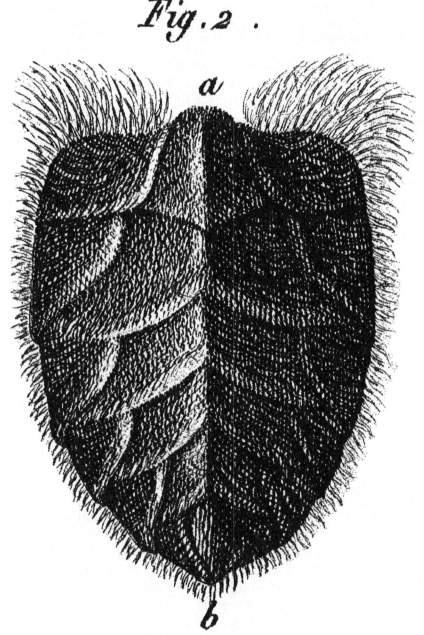

Volume 2 Plate II Fig 2—Closeup of worker abdomen.

Volume 2 Plate II Fig 1—Underside of a worker showing plates.

The underside of the belly of the bee (Plate II, fig. 2) presents nothing on the outside which is not common with the abdomen of wasps and several other hymenopters, they are demi-segments partly overlapping one another, but they are not flat, as are those of most insects of the same family; they are arched; for the abdomen of the bees is noticeable in an angular prominence which exists from one end to the other (a, b, fig. 2).

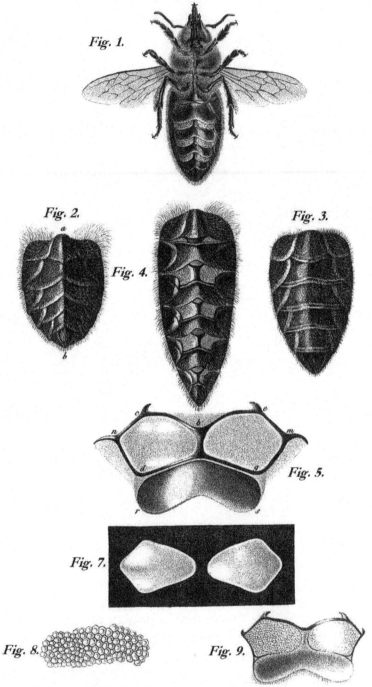

Volume 2 Plate II—Organs of Wax Secretion.

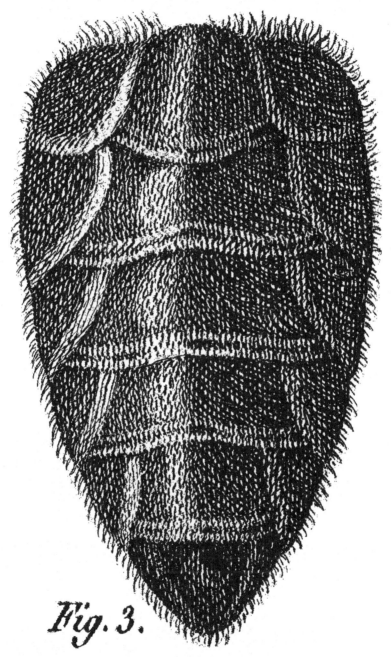

Fig. 3.

Volume 2 Plate II Fig 3—Abdomen partly distended.

Fig.4.

Volume 2 Plate II Fig 4—Abdomen completely distended

The form of these pockets or reservoirs, which was not noted by this author and which Swammerdam and so many other naturalists who studied the bee overlooked, yet deserved the greatest study, since it belongs to a newly found organ.

The edge of these segments is scaly, but if they are lifted, or if we stretch the abdomen of the bee by drawing it gently at one of its extremities, we disclose the part which was concealed, in ordinary conditions, by the upper edge of the other segments (figs. 1 & 4).

Volume 2 Plate II Fig 5—Base of abdominal ring.

This part (c, d, e, g, fig. 5) which must be considered as the base of each ring since it adheres to the body of the insect, is a membranous, soft, transparent and yellowish white substance; it occupies at least two thirds of each segment; it is divided into two by a small horny ridge (a, b,) which corresponds exactly with the angular projection of the abdomen. This ridge, starting from the center of the scaly edge (d, g, r, s) going towards the head, crosses the membranous part bifurcates at its extremity and divides into a bow shape right and left, supplying a solid edge to both sides of the membrane (n, c, b, e, m, g, fig. 5): the scales of wax are found in nature upon these two small areas (fig. 7). Their outline, formed of both straight and curved lines joined together, exhibit at first sight the appearance of two ovals; but when we analyze their composition, we recognize that they are of irregular, pentagonal shape. The membranous areas are sloping, like the sides of the body itself; they are entirely covered by the edge of the preceding segment and form, with the latter, small pockets open only on the lower side. The segments, or the two plates which form the wax cavity, are united together by a sort of membrane, like the two parts of a portfolio.

*Volume 2 Plate II Fig 7—Wax scales on black cloth for con-
trast.*

The scales of wax (fig. 7) are exactly of the same shape as the membranous areas upon which they are found. There are only 8 in each individual bee; for the first and last ring, being of different shape from the rest, do not have any. The size of the scales decreases with the diameter of the rings whereon they are molded; the largest are under the third and the smallest under the fifth.

We noticed that the wax scales were not alike in every bee; a difference was perceptible in their shape, their thickness and their consistency.

Upon some of the bees, they were so thin and so transparent that a magnifying glass was necessary to perceive them; upon others we could discover only crystals in needle shape such as are seen upon freezing water.

These spiculae, or scales did not rest immediately upon the membrane; they were separated from it by a slight coat of liquid substance, perhaps serving to lubricate the junctures of the rings, or to render the extraction of the scales easier, as otherwise they might adhere too firmly to the walls of the cells.

Finally some other bees had scales so large that they projected beyond the rings, their form more irregular than that of the previous ones; their thickness, altering the transparency of the wax, made them appear of a whitish yellow color; one could perceive them without raising the segments which usually cover them entirely.

These shades of difference in the scales of different bees, this progression in their shape and thickness, the fluid interposed between them and the walls of their cells, the relation between their size and shape, all those circumstances together appeared to indicate that the transudation of this material through the membrane which moulds it.

We were confirmed in this opinion by a singular fact. On piercing the membrane, whose internal surface seemed to be applied to the soft parts of the belly, we caused the escape of a transparent fluid which coagulated in cooling; in this condition it resembled beeswax: when submitted to the influence of heat, it liquefied again.

The same experiment made upon the wax scales, had similar results; they became liquid and coagulated again according to the temperature, exactly as does beeswax.

We carried our researches further upon the analogy of this substance with finished beeswax; for this purpose we selected the whitest fragments of wax that we could find, taking them from newly built comb, to make the same test; for wax from old combs is always more or less colored.

1st *Experiment: Comparing scales to beeswax.*

We dropped into spirits of turpentine a few scales taken from under the rings of workers; they were dissolved and disappeared before reaching the bottom of the vessel, without rendering the fluid turbid; but an equal amount of the spirit could not dissolve, either as completely or as quickly the white fragments of worked wax, with many particles remaining suspended in the liquid.

2nd *Experiment: Comparing scales to beeswax.*

We filled with sulfuric ether two vessels of equal size; the one was appropriated for wax from the rings of bees, the other for fragments of beeswax of equivalent weight. Scarcely had the fragments of wax from combs touched the ether when they divided and fell in powder to the bottom of the vase; but the scales taken from the bees themselves were not disintegrated; they preserved their shape and only lost their transparency, becoming of a dull white color. No change took place in either of the vessels in the space of several days. On evaporating separately the ether from each, a thin coat of wax was found on the glass; we repeated this experiment frequently, the fragments of combs were always reduced to powder; the scales on the contrary, were never dissolved by the liquid; after several months the ether had dissolved but a very small proportion of them.

From the experiment the evidence was that the wax of the bees' rings was less compounded than that which had been built into cells, since the latter was dissolve by the ether while the former remained whole; the one was dissolved by turpentine only in part, while the other was completely dissolved by it.

If the substance taken from the rings of the bees is crude wax, it must undergo some preparation after leaving its cells and the bees must be capable of impregnating it with a substance giving it the ductility and whiteness of true wax. Hitherto, we knew only of its fusibility, but such being the chief property of the combs, we could not doubt that the scales enter in their composition.

Volume 2 Plate II Fig 8—Wax producing organ removed.

Looking for the wax glands

In the hope ascertaining the primary source of the waxy matter, we had recourse to the dissection of the wax organs, but though undertaken by a skillful hand, it did not fulfill our expectations.   (See "The Analysis of Wax Glands by Miss Jurine" following this chapter).

No direct communication would be found between these organs and the interior of the abdomen; no vessels were found appearing to connect them, with the exception of a few tracheae, doubtless intended to admit the air into these parts.   But the membrane of the wax-producing organs is covered with a network of hexagonal meshes (Vol 2 Plate II, Figs. 8 & 9) to which we must perhaps attribute some function connected with the secretion of wax.   This network is not found in the males, but it exists in queens with modifications which alter its texture, and occupying in them two-thirds of each segment.

(Translator—The next paragraph is not intelligible, probably owing to some error in the publication, it appears to be self-contradictory. We omit it. Transcriber—Here is the original French: "Chez les bourdons velus (apis bombilius) qui produisent de la cire, on retrouve ce réseau, don't la structure est absolument la meme que chez l'abeille ouvrière, il n'en diffère que parce qu'il occupe toute la partie antérieure des segmens; mais nous remarquerons ici que l'on n'aperçoit point de loges à circe chez ces insects, leur abdomen est formé comme celui des hymenopters de la meme section."—Tome Second pg 51)

The network in question is separated from the other internal parts by a grayish membrane which lines the entire abdominal cavity; when the stomach is full of the juices elaborated by it, it may allow them to transude through its very thin walls; and these juices, traversing the grayish membrane which is not thickly woven, may come in contact with the network of hexagon meshes. It is not impossible that, by a sort of digestion through this network, these juices be reabsorbed, producing the secretion of wax.

Volume 2 Plate II Fig 9—Wax producing organs in place in the lower segment of the abdomen.

Although it is as yet impossible to decide upon anything on this point, it seems admissible, without breaking physiological laws, to consider this matter as produced by a particular organ after the manner of other secretions.

The discovery of wax scales, of the wax-producing areas, of their transudation, by overthrowing ancient theories, opens a new epoch in the history of bees. It raises doubts upon several points which were considered as solved and which may not be any longer explained without the acquisition of additional information. It brings up a host of questions, and offers a wider field to the researched of physiologists and amateurs of natural history; it opens new vistas to chemists, by exhibiting to them, as an animal secretion, a substance which appeared to belong to the vegetable kingdom. In a word, it is the corner stone of a new edifice.

Volume 2 Plate III—That section where worker wax organs are, of each caste: worker, queen and drone.

Plate III is intended to represent the lower segments of the abdomen of the three sorts of bee: fig. 1, segment of the worker; fig. 2, segment of the queen; fig. 3 segment of the male.

Figs. 4, 5 and 6 are the same, viewed in profile, to show the inclination of the pieces of which the segments are composed.

A . *Fig . 1 .*

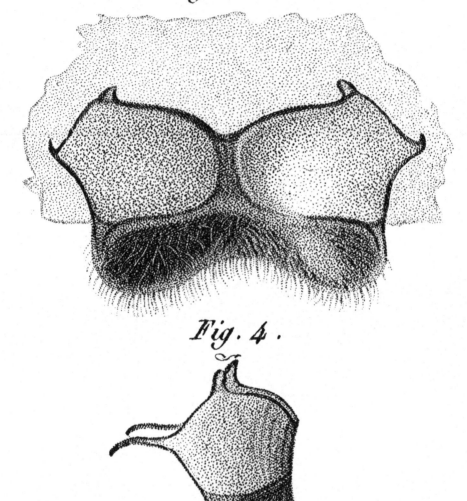

Fig . 4 .

Volume 2 Plate III Figs 1 & 4—Dissection of the lower segment of the abdomen (wax organs) of worker bee, front and
side views.

B . *Fig . 2 .*

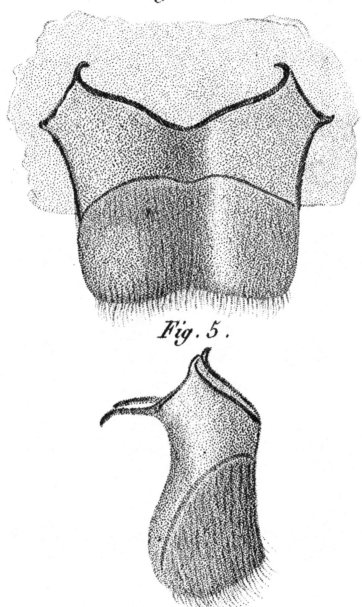

Fig . 5 .

Volume 2 Plate III Figs 2 & 5—Dissection of same lower segment of the abdomen of the queen bee, front and side views.

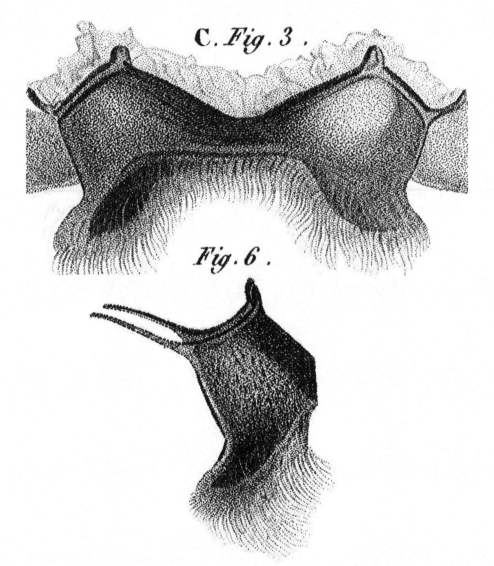

Volume 2 Plate III Figs 3 & 6—Dissection of same lower segment of the abdomen of the drone bee, front and side views.

The Analysis of Wax Glands by Miss Jurine

Sir, you have desired me to seek in the bees the organs which produce wax; in order to inform you I had to examine the parts which rest upon the segments of the abdomen, where the wax plates are found; compare these parts with those of the female bumblebee (bremus) which also produce a waxy substance, without having, like the bees, glands in which it is molded; establish a similar comparison with the females of some other hymenopters that do not secrete wax, and lastly ascertain whether there are any great differences between queens, males and workers in the structure of these organs.

On carefully removing the four wax segments of a worker, one discovers an adipose membrane, interspersed with trachea, and exactly similar to that which had been recognized by Swammerdam, under the upper segments of the abdomen; this membrane is held under each ring by six little bundles of muscles. Since this membrane is found under all the segments, while wax appears only in the lower ones, it is not presumed to be the secretory organ. To ascertain this, I examined the abdomen of the violet bee (sylocopa violacea), and two species of wasps, and found this membrane existing in the same way.

I examined afterwards the internal surface of the wax segments, and discovered a whitish membrane which coated only the wax-producing parts; I removed this readily by maceration, and placing it under a microscope, it appeared to consist of a pretty net of very small hexagonal meshes, full of a liquid as thick as syrup. If this network was the organ of wax secretion, I could expect to find it under the same segments of the abdomen of bumblebees and it was there indeed; with this difference, that it occupied all their anterior half.

In order easily to perceive this membrane, which is sometimes indistinct, we must select bees that are building their combs; as it is so full of whitish matter, then that it might be taken for scales of wax.

Detaching the network from the ring, to ascertain whether it contained real wax, or only a preliminary preparation for it, I placed it in a vessel, in order to compare it with scales of wax placed into another vessel; and poured boiling water over both; the scales of wax melted while no waxy particles escaped from the former; being but little pleased with this experiment I repeated it twice; but the result was the same, although I had broken the meshes of this network in several places. If the existence of this network was to be considered as an initial step towards the discover of the wax-secreting organs, it was necessary to discover the vessels communicating with it, and how the wax was transuded from the abdomen; for this purpose I dissected a great number of bees, and could only see minute trachea, communicating immediately with the network. In the hope of succeeding better with another plan, I fed some bees on honey colored with lac, but this substance did not reach farther than the digestive organs. I tried injections of mercury in these same organs, with no better success; unable to discover any other vessel, I conjectured that the material of which wax was formed might be supplied by a transudation of the juices of the stomach, which is very much gorged when bees work in wax. To clear my doubts, I examined it in several wax workers, and by repeatedly and gently pressing it, while I avoided rupturing it, I succeeded in causing half of its contents to flow into the abdominal cavity; I tasted this and found in it a sweet and saccharine flavor: these bees having been afterwards exposed to the heat of a moderate fire, this liquid assumed the consistence of dried syrup. Bees having several means of obtaining such pressure upon their stomach, may it not be attained with similar effects, and may not this liquid reach the hexagonal network where it receives a preparation suitable for its conversion into wax?

The researches which I made, to discern how the wax or the liquid found within the hexagonal network passed from the inside to the outside of the body, had no greater success; I could not find any opening, either in the horny part of the segment which is lined with this net or in the membrane which unites the rings; but although I had not seen such an opening, should I conclude that there was none? In this uncertainty I made the following experiments: Among some bees that had just been killed by a brimstone fumigation, I selected such as showed scales of wax; after having fastened them on their back on a board, I stretched their abdomen in order to remove the wax plates more easily; then, pressing the wax producing segments repeatedly with the head of a needle, I saw their receptacle insensibly moistened with a liquid, of the consistence of syrup, observed nowhere besides: when the bees in this condition were exposed to moderate heat, it acquired still greater consistence, however without assuming a waxy appearance.

I repeated this experiment on bees that had been dead several days, and were somewhat dried; the scales broke into fragments when I tried to remove them; by the simple expedient of pressing the wax segments several times, I succeeded in obtaining them entire, which I could ascribe only to the oozing of the syrupy matter which I had noticed in the previous experiment.

The comparison of the abdomen of the queens with that of the workers yielded the following modifications: The reticulated membrane, which in the latter occupies only the wax segments, is replaced in queens by a membrane which extends over the anterior two-thirds of each segment; its consistency is so fine and delicate that it may only be seen with a microscope; after having removed it, I noticed that the scale exhibited a hexagonal tissue much more decided in the half of the segment corresponding with the wax organs of the workers than in the posterior half. While trying to remove what I thought to be a second membrane, I ascertained that it was the scale itself which was thus organized; this lead me to a closer inspection of the scale of the wax segments of the worker which I found perfectly smooth in the part where the wax receptacles are situated and resembling that of the queen throughout the rest of the segment.

As to the difference between the males and the workers, it consists in the following: The drones are entirely deprived of the fatty membrane and the hexagonal network; in their place one sees only very thick muscular fibers, through which trachea exist which are disposed as in the worker; the scale of the male segments displays the same hexagonal tissue as that of the queen. Note: See Plate III. A is a worker segment, B that of a queen, C that of a drone. Figs. 4, 5, 6, show the same segments in profile.

Extract from the Memoir by John Hunter

On Beeswax. *Translated From the English*

In explaining in a new way the formation of beeswax, I shall prove that it could not have the origin which it was supposed to have. I shall first remark that the materials from which the combs are composed are in a different state from that of the stamen dust of any vegetable whatever.

The substance which the bees bring home on their legs, and which is the fecundating dust of flowers, has always been considered as the material from which wax is composed; some authors have even called *wax* the little pellets which our bees bring in from the fields.

Réaumur was of that opinion; I made several experiments in order to ascertain whether there was in this product a quantity of oil sufficient to account for the quantity of wax formed from it, and to learn whether it actually contained oil; I held one near a candle; it burnt but without the smell of wax, and emitted the same smell as stamen dust when exposed to fire.

I remarked that this substance was of different colors on the legs of different bees; but always of the same color on both legs of the same bee; whereas the shade of new made comb is uniform. I observed that the bees of old hives where the combs are complete, gather this substance with more activity, than those inhabiting new hives where they are only begun, which would hardly be the case were it the elements of wax. We may observe also that, when we place bees in a new hive, they spend two or three days before bringing any pellets on their legs, and that it is only after that interval of time that they gather it. Why? Because during those first days they have had time to build cells in which this substance may be stored; a few eggs have been laid and after they are hatched the worms will need this food which will be ready for them, and which will not be lacking if the weather should be moist and the bees became unable to gather it outside.

I have also observed that, when the weather was so cold or so wet in June as to prevent a young swarm from going abroad, as much comb was constructed, nevertheless, as might have been built, if they had been able to fly about the fields.

Wax is formed by the bees themselves; it may be called an external secretion of oil and originates between each plate of the underside of the belly. On first observing it, in examining a worker, I was embarrassed to explain its appearance, and doubted whether new scales were forming, and whether bees cast the old ones like the shells of lobsters, but I soon discovered that this substance would be found only between the scales of the belly. When examining the workers climbing on the inside of the panes of glass hives, I saw that most of them exhibited this substance; it gave the lower and posterior edge of the scales the appearance of being double, or there seemed to be double scales; but I ascertained that this substance was loose and did not adhere.

Having proved that the pellets brought on their limbs were farina from the stamens, apparently destined for the food of the larvae and not for wax making, and having found nothing else which could be supposed to be wax, I conjectured that these scales might be wax itself. I placed several of them on the point of a needle, which I held to the flame of a candle; they melted and formed a globule. I doubted no longer of this being wax and made sure of it in a more positive way by ascertaining that they are never found except during the season that bees construct their combs.

In the remainder of the paragraph the author relates having made useless efforts to seize the moment when they detached the scales from themselves.

He afterwards affirms that it is with this material, transuded through the rings of the abdomen, that they build their combs, but he believes that they add to it a little of the fecundating dust of the stamens, when the wax secretion is not sufficiently abundant for their work.

CHAPTER II: ON THE ORIGIN OF WAX

When nature exhibits a peculiar organization in one of its productions, one may be certain that it is with a useful purpose, an aim which will sooner or later be evidenced to us.

The existence of the wax organs under the rings of the bees, the shape and structure of the membranes upon which the wax scales appear to be molded; the hexagonal network, immediately below, its absence in insects that do not produce wax, its presence in bumble bees with a marked modification; lastly the graduations observed in the plates of wax, from their appearance in the shape of crystals to their projecting outside the rings, the fusibility of this material, which however differs in some regard from beeswax itself, everything indicates organs devised for an important function and we believe they are endowed with the faculty of producing wax.

However we had not discovered the channels which should bring this substance into its reservoirs; its elaboration might be produced by the action of the network of hexagon meshes; but we had no means of ascertaining it: the art assumed in animal and vegetable secretions will perhaps always escape our analysis, for the metamorphoses of liquids in organized beings, when secreted by the glands and viscera in which they are elaborated appear to be carefully veiled by nature.

The means of simple observation thus being obstructed for us in this research, we felt it necessary to employ other methods for ascertaining whether wax is actually a secretion, or whether it resulted from the collection of a particular substance.

Providing it were a secretion, we had first to verify the opinion of Réaumur, who conjectured that it came from the elaboration of pollen in the stomach of bees, though we did not believe, as he did, that it was disgorged through the mouth. Neither were we disposed to adopt his views regarding its origin; for we had been struck, as was Hunter, with the fact that swarms newly gather in empty hives do not bring home any pollen and yet construct combs; while the bees of old hive, having no new cells to build, gathered it abundantly.

It is singular that Réaumur, who had made this observation, had yet failed to realize how unfavorable it was to the common view; however well he was, more than any one, free from prejudice.

We decided to make extensive experiments, to learn definitely whether bees deprived of pollen, for a series of days, would still produce wax; this was important, for we remembered that Mr. de Réaumur, in order to explain his suppositions, had assumed that it took a certain time for the elaboration of pollen within the body of the bees. The indicated experiment was to retain the bees within the hive to thus prevent them from gathering or eating fecundating dust. It was on the 24th of May that we made this experiment upon a swarm which had just left the mother hive.

1st Experiment: To see if bees can make wax without pollen

We placed this swarm in a straw hive with sufficient water and honey for the consumption of the bees; we carefully closed the entrances so as to prevent all possibility of escape, leaving free access for the air needed by the captive bees.

The bees were greatly agitated at first; we succeeded in quieting them by placing the hive in a cool and dark place; their captivity lasted five days; at the end of that time we allowed them to take flight in a room the windows of which were carefully shut; we were then able to examine their hive conveniently; they had consumed their provision of honey; but the hive which did not contain an atom of wax when we placed them in it, had acquired five combs of the finest wax, during those five days; they were suspended from the arch of the skep; the substance of them was of pure white color and of great fragility.

This result, from which we did not as yet draw any consequences, was very remarkable; we had not expected so prompt and complete a solution of the problem. However, before concluding that the bees had been enabled to produce wax from the honey with which they were fed it was necessary to make sure, through other experiments, that no other explanation was possible.

The workers, though held captive, might have gathered the pollen at the time when they were at liberty, on the eve or on the day of their imprisonment and have enough of it in their stomach or in their pollen baskets to extract from it all the wax that we had found in the hive.

But if such was the case, this source was not inexhaustible, and the bees being unable to procure more, would soon cease to build combs, they would fall into absolute inaction; so it was necessary to prolong the test in order to make it decisive.

2nd Experiment: To insure there was no stored pollen in the stomach of the bees and only honey available

Before proceeding to this second Experiment, we deprived the bees of all the combs which they had built during their captivity. Burnens, with his usual skill, made them return to the hive and closed them in, as before, with a new ration of honey. This test was short; on the following day we perceived in the evening, that the bees were working with new wax; on the third day we visited the hive and actually found five new combs, as regular as those that they had built during their first imprisonment.

The combs were removed five times successively, always under the precaution of preventing the bees from escaping outside. The same insects were preserved, and were fed exclusively with honey, during this long captivity that we might have prolonged with equal success, had we thought it necessary. On each occasion that we supplied them with honey they produced new combs; so it is beyond doubt that this substance effects the secretion of wax without the help of fecundating dust.

Since it was possible that the pollen might have similar properties, we did not delay in making the matter clear by another experiment which was only the reverse of the preceding one.

This time, instead of giving honey to the bees, we gave them nothing but fruits and pollen for food; we enclosed them under a glass bell, with a comb the cells of which contained only accumulated pollen: their captivity lasted eight days, during which time they did not produce any wax, nor where scales seen under the rings: could any doubt then exist upon the real origin of beeswax?   We entertained none.

3rd Experiment: *To insure there was no wax in the honey*

Could it be argued that wax is contained in the honey it-self and that the bees preserved it out of this liquid in order to use it when needed? This last objection had some likelihood, for honey nearly always contains parcels of wax; one may see it rise to the surface when the honey is diluted in water; but the microscope, by exhibiting to us the fact that these particles belonged to previously built cells, that they were of the same shape and thickness as the broken walls of cells, gave us an indication of the lack of weight of this argument which had stopped us for a moment.

In order to formally obviate this objection and to enlight-en ourselves on a particular opinion of our own, that is: that the sweet principle was the true cause of the wax secretion; we took a pound of white sugar reduced to syrup and gave it to a swarm confined in a glass hive.

We made this experiment still more positive by establish-ing for comparison, two other hives, in which two swarms were hived, one fed with very dark brown sugar and the other with honey. The result of this triple test was as satisfactory as it was possible to wish it.

The bees of all three hives produced beeswax; those that had been fed with sugar of different grades gave more of it and in greater abundance than those that were fed with honey only.

Amounts of wax produced from various sugars

A pound (453 grams) of white sugar, reduced to syrup, and clarified with the white of an egg, produced 10 gros 52 grains (1.5 ounces or 42 grams) of beeswax darker than that which bees extract from honey. An equal weight of dark brown sugar yielded 22 gros (3 ounces or 84 grams) of very white wax; a similar amount was obtained from maple sugar.

We repeated these experiments seven times in succession, with the same bees and we always obtained wax in nearly the same proportions as above. It therefore appears demonstrated that sugar and the saccharine part of honey enable the bees that feed upon it to produce wax, a property entirely denied to the fecundating dust.

The facts which these experiments gave us were soon confirmed in a more general way. Although there was no uncertainty upon these questions, it was well to ascertain whether the bees, in the natural state, would follow the same course as those which we had held captive: a long course of observations, of which we will give but a sketch, proved to us that when the fields offer to the bees a great crop of honey, those of the old hives store it eagerly, while those of the new swarms convert it into wax.

I did not then own a large number of colonies, but those of my village neighbors served for comparison, even though they were constructed of straw and did not offer the same conveniences as my own. Certain remarks which we made upon the appearance of the combs and of the bees themselves when working in wax enabled us to avail ourselves of those hives so unfavorable for observation.

Beeswax is originally white, soon afterwards the cells become yellow, and brown with time; when the combs are very old their color is of a blackish hue. It is therefore very easy to distinguish the new combs from those where were built previously, and therefore to know whether the bees are building combs or whether they work is suspended, merely by raising up the hives and glancing at the edges of the combs.

Two kinds of workers in the hive

The following observations may also furnish indications of the presence of honey in the flowers. They are based upon a remarkable fact which was unknown to my precursors; it is that there are two kinds of workers in the hive; the ones which may attain a considerable size when they have filled themselves with all the honey that their stomach may contain, are in general destined to the elaboration of wax; the others whose abdomen does not perceptibly change in appearance, retain only the quantity of honey which is necessary for their sustenance and immediately hand out to others that which they have harvested; they are not in charge of the provisioning of the hive, their particular function being to care for the young: we will call them nurse bees, or small bees, in opposition to those whose abdomen may be dilated and which deserve the name of wax-workers.

Although the external difference by which the two sorts may be recognized be inconsiderable, this distinction is not imaginary. Anatomical observations have taught us that there is a real difference in the capacity of their stomach. We have also ascertained that the bees of one sort cannot fulfill all the functions shared among the workers of a hive. In one of these tests we painted with different colors the bees of each class, to observe their behavior, and we did not see any interchange. In another test, we gave the bees of a queenless colony both brood and pollen and we at once saw the small bees busy themselves with the food of the larvae, while those of the wax-working class paid no attention to them. Note: Huber did not then know what we learned later, by the introduction of Italian bees, that the difference in functions is due to the difference in age, of the bees of the colony.—Translator.

When the hives are full of combs, the wax-working bees disgorge their honey into the usual magazines and make no wax; but if they have no reservoir in which to deposit it, and if their queen does not find already built cells to deposit her eggs, they retain in their stomach the honey which they have gathered, and at the end of twenty-four hours wax exudes through the rings; then the labor of comb construction begins.

One might believe that, when the country does not furnish honey, wax builders may encroach upon the provisions stored up in the hive; but they are not permitted to do it; a part of the honey is carefully put away; the cells in which it is deposited are protected with a wax covering which is removed only in case of extreme need and when there is no other way to procure it elsewhere; they are never opened during the good season; other reservoirs, always open, supply the daily needs of the community; but each bee takes only that which is absolutely necessary for present requirements.

The wax-workers appear with large bellies at the entrance of the hive only when the country supplies an abundant crop of honey; they produce wax only when the hive is not full of combs. It may be conceived, from what we have said, that the production of the waxy matter depends upon a concourse of circumstances that do not always appear.

The small bees may also produce wax, but in a very inferior quantity to that produced by the real wax workers.

Another characteristic, whereby an attentive observer cannot fail to recognize the time when bees collect sufficient honey to produce wax, is the strong odor of both these substances which is produced from the hives at that time and which does not exist with such intensity at any other time.

From such data it was easy for us to recognize whether the bees worked upon their combs in our hives and in those of the cultivators of the same district.

Observations on conditions when wax building occurs
In 1793, the inclemency of the season had retarded the departure of swarms; there were none in the country before the 24th of May; most of the hives swarmed in the middle of June. The country was then covered with flowers, the bees collected much honey, and the new swarms worked in wax with activity.

On the 18th, Burnens visited 65 hives and saw wax workers before the entrances of all; those that entered into the old hives speedily stored their harvest, and did not build any combs; but those of the swarms converted their honey into wax and hastened to prepare lodgings for the eggs of their queen.

The 19th was showery, the bees went out, but we did not see any wax workers; they brought in only pollen. The weather was cold and rainy until the 27th; we became anxious to learn what had resulted from this atmospheric condition.

On the 28th we raised all the hives. Burnens then saw that the work had been interrupted; the combs which he had measured on the 9th had not received the least accession, they were of citron yellow, there were no longer any white cells in any of the hives.

On the 1st of July, the weather being warmer, and the chestnut and linden trees in bloom, we again saw the wax workers; they brought in much honey; the swarms lengthened the combs; we saw everywhere the greatest activity: the gathering of honey and the work in wax continued until the middle of the month.

But on the 16th of July, the heat having risen above 20° R (Note: Dadant's translation just says 77° F while the original French version which consistently uses R says 20° which is 77° F or 25° C. Yet Huber seems to indicate it is very hot. Perhaps it was a typographical error in the original.—Transcriber.), the country felt the drought; the flowers of the meadows and those of the trees just mentioned were entirely faded, they no longer yielded honey; their pollen alone attracted the bees, they gathered abundantly of it, and there was no wax produced. The combs were not lengthened, those of the swarms made no progress.

It had not rained for six weeks; the heat was great; neither did any dew temper it during the night, and the buckwheat which had bloomed for several days gave no honey to the bees, they found only pollen in it; but on the 10th of August, it rained for several hours; the following day they exhaled the odor of honey and we saw it actually glitter in the open blossoms, the bees found enough for their food, but too little to be induced to work in wax.

The drought returned on the 14th and lasted until the end of the month; we then examined the 65 hives for the last time, and saw that the bees had not worked in wax since the middle of July; and they had stored much pollen, that the provision of honey had diminished considerably in the old hives and that there was scarcely any in the new swarms.

The year was therefore very unfavorable to the labor of bees; I attribute it mainly to the condition of the atmosphere which was not charged with electricity; a circumstance which has great influence on the secretion of honey in the nectaries of flowers. I have noticed that the harvest of the bees is never more abundant nor the work in wax more active than when a storm is preparing and the wind is in the south, the air moist and warm; but heat too long protracted and the drought ensuing, cold rains and north wind entirely suspend the elaboration of honey in plants, and consequently the operation of bees.

When we confined the bees for the purpose of discovering whether the honey was sufficient for the production of wax, they supported their captivity patiently; they showed astonishing perseverance in rebuilding their combs, as fast they were removed by us: had we left a part of those combs to them, their queen would have laid eggs in the cells, we would have seen in what manner the workers conducted themselves towards their young and what would have been the effect upon the latter of the deprivation of the fecundating pollen; but since we were occupied solely with the question relating to the origin of wax we preferred to make a separate treatment of that which concerns the feeding of the young.

4th Experiment: Proving that pollen is necessary to raise brood

The experiment to be made required the presence of larvae in the hive; honey and water were needed; the bees must have combs containing brood and must be carefully confined, so that they might not go to the field after pollen; we chanced to have a colony which had never become useless from sterility of the queen; we sacrificed it for this experiment; it was in one of my leaf hives, both ends of which were glazed: we removed the queen and substituted, for the first and last combs, some combs filled with brood, eggs and young larvae, but no cells with fecundating dust; we removed every parcel of this matter which John Hunter conjectured to be the basis of the food of the young.

The behavior of the bees in these circumstances is worthy of some attention. On the first and second day of the experiment nothing extraordinary happened; the bees brooded over their young and appeared to care for them.

But on the third day after sunset, we heard a great noise in this hive; impatient to discover its cause we opened a shutter and saw all in confusion; the brood was abandoned, the workers ran in disorder over the combs; we saw thousands rush towards the lower part of the hive; those about the entrance gnawed fiercely at its grating; their intention was not equivocal, they wished to emerge from their prison.

Some imperious necessity obliged them to seek elsewhere what they could not find in their home: I feared to see them perish if we restrained them longer from their instinct; we set them at liberty. The entire swarm escaped, but the hour was not favorable for the harvest; so the bees did not depart from the hive, they flew about it. The increasing darkness and the coolness of the air soon compelled them to re-enter. Probably the same cause calmed their agitation, for we saw them remounting peaceably upon their combs; order seemed re-established, and we profited of this moment to close the hive.

The next day, July 19th we saw the rudiments of two royal cells that some bees had outlined upon one of the brood combs. In the evening at the same hour as the preceding day, we again heard a loud buzzing in the enclosed hive, the agitation and disorder being manifested at the highest degree; we were again obliged to let the swarm escape; but it was not out long; the quieted bees returned as before.

On the 20th we noticed that the royal cells had not been continued as they would have been in ordinary conditions. A great tumult took place in the evening the bees appeared in delirium; we set them at liberty and order was restored on their return.

The captivity of these bees having endured five days, we though it useless to protract it further; besides we wished to know whether the brood was in good condition, whether it had made the usually progress, and try to discover what might be the cause of the periodical agitation of the bees. Burnens having exposed to the light of day the two combs of brood which he had given them, he first noticed the royal cells, but did not find them enlarged; indeed why should they be, since they contained neither eggs nor worms, nor that peculiar kind of jelly given to the individuals of their calls? The other cells were vacant also; no brood, no pap; the worms must have died of hunger. By removing all the fecundating dust, had we taken away from the bees all means of nourishing them? To decide this question it was necessary to confine other brood to the same bees to care for, while giving them an abundance of pollen. They had not been able to make any harvest while we examined their combs; for on this occasion they had been set at liberty in a room all of the windows of which were closed; after having substituted young worms for those which they had allowed to perish, we returned them to their prison.

Continuing the experiment by providing pollen

The next day, the 22nd, we noticed that they had resumed courage; they had strengthened the combs which we had given them and were clustered upon the brood. We then provided them with fragments of combs into which other bees had stored up fecundating dust; but in order to observe what they would do with it, we took some of the pollen out of a few cells and spread it upon the hive stand. The bees immediately discovered both the pollen in the combs and that we had exposed; they crowded upon the cells and also upon the bottom of the hive, took the pollen, grain by grain, in their mandibles and conveyed it to their mouths: those that had eaten of it the most greedily climbed upon the combs before the rest, stopped upon the cells containing the young worms, inserted their heads in them and remained them for a certain time.

Burnens opened gently one of the windows of the hive and powdered the workers which were eating pollen, for the purpose of recognizing them when they would ascend upon the combs. He observed them during several hours and by this means ascertained that they took so great a quantity of pollen only to impart it to their pupils.

On the 23rd we saw royal cells outlined; on the 24th we removed the bees which concealed the brood and found that all the young worms had jelly as in the ordinary hives, that they had grown and had advanced in their cells; that others had been lately closed up because they were nearing their metamorphosis; finally we had no longer any doubt of order being restored, when we saw the royal cells lengthened.

Out of curiosity, we removed the parcels of comb which we had laid upon the stand of the hive and saw the quantity of pollen in them had been sensibly diminished; we returned them to the bees, increasing their provisions still further, so as to prolong the actions which we witnessed. We soon saw the royal cells sealed as well as several of the common cells; we again opened the hive, everywhere the worms had prospered; some had their food still before them; others had spun and their cells were sealed with a wax covering.

The result was already very striking, but what excited our astonishment above all was, that in spite of their captivity so long protracted, the bees seemed no longer anxious to go out; we could not see the agitation, the increasing periodical trouble, the general impatience which they had manifested in the first part of the experiment; several bees, indeed, attempted to escape in the course of the day; but when they found it was impossible they returned peaceably to their young.

This trait which we have witnessed several times, always with the same interest, proves so undoubtedly the affection of bees for the larvae whose education is entrusted to them, that we shall not seek for any other explanation of their conduct.

Feeding sugar rather than honey for too long changed their instincts

Another fact, no less extraordinary, and the cause of which is more difficult to discern, was that exhibited by bees which were constrained to work in wax, several times successively, by giving them sugar syrup. During the first part of the tests they gave their young the usual care; but at the last they ceased to feed them, they even frequently dragged them from their cells and carried them out of the hive.

Not knowing what this disposition should be ascribed to, I endeavored to revive the instinct of these bees by giving them other brood to care for; but this attempt was unsuccessful; the bees did not feed the new larvae, although they had pollen in store. We offered them honey, hoping to supply thus a more natural method of alimenting their young; but it was useless; all the brood perished; perhaps the bees could no longer produce the jelly which is the food of the larvae; except in this particular they appeared to have lost none of the faculties, they were equally active and laborious. At last, from motives unknown to us, all deserted their hive together one day and did not return to the hive.

Whatever be the cause of the alteration which we noticed in the instinct of the bees which have been fed too long with sugar, one may not see without admiration that this substance is modified in the flowers so as to be used by bees without inconvenience; but everything in nature is adapted for long continued use, and the elements are combined with so much foresight that they never act in isolation but with all the energy proper to them.

CHAPTER III: ON THE ARCHITECTURE OF BEES

The great problem that bees present to us by their astonishing industry does not exclusively belong to the exact sciences: physics, chemistry, anatomy even would find application in it; but their efforts would be insufficient without the help of natural history, which observed the habits of animals and studies all the circumstances of their active life. It is natural history which by raising the veil, uncovers facts to us under their diverse disguises; and leads the other sciences upon the way of other researches to which they are adapted.

Thus when we demonstrate that wax is an animal secretion, and that it proceeds from the sweet part of honey, we leave it for the chemists to decide in what manner this secretion operates, whether sugar or one of its constituents changes to wax, or whether it is only a stimulating cause of a particular action, and we also invite the anatomists to seek for the organs which have escaped our attention.

It is time to examine how bees use the substance exuding from their rings, and to discover how they prepare it to convert it into true beeswax, for this substance does not leave the lodges where it is molded in a perfect state, it differs in several respects from what it is after having been carved; it has only the fusibility of wax, it is friable and brittle, it does not have the ductibility which it will acquire later; it is still as transparent as plates of talc, whereas that which constitutes the cells is opaque and of a yellowish white color.

We must also watch the bees when they are busy removing the scales of wax from under their rings, we must learn how they trim the bottoms of their cells, the prisms composed of trapezes; observe the manner in which they join the bottom of each cell with that of three other cells, how they give to their design the proper slope, etc., etc.

The brightest conceptions are insufficient without observation

We might form ingenious suppositions upon all these marvels but we cannot divine the processes of insects; we must observe them. The most simple methods may not present themselves to our mind; we usually seek to explain the behavior of animals after our own faculties, according to our lights and our means; but the being which directs their instinct takes His views outside of the limits assigned to us and in a sphere of ideas in which our most learned designs, our most specious reasoning betoken the limits of our nature.

We have been able to ascertain, through the hypotheses of a celebrated writer, how insufficient are the most extensive knowledge and the brightest conceptions without the concourse of observation, to explain, in a plausible manner, the art displayed by the bees in constructing their cells. Consummate naturalists failed when they attempted to penetrate this mystery: Réaumur, who had come nearest to the discovery of the truth, had passed judgment in too fleeting a manner to satisfy our curiosity and his own, so he candidly acknowledges that that he gives only conjectures upon this point. Hunter, the most enlightened of modern observers, did not succeed in following the bees as to the use they made of the scales of wax which he had discovered under their rings; could I hope to be more fortunate than savants who were provided with such perfect organs and were so well drilled in the art of nature study?

Perhaps new methods which I employed by helping our efforts have contributed in throwing some light upon a subject which excited a keen interest in my mind

The tools of wax working

One may suppose that bees are provided with instruments similar to the angles of their cells; for one must explain their geometry in some way; but these instruments can only be their teeth, their claws and their antennae. Now there is no more similarity between the shape of the teeth of the bees and the angles of their cells than there is between the sculptor's chisel and the work which emerges from his hands. Their teeth

(Pate IV, figs. 1, 2, 3) are in effect hollow chisels, cut obliquely in gouge-shape, born upon a short pedicle and divided into two longitudinal cavities by a scaly projection, their edges meet above and rest against each other (fig. 1); the underside shows a sort of throat divided by the projection and bordered with long and strong hairs which are probably intended to hold the particles of wax during the work in the combs (figs. 2, 3). When the teeth are brought together they form an acute curvilineal angle, and the inner angle which they form when working apart is still less open. There are none of the angles of rhombs and trapezes of the cells.

The triangular shape of the head, which presents only three sharp angles, explains no better the choice of these figures; for even if we suppose that one of them be analogous to the acute angle of the lozenges, where would we find the measure of their obtuse angles?

Volume 2 Plate IV Fig 1—Teeth.

Shall we seek in the legs of the bees some connection with the regular work which these insects execute? They are composed, as those of most other insects, of the haunch (a), the thigh (b), the leg (c), and of the foot or tarsus (Plate IV, Fig 4, de).

Volume 2 Plate IV Fig 2—One tooth.

Volume 2 Plate IV Fig 3—Teeth (Obverse).

The first three parts have nothing in them distinguishable from those of most other hymenopters, with the exception of the leg proper of the third pair; it is this limb in shape of basket which Réaumur calls the "palet" and upon which the bees carry the fecundating dusts (c, figs. 4 & 5): it is triangular, smooth, with a row of hairs, lengthwise along its exterior edge, those of the base arise, he says, and curve up towards the upper part of the leg, so that all these hairs form the edge of a sort of basket, the outside face of which would be the bottom.

Fig. 4 .

Volume 2 Plate IV Fig 4—Leg with basket and comb.

Fig. 5.

*Volume 2 Plate IV Fig 5—Obverse of lower portion of leg in
Fig 4 showing comb and basket.*

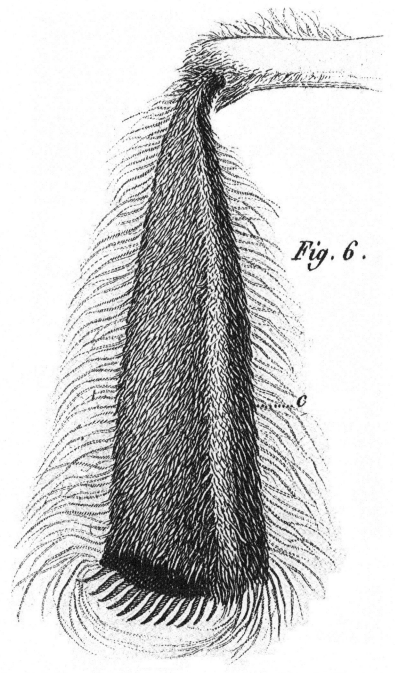

Fig. 6.

Volume 2 Plate IV Fig 6—Upper portion of leg in Fig 4 show-ing comb or brush.

Aside of the triangular palet, the most remarkable thing about the legs of bees is the tarsus, of which the first articulation is much larger than the rest and all three pairs is of a very different form from those of other insects of the same genus (d, figs. 4 & 5).

The first articulation of the tarsus is called the brush, from the well-known use of this part, which is employed in gather the pollen grains scattered over the body of the bee as she collects them. In the legs of the first pair, it is lengthened, rounded and entirely hairy, all the hairs being turned towards the extremity of the tarsus. In the legs of the second pair, the brush is oblong of irregular shape, flattened smooth on the outer side, much covered with hairs on the opposite side; these are all turned downwards: it is joined exactly in the middle of the other piece, into which it fits.

The brush of the third pair offers some very remarkable peculiarities which will appear the more so when we make their use known; this piece is shaped very differently from that of the second pair of legs; the only resemblance they have to each other is to be both flat, smooth on the outside and hairy on the other side; but the brush of the third pair (d, figs 4& 5) is larger than that of the second and of a peculiar shape. It appears at first sight as a rectangular parallelogram: it was first designated as "square piece" to distinguish it from the palet, the edges of which are triangular, but when examining it carefully we notice that it diverges from the shape described. The rising edges of it cease to appear parallel, when we notice that they are not exactly in straight line and that they tend to come together at one of the extremities; the underside is slightly notched, the upper side, is more so and is prolonged in the shape of a very sharp and projecting tooth, while at the other end it rises in the shape of an arc to supply a joint with the leg; but this movable piece is not joined into the middle of the base of the other as in the other pairs; it is on the forward angle of the triangular piece that we find the joint which unites them, and the inferior face of the palet being about straight, it forms a real claw with the upper edge of the brush.

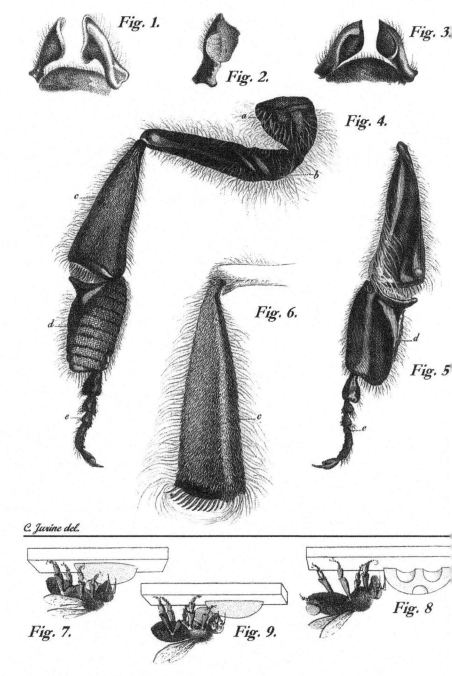

Fig. 1.

Fig. 2.

Fig. 3.

Fig. 4.

Fig. 6.

Fig. 5

C. Jurine del.

Fig. 7.

Fig. 9.

Fig. 8

Volume 2 Plate IV—"Tools" of Comb Building.

Réaumur who gave the description of these two pieces had not noticed that they could spread apart and make an angle the upper edge of which is represented by their joint: he had not noticed that the edge (ab) of this angle was smooth on its outside and that the hairs which form the edge of the basket at that spot come from the sides of the palet; that these hairs, of great length, curve towards the base and form a sort of arch by coming together; but if the outside of the palet is smooth at that spot, it is not the same on the opposite side (Plate IV, fig. 6): we see there a row of scaly teeth, similar to those of a comb, almost straight, parallel to each other; of equal length, very acute and slightly sloping towards the opening of the pincers: corresponding with bundles of very strong hairs with which the neighboring portion of the brush is provided.

The scaly projection supplied by the brush at its extremity is slightly turned outwards, and when the two parts of the pincers meet their ends do not correspond exactly with the edge of the palet, so that the teeth of the one cross with the hairs of the other.

This organization is too obvious not to have a particular aim; indeed nothing similar appears on the legs of either males or queens; but is seen only in bumble bees (bremus) a race very near to the honeybee and whose habits have some analogy with hers. We will soon show its usage among the bees; but it is evident that it cannot in any way serve as a model for the angles by which the different sections of cells are joined.

The tarsus is composed also of three conical articulations very small and elongated and terminating in two pairs of claws. Réaumur may be correct in considering this as two articulations, one of which is conical and elongated, the other a fleshy part, with claws arming the foot.

Do the antennae posses these direct pattern for the geometrical forms of the pyramidal bases of which we have as yet found no pattern on the body of the insect? They are bent and composed of twelve articulations; the first two form a peculiar section, which moves in every direction on its base and served to support the next section composed of the other ten. The first articulation of the antenna is globular, the second cylindrical and much elongated; the third, which is the first of the second section, is conical and very short, the second very long and conical, the remainder are all cylindrical and the last is terminated in a soft point. This organization enables the antenna to make all sorts of motions, and it can, through its flexibility, follow the outline of every object; though its position it may encircle body of small diameter, and extend in every direction.

There is no pattern for the structure of comb in the anatomy of the bee

Thus neither the antennae, the teeth, nor the legs of bees are able to serve as patterns for the structure of cells; but the chisel, pincers and compass which they represent are proper instruments for the building of all the parts of a cell; the result which they produce depends entirely upon the aim of the insect.

If the workman is not supplied with a model for his work, if the pattern upon which he cuts each piece is not outside of himself and his sight, we must admit that some intellect directs his operations.

It is true that we might suppose that the scales of wax, when they emerge from under the rungs, have already a shape similar to that which is intended; but we know that the shape of these scales is an irregular pentagon, which resembles neither the trapezes nor the lozenges of which the cells are composed.

Hunter, having noticed that the thickness of the bases was about that of one of the scales, inferred that the bees used them as produced and accumulated them upon each other to form the sides which appeared of heavier thickness. We should then take it for granted that the bees were taught to trim these scales and arrange them in regular order; but these are only conjectures and facts are necessary to solve as complicated a question as this.

Réaumur, even with glass hives, had not solved the mystery of comb building; he thought that one could gain a correct idea of their operations without witnessing their work; this mistake deprived him of the pleasure of seeing in action the most singular work of all those that insects display. I thought that it was indispensable to witness it, in order to understand the process of building and I sought more proper methods for this than any of my predecessors had used.

One may imagine that glass hives of four sides are sufficient to see the bees construct their combs and that the only other requirement is assiduity and attention; but their architecture is always concealed from our view by clusters of bees several inches in thickness. It is in this cluster, and in darkness, that the combs are built; they are fastened at their inception, to the ceiling of the hives; they are prolongated downwards, more or less, according to the time of building, and their diameter is increased in proportion to their length.

A hive to observe wax building

I saw the necessity of witnessing their initial work; but how is one to see in the midst of such a host of insects, how could we hope to reach the center of a sanctuary guarded by so great a number of stings and such courageous guards? For this purpose it was indispensable to lighten the upper part of the hive; for *there* was the work which I was anxious to witness. I hoped to succeed with the following apparatus; but experience showed me that it had to be modified. It was a large bell-shaped receiver; which I hoped to use in place of an ordinary hive; there was nothing in its curves very different from the shape of skeps in which we hive bees; but I had not foreseen the inability of the bees to hang in clusters under this slippery arch. A few bees managed to hang to it, but were unable to sustain this scheme, but I retained this plan as closely as I could. Understanding that the bees need supports I attempted to satisfy them by gluing thin wooden slips at certain intervals to the arch. I thought that they would work between these slips and that I would be enabled to watch them; but they did not consult my convenience and fastened their cells to the wooden slips; I was, however able to take some advantage of this arrangement.

We introduced into this hive a swarm of a few thousand workers, a few hundred drones and a fertile queen. They at once ascended to the highest point of their home, and those first reaching the slips, fixed themselves to them with the claws of their forefeet; others scrambling up the sides, joined them, by hanging to their third pair of legs with their own firsts pair. Thus they made chains fastened by their two ends to the upper parts of the receiver which served as a bridge or ladders for the workers joining their gathering; this formed a cluster with its extremities hanging clear to the bottom of the hive, like an inverted pyramid or cone, the base of which was at the top of the hive.

The country then afforded but little honey; but it was important that the object of our researches be not too much delayed, for we could not leave the hive a single instant without running the risk of losing the opportunity of witnessing the beginning of the combs. Had we left the bees to their natural state, we should have had to watch them for several days before seeing them occupied with building; so we fed them with sugar syrup, in order to hasten their work.

They crowded to the edge of the manger containing it, then returned to the pyramidal cluster. Soon we were struck with the appearance of this hive, through the contrast of the usual agitation of bees with their present inaction. All the external layers of the cluster constituted a kind of curtain formed exclusively of wax workers; hanging together they displayed a series of festoons crossing each other in every direction, and in which the back of most of the bees was turned towards the observer: This festoon had no other motion than that which was communicated to it from the inner layers, whose fluctuations were displayed in it.

However, the small bees appeared to have retained all their activity, they alone went to the fields, brought back pollen, kept guard at the entrance of the hive, cleansed it and stopped up its edges with odiferous resin, known as propolis; the wax workers remained motionless above fifteen hours; the curtain consisted of the same individuals and we made sure that none replaced them. Some hours later, we noticed that almost all the wax workers had scales under their rings. The next day, this phenomenon was still more general; the bees on the outside of the cluster had slightly changed their position; one could see the under part of their abdomen distinctly. By the projection of the scales, their rings seemed edged with white; the curtain wax rent in several places; less tranquility reigned in the hive.

Convinced that the combs would first appear in the center of the swarm, and that they would soon be noticeable, we concentrated our attention upon the vault of the receiver. The area of the base was in a good light, we could distinctly see the first links of the festoons of bees which hung from the top of the vault. The concentrical layers which the bees formed, equally crowded together, left no intervals; but the scene was about to be shifted and we witnessed it.

Observing comb building

A worker at this time detached herself from one of the central festoons of the cluster, we saw her spread her companions apart, driving away with her head the leaders fastened at the middle of the arch and by turning around form a space in which she could freely move. She then suspended herself in the center of the field which she had just cleared, the diameter of which was 12 or 13 lines (about one in. or about 27 mm).

We saw her at once seize one of the scales which projected from her rings (Plate IV. Fig. 8); for this purpose she brought towards her abdomen one of the legs of the third pair, rested it against her body, opened the pincers which we have described, inserted skillfully the edge of her brush under the scale that she wished to remove, closed up on this instrument, pulled the scale of wax from its ring and took it with the claws of her anterior legs, to bring it up to her mouth (figs. 7 & 8).

Volume 2 Plate IV Fig 7—Scale of wax being brought to mouth.

Volume 2 Plate IV Fig 8—Scale of wax being brought to mouth by anterior leg.

Volume 2 Plate IV Fig 9—Scale of wax being brought to mouth.

The scale is broken into parcels

The bee then held this scale in a vertical position: we noticed that she turned it between her jaws with the help of the claws of her front legs, which held it by its opposite edge and could give it a suitable direction. The tongue, folded on itself, served as a support; by raising and lowering it she could pass every part of the circumference under the edge of the jaws and the edge of the scale was soon broken to pieces. The parcels of wax that fell from it stopped in the hairy cavity which we described when we spoke of bees' teeth. These fragments having accumulated with others freshly cut, were crowded towards the mouth and issued from it as from a drawing-plate in the shape of a very narrow ribbon.

Wax is impregnated with frothy liquid from the mouth

They next passed through by the tongue which impregnated them with a frothy liquid similar to pap. The tongue in this operation made most varied maneuvers; it assumed most varied shapes, now flattening like a spatula now acting like a trowel applied upon the ribbon of wax; at other times it appeared like a pointed brush.

After having imbued the entire substance of the ribbon with the liquid that loaded it, the tongue forced this ribbon forward and passed it again through the same drawing-plate, but in the opposite direction; this motion brought it towards the sharp edge of the jaws, where it was again chopped up under their carver.

The liquid makes the wax more opaque, more pliable and promotes adhesion

At length, the bee applied these particles of wax to the vault of the hive. The gluten which impregnated them promoted their adhesion; she separated them with a cut of her jaw, from the portion not yet to be used; then with the same instruments she gave them direction which she intended for them.

The liquid which she mixed with the wax gave it a whiteness and opacity which were wanting when the scales left the rings; doubtless the purpose of this process was to give the wax that ductility and tenacity which it posses when perfect.

The founding bee (this denomination is well deserved) continued this maneuver until all the fragments, which had been worked up and impregnated with this whitish fluid, were attached to the vault; she then manipulated between her teeth the remainder of the scale which she had kept apart during the working of the ribbon. All the portion which had been thus kept intact during the first operation was employed then, and in the same manner. The worker applied to the underside of the vault all the material prepared, fastened additional material under and on the side of it, and continued until she had entirely exhausted the material supplied.

Second and third scales were treated thus by the same bee, yet the work was only sketched, for it was only material ready to assume any shape wanted; the worker did not attempt to shape the molecules of wax which she assembled; she was satisfied to accumulate them together, this required no effort.

The work is done sequentially by many bees

However, the founding bee quit the spot and disappeared among her companions, another with wax under her rings succeeded her; she suspended herself at the same spot, seized with the pincers of the posterior legs one of the scales of wax, and passing it up to her teeth, proceeded with the work.

She did not deposit haphazard the fragments which she manipulated; for the little pile which her companion had built directed her and she put her own in the same alignment, uniting the two at their extremities. A third worker, detaching herself from the interior of the cluster, suspended herself to the ceiling, reduced some of her scales to paste and put them near the materials accumulated by her companions, but not in the same manner, they were places at an angle with the others: another worker appeared to notice it and removed the mis-placed wax before our eyes, carrying it to the former heap; she deposited it in the same order, following exactly the indicated direction. From all these operations was produced a block of rugged surface, hanging perpendicularly from the vault. One could not perceive any angle, any trace of the figure of cells in this initial work of the bees; it was a simple partition, in a straight line, and without the least inflexion; six or eight lines in length (about ½ in. or about 15mm); about two thirds of the diameter of a cell in height and declining towards its extremities: we have seen other blocks from an inch to an inch and a half long, the form was always the same, but none were of greater height.

The empty space in the center of the cluster permitted us to see the first maneuvers of the bees and to discover the art with which they lay the foundations of their edifice, but this space was filled too promptly for our wishes, too many bees collected on both sides of the block obstructing the view, so that it was no longer possible to follow their work.

But if we were unable, with this apparatus, to see as much as we should have wished to learn, we considered ourselves very fortunate in doing justice to Réaumur, who thought he observed the wax discharged from the mouth of the bees in the shape of pap; doubtless it was this whitish and frothy liquid with which they moisten the waxy substance to give it properties which it does not possess in the origin, and which he mistook for the wax; this observation, by indicating the cause of the opinion of this naturalist; solved one of the greatest difficulties of the subject of which we are speaking; for one cannot reject a fact advanced by so judicious a writer without explaining the cause of his error.

CHAPTER IV: CONTINUATION OF THE ARCHITECTURE OF BEES

Section I: Description of the usual shape of cells

Natural history does not present any phenomenon whose final causes are more tempting to seek than bee architecture. The order and symmetry which reign in their combs invite us to these researches, which please both the heart and the mind at the same time.

I shall not investigate as to whether some error has been made in the attribution of these causes and whether nature had not been credited with narrow aims in planning such strict economy among the bees. I shall not decide whether the fine problem solved by Koenig, Cramer, Maraldi, is rigorously applicable to the work of these insects, or whether we should not, in the actions of insects, admit of a certain freedom of action which is not needed in purely physical matters; the reckoning of the modern geometers appears to be in harmony with the liberal views of the Author of nature, when they figure upon intended economy as only a secondary object in the plan followed by the bees.

There is, indeed, a more important requirement for these insects, which could not have been fulfilled, if their art was confined to this sole and meritorious purpose.

When I undertook the researches which I am about to relate, I was far from foreseeing that they were to lead me to new conclusions on the structure of combs.

Distinguished observers had made this a subject of meditation, and appeared to have fully developed a theory on the pyramidal bases of the combs; even their names appeared to confirm the accepted ideas concerning this matter, and I did not expect to discover important facts unknown until then, through instructions given by me to a simple villager.

But the most interesting discoveries are not always those that require the most effort. A glance, to the base of newly built combs, suggested to us that the details of their constructions had not yet been sufficiently studied. The anomalies which they presented appeared to us to be of the greatest importance; I will recall in a few words the usual shape of the cells, in order to describe the traits which seem to furnish a key to the architecture of bees.

The cells which any one may examine are composed of two parts, a prismatic hexagonal tube, and a pyramidal base (Plate V, fig. 1). The latter (bcdg), which must be considered the most delicate and essential part of the entire work, is formed of three rhomboids or lozenges, equal and similar, united together in a common center and inclined in a deter-mined angle so as to produce a slight cavity.

While these three pieces produce a depression on one of the sides of the comb, they produce a projection (fig. 2) on the other side: and here each corresponds to two other pieces which, through their inclinations, help to form similar pyramidal bases; that is why each cell is fastened to three other cells by a common base.

On the edge of each pyramidal base (fig. 1) they pris-matic hexagonal tube rises, the six sides of which are cut at right angles at the orifice of the cell, and are shaped at their lower extremity so as to fit the angular contour of the pyrami-dal base.

These cells, by their shape and combination fulfill proba-bly all the conditions that we might expect from the work of the bees; but are they capable of becoming fastened with sufficient strength to the part of the hive which is to sustain them? This is a very important point which seems to have been over-looked.

A very simple figure (fig. 3) is sufficient to show us that hexagonal prisms, placed side by side can be fastened by only one of their angles to the surface of the ceiling and would leave large vacuities between these angles. And yet the combs need to be solidly fixed.

This condition is so important that it is taken in consider-ation by nature, at two different times, if we may so express it.

First, when the combs are built; secondly when those have become too heavy to be trusted with so frail a support.

The following observations showed us by what precautions the bees provide for the stability of their constructions.

Having directed our attention upon the base of the combs in a newly stocked hive, we were impressed by the appearance of the first row of cells, through which the comb is fastened to the ceiling of the hive. It was different from the rows below it, in such remarkable peculiarities, that we saw fit to examine a number of others for comparison. We found, indeed, that even those of most recent building presented a similar contrast between the fundamental cells and those of which the comb is composed; so that what had first impressed us as an anomaly was really a rule (fig. 11).

The upper part of the combs being always partly hidden from view by the edge of the supports, I realized that they would not promote our observations; that it was necessary to take possession of the work and remove from it the workers whose vigilance would incommode us: but it was important not to alter their masonry, and especially to preserve intact the cells of the first row, which attracted our curiosity. So I had such combs removed from my leaf hives as I wished to examine; we left them for this purpose in the frames in which they had been built; without such precaution we should have failed in our purpose: it was then only that we were able to examine the shape and arrangement of the cells of the first row.

Their orifice, instead of a hexagon, presents the shape of an irregular pentagon (fig. 4): a horizontal line which is that of the hive ceiling two vertical and perpendicular lines and two oblique lines united at the bottom in an obtuse angle, formed the contour of the cell; so the wax tube was composed of only four pieces, two vertical and two oblique, the ceiling forming a fifth side.

These are not the classical shapes to which we were accustomed. We desired to know whether the bottom of the cells corresponded with the shape of their edges; in order to see this more distinctly we cut the tubes away from their bearings; we saw then that their bases were very different from those of the ordinary cells.

We retained only the wall which separates the cells on both sides (fig. 4 and 5). It displayed angular projections and recesses; but as it was throughout of about even thickness, that which was a projection on one side proved to be recess on the opposite side.

However on one side the base of each cell was composed of three pieces while on the other it had but two, because these cells alternately opposite, were unequal: this requires a greater explanation.

Of the three pieces which compose the base of the cells of the first row, on one side which we shall call the *anterior* side, only one of them was in the shape of a rhomb; the other two were irregular quadrilaterals, or trapezes. These hanging (a, b, fig. 5) from the ceiling by their short side, descended perpendicularly; their vertical edges were parallel; but one was joined together in an obtuse angle; the fourth edge, the lower one of these pieces, was oblique; and it was between the oblique edges of these trapezes that the rhomb was fastened which forms the bottom of the cavity. It is easy to understand the cause of its inclination, since the top of one of its obtuse angles was below the joint of the two trapezes; and its sharp angles at the lower extremity of the large edges of these trapezes, and consequently a little lower. Thus the rhomb is slanting or inclined as are the lower edges of the trapezes (fig 8).

On the opposite side of the comb, the bases of the cells of the same row are composed of only two trapezes (fig. 9) similar to those that form a part of the base of the cells just described, only they appear turned differently, for they are joined to the base of the cell by their greater sides: they make, with each other, an angle exactly equal to that which unites the trapezes of the anterior face, they form the back of two neighboring cells: so the cells of this face can only correspond in their base to two opposite cells. On the contrary, those of the anterior face having one more piece, must correspond with three cells (fig. 14 and 15); the rhomb c which they show fills the space between two cells of the posterior face, and is the first piece of the cells of the second row, which are themselves composed of three rhombs.

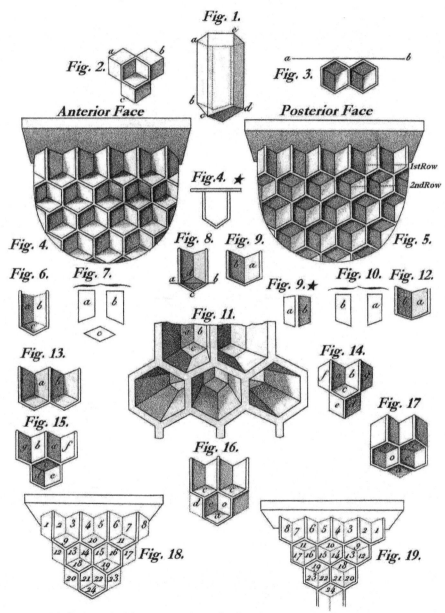

Volume 2 Plate V—Comb Construction Sequence.

Through these simple arrangements the stability of the comb is assured, for it reaches the ceiling of the hive in the greatest possible number of points.

We see another aim in this arrangement through the influence of the composition of the first row upon the formation of cells with pyramidal bases; but we will mention it in a few words only, referring those who desire to exhaust the subject to the notes which follow this chapter.

The rhomb situated at the base of the cells of the first row, on the anterior face, having a determined inclination because of its position at the base of the trapezes whose obliquity it follows, and this rhomb belonging on the opposite face to the pyramidal base, its inclination is partly indicated, for if we add two similar pieces below the rhomb, when joined together they will have a similar inclination and will form a pyramidal base on the posterior face.

Regarding the pyramidal bases of the anterior face they will have their origin in the same pieces on the opposite side, of which they are the reverse; thus all the properties of the pyramidal base appear to be derived from the structure of the cells of the first row.

Figure 1 is that of an ordinary cell, resting upon its base and seen in perspective. Its tube (ae) rises above the pyramidal base bcd; one must notice the angular edges of the base and realize why the tube is composed of irregular quadrangles.

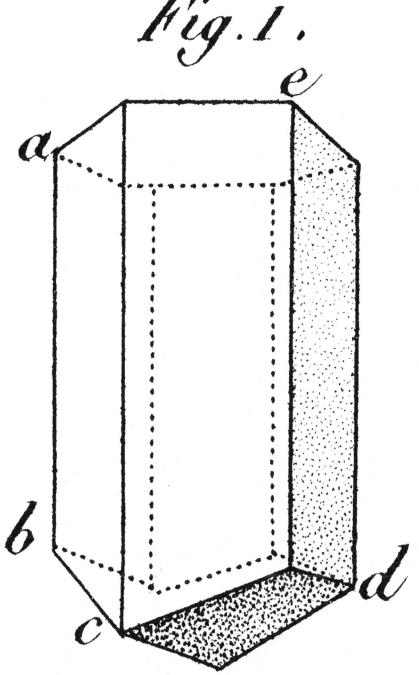

Volume 2 Plate V Fig 1—Cell resting on its base.

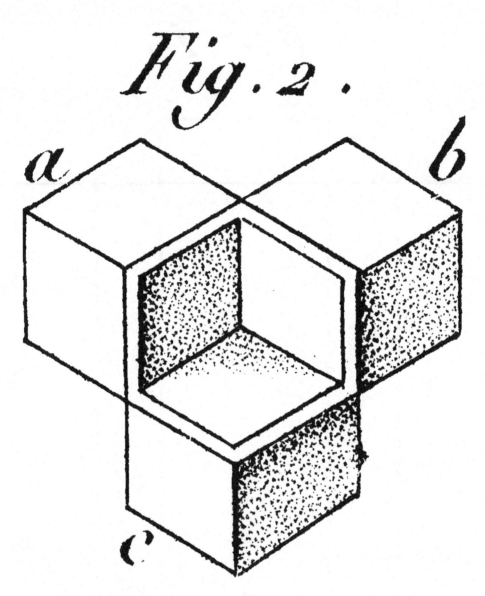

Volume 2 Plate V Fig 2—The bottom of a cell, front view. It is backed by three other cells, a, b, c, whose bases are seen from the rear.

Volume 2 Plate V Fig 3—Two pyramidal bases; (ab) is a line which they touch in only one spot.

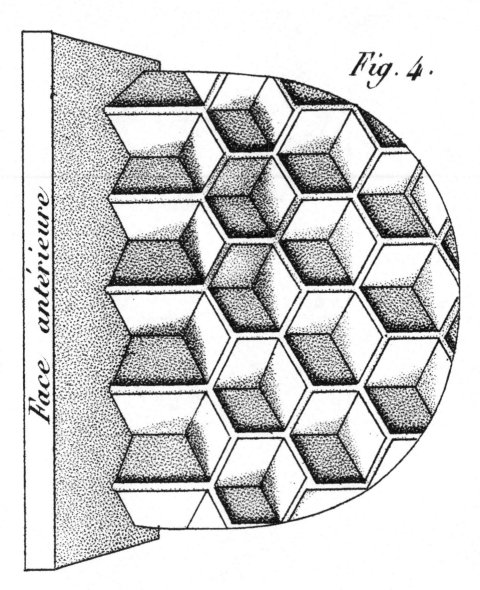

Fig. 4.

Face antérieure

Volume 2 Plate V Fig 4—A piece of new comb, fixed to the ceiling of the hive.

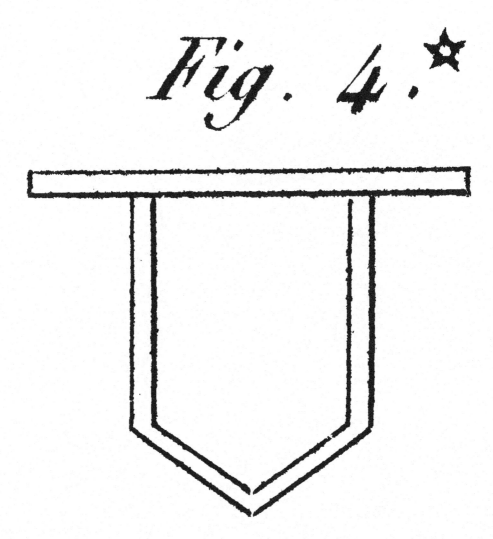

Volume 2 Plate V Fig 4*—Represents the edge or orifice of a cell of the 1st row.

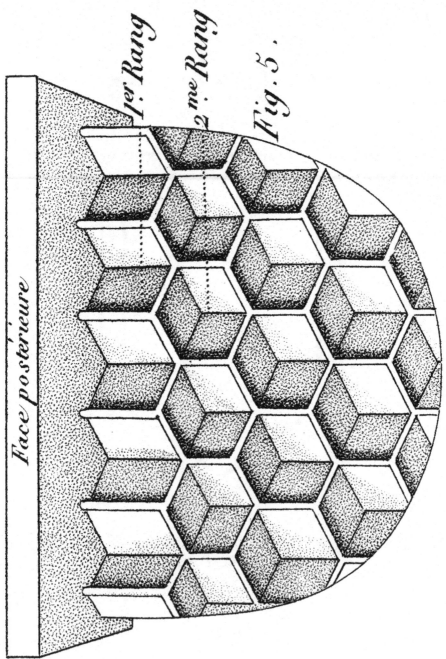

Volume 2 Plate V Fig 5—Opposite side of the comb in Figure 4.

Figure 5 represents the same comb shown from the opposite side; in each of them the tubes of the cells have been
removed, with only a small edge left to distinguish their contour. The bases of the first cells, immediately below the ceiling
are those which I call cells of the 1st row.

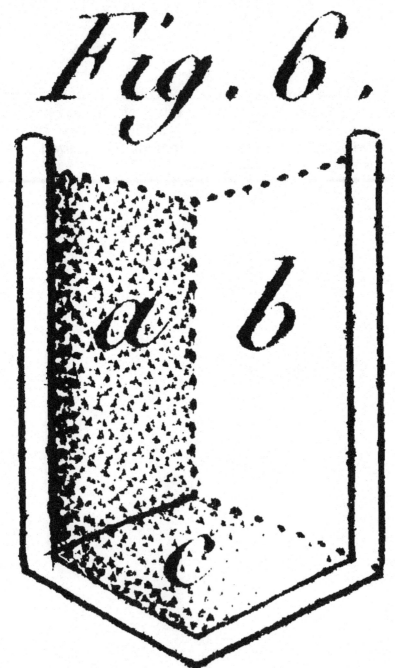

Volume 2 Plate V Fig 6—Base of an anterior cell of the 1ˢᵗ row.

Figure 6 shows the base of an anterior cell of the first row, detached from the comb; (ab) its trapezes (c) the rhomb which terminates it. In figure 9 we see the base of the posterior cell of the first row, formed of only two trapezes. In figure 9 we see the same pieces, but on their opposite face and in the same position as they are in figure 13 (ab). As these are drawn in perspective, which alters the appearance of their pieces to a certain extent, owing to the recess of the cells, they are shown flat and separate in figures 7 and 10, under braces which indicate their union; we thus see their geometric shape.

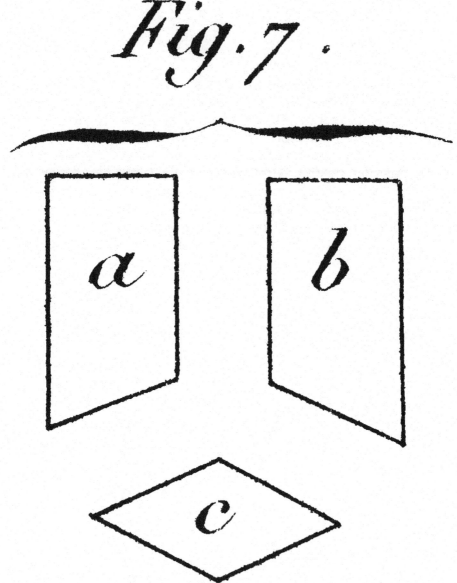

Volume 2 Plate V Fig 7—Many of these are drawn in perspective, which alters the appearance of their pieces to a certain extent, owing to the recess of the cells, the parts of Fig. 6 are shown flat and separate in figures 7 and 10, under braces which indicate their union; we thus see their geometric shape.

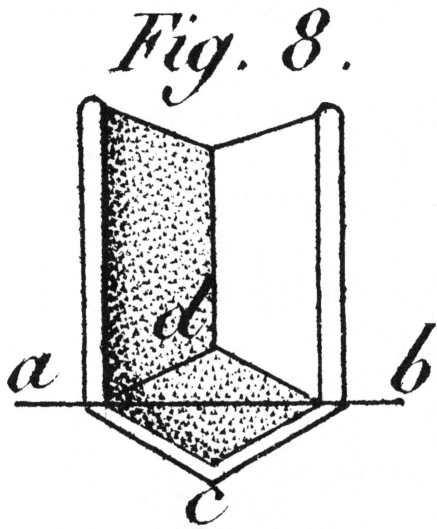

Volume 2 Plate V Fig 8—Exhibits the projection of the rhomb, projecting beyond a line (a, b) drawn from one of its acute angles to another; the part (acb) projects beyond the cavity, while the part (adb) is within it: so the rhomb projects in exactly half of its length; it slopes in the direction of its short diagonal, but is horizontal in its long diagonal.

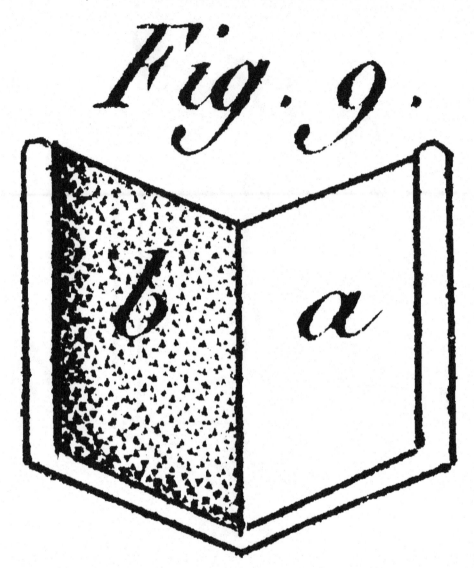

Volume 2 Plate V Fig 9—The base of the posterior cell of the 1st row, formed of only two trapezes.

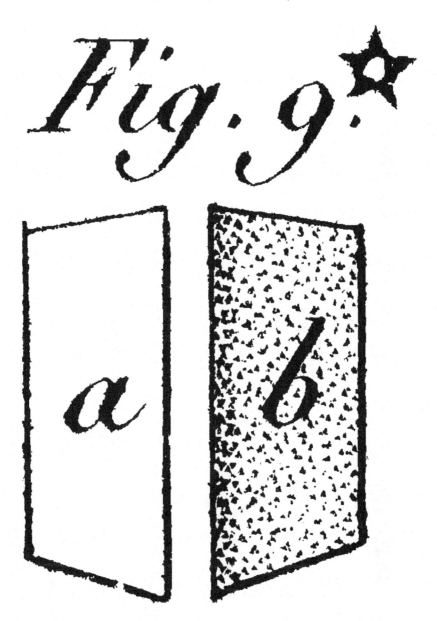

Volume 2 Plate V Fig 9*—We see the same pieces, but on their opposite face from Fig. 6 and in the same position as they are in figure 13 (ab).

Volume 2 Plate V Fig 10—Pieces of top row separate to show them not distorted by perspective.

As most of these are drawn in perspective, which alters the appearance of their pieces to a certain extent, owing to the recess of the cells, they are shown flat and separate in figures 7 and 10, under braces which indicate their union; we thus see their geometric shape.

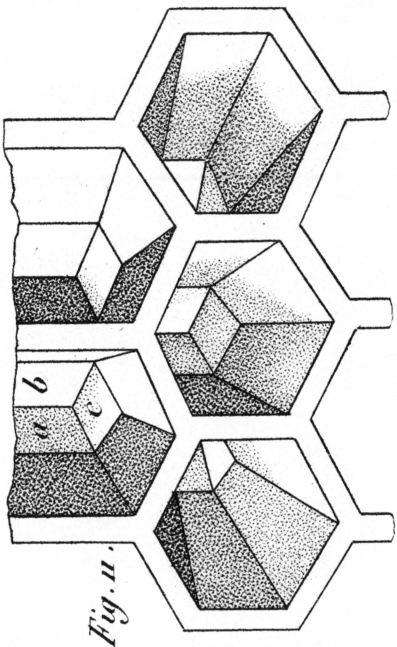

Volume 2 Plate V Fig 11—Front view of the cells of the 1st row with their enlarged tube in perspective, abc being the base.

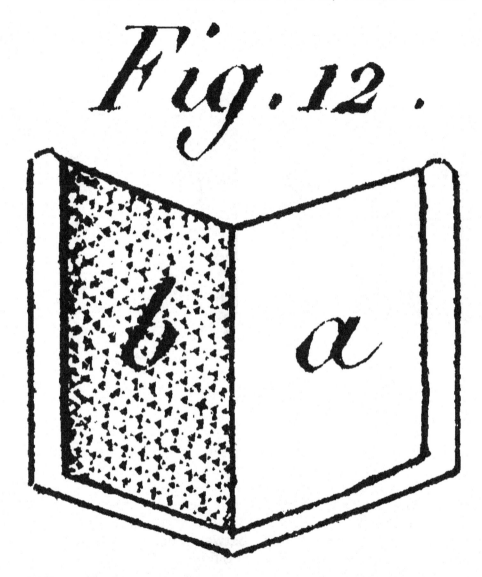

Volume 2 Plate V Fig 12—Figures 12 and 13 show the bases of three cells which would be back to back; figure 13 showing two anterior cells and figure 12 a posterior cell fitted between these two, b being the back of b, and the back of a. See fig 9*.

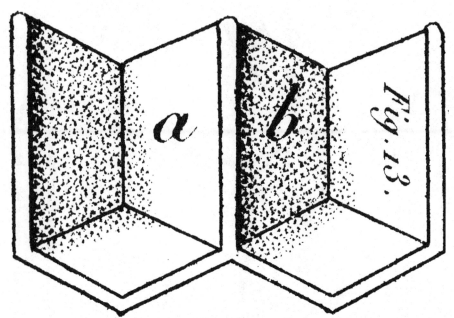

Volume 2 Plate V Fig 13—Two anterior cells.

Figures 12 and 13 show the bases of three cells which would be back to back; figure 13 showing two anterior cells and figure 12 a posterior cell fitted between these two, b being the back of b, and the back of a. See fig 9*.

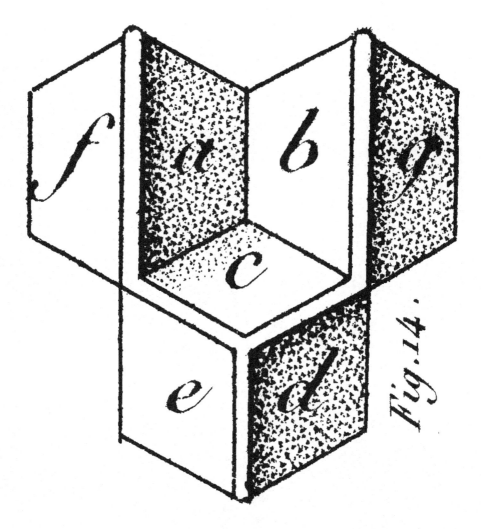

Volume 2 Plate V Fig 14—Inverse of Fig. 15, base of 1ˢᵗ Row.

Figures 14 and 15 are the inverse of one another; the first shows a base of the first row; with the back of three cells that meet it on the opposite side; two of the first row (f, a and g, b) and one of the second row (c, e, d).

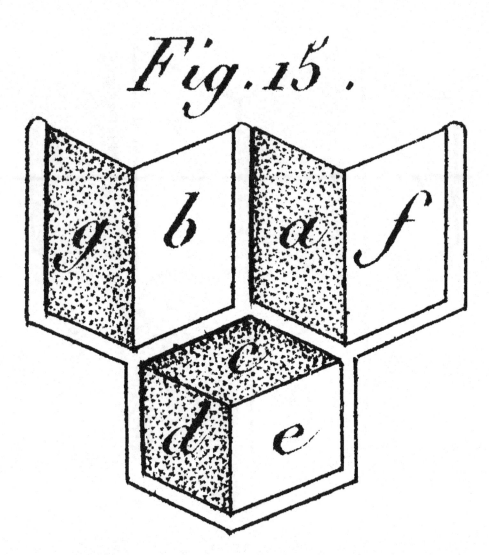

Fig. 15.

Volume 2 Plate V Fig 15—Inverse of Fig. 14, base of 1st Row.

Figures 14 and 15 are the inverse of one another; the first shows a base of the first row; with the back of three cells that meet it on the opposite side; two of the first row (f, a and g, b) and one of the second row (c, e, d); we make sure of this by looking at figure 15, in which the three posterior cells (g, b) (f, a) and (c, d, e) shown facing are backed to the anterior cell of the first row (b, a, c), shown here from the rear, the piece (c), which is opposite the rhomb (c) of the anterior cell becomes here the upper piece of the pyramidal base (d, c, e), formed below the cells (g, b) and (a, f) figure 15.

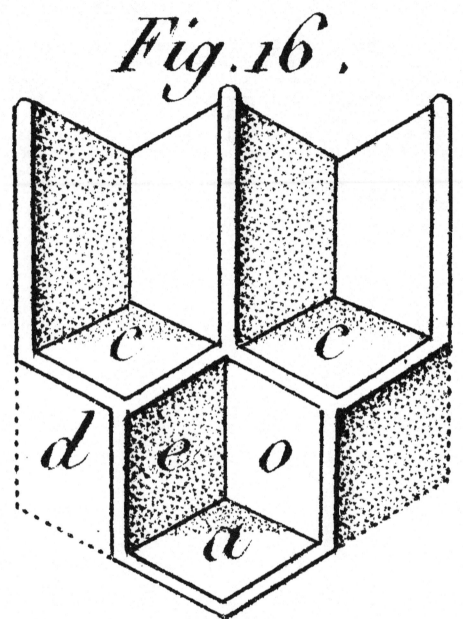

Volume 2 Plate V Fig 16—Two anterior cells of the 1ˢᵗ row and one Anterior cell of the 2ⁿᵈ row (Inverse of Fig. 17).

Figures 16 and 17 are also the opposite of each other placed on the same line so that we may understand the manner in which the cells are joined.

Fig. 16 represents a small piece of comb composed of two anterior cells of the first row and one anterior cell of the second row.

We notice here that the pyramidal base of the anterior face, figure 16, is composed of two rhombs situated in the interval between the cells of the first row, but the two pieces (eo) are the same as (eo) figure 17, which belong to two cells of the posterior face; lastly, the rhomb (a) completing the cell of figure 16, belongs on the opposite side to the space between two cells, or to a cell of the third row.

Volume 2 Plate V Fig 17—One posterior cell of the 1st row and 2 posterior cells of the 2nd row (Inverse of Fig 16).

Figures 16 and 17 are also the opposite of each other placed on the same line so that we may understand the manner in which the cells are joined.

Fig 17 shows one posterior cell of the first row and two posterior cells of the second row.

We notice here that the pyramidal base of the anterior face, figure 16, is composed of two rhombs situated in the interval between the cells of the first row, but the two pieces (eo) are the same as (eo) figure 17, which belong to two cells of the posterior face; lastly, the rhomb (a) completing the cell of figure 16, belongs on the opposite side to the space between two cells, or to a cell of the third row.

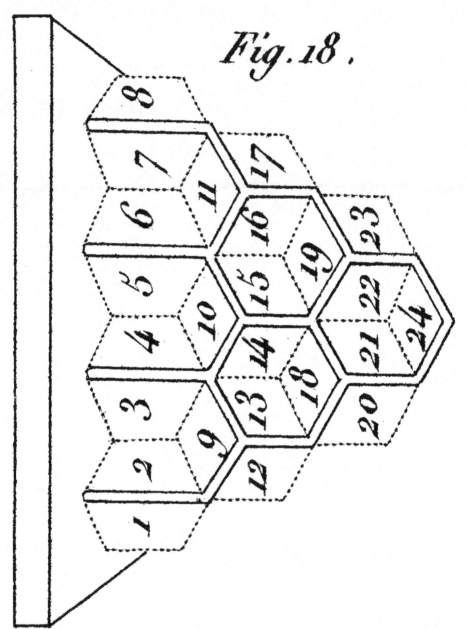

Fig. 18 .

*Volume 2 Plate V Fig 18—Figures 18 and 19, which represent
two small pieces of comb without any shading, give us
opportunity to compare each piece of the bases of the cells
on both sides.*

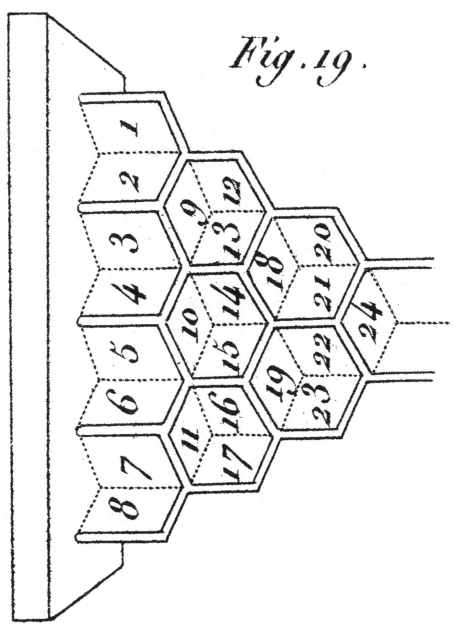

Fig. 19.

Volume 2 Plate V Fig 19—Figures 18 and 19, which represent two small pieces of comb without any shading, give us opportunity to compare each piece of the bases of the cells on both sides.

Fig. 1.

Fig. 2.

Fig. 3.

Fig. 4.

Fig. 5.

Volume 2 Plate VI—Larger details of the way the cells fit together.

Explanation of the Figures of Plate VI

The figures of this plate are on a larger scale than on the previous one. The first represents a very small portion of comb, shown as if the prisms were transparent, so as to exhibit the connecting wall to which the bases of both sides are built. These prisms are delineated only in their edges and their orifices. As they are shown here in their entire length, the mid ribs of the bases appear a little short: the eye is supposed to be in a position to see both the bases and the orifices.

Fig. 1.

Volume 2 Plate VI Fig 1—Cutaway view of anterior of the first three rows of cells.

As figure 1, we see two cell bases of the first row, beneath which a pyramidal base is displayed. The adjacent pieces to this cell have been retained, so that those of the posterior plan may be full; thus we see in this figure the back of four posterior cells, one in the first row, two in the second, and one in the third: this figure corresponds with figure 16 of Plate V, where the bases of these cells are seen in front view.

Horizontal lines have been drawn from all the angles of the contour of these bases; by their union they represent the prismatic tubes the openings of which are seen at the other extremity; the lines emerging from the posterior angles represent those of the cells on that side.

Fig. 2.

*Volume 2 Plate VI Fig 2—Cutaway view of posterior of the
first three rows of cells.*

Figure 2 represents the same piece of comb inverted so that we may see obliquely the bases of the cells of the posterior side; it corresponds to figure 17 of Plate V. which shows the bases of similar cells in front view. We see here, facing us, the bases of the cells which we saw in the rear in figure 1; the bases of the cells on the anterior side show only their back. Glancing at the orifices of those cells, we are impressed by the difference between those of the first row and those of the lower rows; by following the lines from the mouth of the cells inward, we reach the angles of the bases which belong to those same cells.

Fig. 3.

Volume 2 Plate VI Fig 3—Interior face of intermediary wall.

Figure 3 represents in profile the intermediary wall; it is shown here on its interior face, we may notice the angular shape of the contours of all the bases of which it is formed.

The side walls are lengthened to the orifice; four cells are represented two of the first row and two of the second row, so that their position be better grasped.

We see, by this figure, that the walls situated on the vertical edges of the trapezes are rectangular quadrangles, and that all other walls are shaped obliquely near the bottom and at right angles at their other extremity.

Volume 2 Plate VI Fig 4—An anterior cell of the 1st row, detached from the group of figure 3.

Volume 2 Plate VI Fig 5—An isolated posterior cell of the same row as Fig 4.

Section II: Shaping the Cells of the 1ˢᵗ Rows.

The details which we have just presented, upon the composition of the cells of the first row, appeared to us to indicate a progressive march in the work of the bees; but we could form only conjecture upon their method of action.

In order to secure a more complete idea, it was necessary to see these insects build the foundations of their combs and construct these cells in such different shape from what had been recognized until then; it was important to follow the building of these pyramidal bases which display at the same time the skill of the worker and the talent of the architect. We could there catch nature in action and observe instinct in one of its finest developments.

Since we had discovered new facts which could lighten our way, a still more active curiosity possessed us, and in spite of the difficulties of all kinds which opposed our efforts, we did not lose our courage.

As I have already stated, it was impossible to follow the work of these insects within the cluster which surrounds the workers in charge of the architecture. I had vainly thrown daylight upon the base of the cluster hanging to the dome of the hive; I had been able to see only the preparations for their masonry. I did not attempt to isolate a handful of them, for I knew that they work only when they are gathered in great numbers. To drive them away while the work progressed would not have fulfilled the purpose any better: I did not desire to see only the progress of their work, I wanted to witness their actual work.

After mature reflection upon the means which might be provided through the habits of the bees, and having found nothing which fully answered my purpose, or that did not prove more or less inconvenient; I attempted to thwart their habit in some particulars, hoping thereby that when they were compelled to act under new conditions, they might allow us to perceive some traces of the art which had been taught them. But the choice of methods was difficult; it was desirable to keep away all the workers that were not indispensable in the construction of the combs, without discouraging those from which we expected to secure some information; it was especially indispensable not to drive them from their natural conditions.

As the bees always begin the foundation of their combs at the ceiling of their hive a the exact spot where their cluster hangs which is formed from the gather together of the swarm, it seemed that the only way to isolate the wax workers was to induce them to change the direction of their masonry; but I did not foresee how I could compel independent beings to do this.

I finally decided to make an attempt which would not compel them in any way, but would even permit them to follow their usual routine, and even to dispense with building any combs at all if the work devised by me should be too much against their usages.

I wished to compel these bees to construct their combs upwards; that is to say, the reverse way from their daily custom, which however is not without examples among them: so I devised the following apparatus:

I had a box made, eight or nine inches high and twelve inches wide, at the bottom of which we cut an entrance; the upper side or lid could be removed at will and was made of a single piece of glass, in a movable frame I selected combs full of brood, honey and pollen, from one of my leaf hives, so that they would contain all that the bees could wish. I cut them in strips a foot long and four inches high and adjusted them vertically lengthwise, in the bottom of the box, leaving between them such spaces as the bees usually arrange themselves. (Plate I, figure 5a).

We then covered the upper edge of each of these combs with a slat or lath, which did not project beyond it and allowed free communication between all the parts of the hive. These laths, resting upon the combs four inches high, gave the bees opportunity of building above them in the remaining space five inches deep by twelve inches long; it was not likely that those bees should attempt to build combs upon the underside of the horizontal glass ceiling, since they cannot hang in clusters on the slippery surface of the glass; it was necessary for them to build the combs upwards from the laths, and I felt certain that I would have better success by this process than before.

Volume 2 Plate I Fig 5a—Hive to Observe Comb Building

But it was only a small step to have invented an apparatus which could better serve our purpose; I must repeat here with a feeling of gratitude and with the satisfaction felt when we acknowledge modest merit if I have made a few steps forward in this career, I owe it to the assiduity, the courage, and the correct eye of the indefatigable man who assisted my efforts; I owe it to Burnens. These difficult observations required minute precautions; a sudden unexpected light, a neglected opportunity, an instant of suspended attention, could lead us away from the facts into some erroneous system.

Having noticed that the horizontal glass plate, interposed between his eyes and the objects to be studied, altered their perspective or their appearance in some respects, Burnens decided to set aside this chance of error; in spite of my protests and with the chances of danger that he incurred, he watched unprotected all the details relating to the architecture of the bees; the gentleness of his motions and the habit of repressing his respiration when near the bees, could alone preserve him from the anger of these formidable insects; so that I did not have the regret of paying too dearly for his devotion. This action, worthy of the most passionate lover of natural history, shows what may be achieved through the desire for knowledge and must certainly increase the confidence of my readers in the observations that resulted.

After Burnens stocked this hive, the swarm established itself, as we had foreseen, among the combs in the lower part of the box, and we then observed the small bellied bees displaying their natural activity; they dispersed throughout the hive to feed the young larvae, to clear their lodgment and adapt it for their convenience. Evidently the combs which had been given them and which had been roughly cut to fit the bottom of the box, and damaged in several places, appeared to them shapeless and ill-conditioned; for they commenced their repair at once; we saw them cut up the old wax, knead it between their teeth and form bindings to consolidate the combs. We were astonished beyond expression to see this multitude of workers, employed together in a work for which it did not appear they should have been called, such agreement, zeal and prudence, *in beings that have no right to thoughts.*

Volume 2 Plate VII—Comb Attachment—building the foundation of the comb.

But it was still more surprising to see about half of this numerous population taking no part in the labor and remaining motionless while others fulfilled the functions which appeared to be required of them.

You will understand that the wax workers, in a state of absolute repose, recalled our former observations. Gorged with the honey that we had put within their reach, at the end of 24 hours of complete inaction they secreted this substance so long believed to have been gathered upon the anthers of flowers. The wax, wholly formed under their rings was ready to be put to use, and with great satisfaction we saw a little block rising upon one of the laths that we had prepared to serve as base for their new constructions. In this regard, those insects fulfilled our anticipations and as the cluster was established between the combs and below the laths, there was no obstacle through its bulk to the progress of our observations.

Upon this occasion we witnessed for the second time the work of the founding bee and the successive labors of several wax workers to erect the block upon which we were building our hopes.

When the material was thus prepared, these architects gave us the most complete display of the art with which nature has endowed them. Would that my readers could share the interest which this sight inspired; but it is difficult to form a correct idea of it, unless one follows step by step the work of the bees while comparing with the greater care the text and the figures.

Although I aimed to simplify this part of the work as much as possible, I realize that it may be unintelligible to a great many readers; but I feel certain that the true lovers of natural history will not allow the difficulty of the subject to discourage them and will find compensations in the novelty of the observations. But in order to help relieve from mind fatigue those who do not care to deeply study the matter I will prelude with a slight sketch. (See figures of natural size Plate VII A. These natural size cells measure 4.0mm o.c. in the original 1814 plate—Transcriber We should bear in mind that the block rises perpendicularly above the lath, and that it is thus in the position in which we see it when we hold the book vertically).

It was in this block (of wax), at first very small but successively enlarged, as the work of the bees progressed, that the bases of the first cells were carved.

We understood from the first moment why they were intertwined; the bees built before our eyes, this first row, which gives the key to all their architecture.

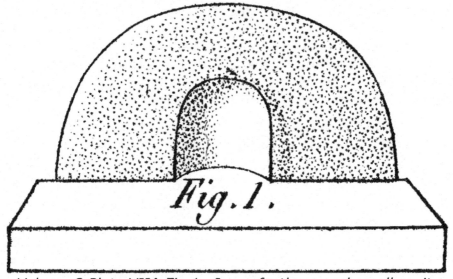

Volume 2 Plate VIIA Fig 1—Imperfectly carved small cavity the width of an ordinary cell.

They imperfectly carved a small cavity of the width of an ordinary cell, on one side of the block (Plate VII A. Fig. 1); it formed a sort of fluting the edges of which were made to project by the accumulation of wax. On the reverse side of this cavity, opposite, two others, contiguous and equal, (fig 2) were made similar to the first but a little shorter. These three cavities, of like diameter, were partly backed against each other, since the center of the one was opposite the edge between the other two.

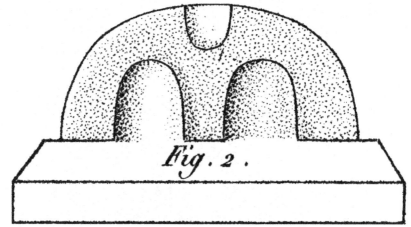

*Volume 2 Plate VIIA Fig 2—Imperfectly carved small cavity
the width of an ordinary cell. Obverse of Fig 1.*

The first of these cavities, being longer, corresponded on the other side with a still uncut portion of the block, above the cavities of the first row, and it was in this spot that the outline of the first pyramidal base was begun (fig. 2).

Thus a single fluting, on the anterior face, corresponded with three cavities on the opposite side, two of them on the first row and one on the second.

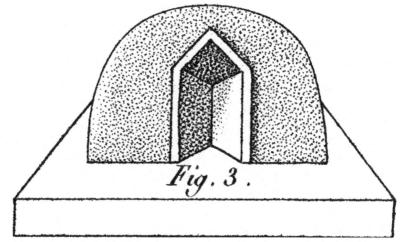

*Volume 2 Plate VIIA Fig 3—Raised edge converted by the
bees into two rectilinear prominences*

The raised edge of these flutings having been converted by the bees into two rectilinear prominences, which together formed an obtuse angle, each of the cavities of the first row became pentagonal, if we considered the lath as one side (fig. 3 and 4).

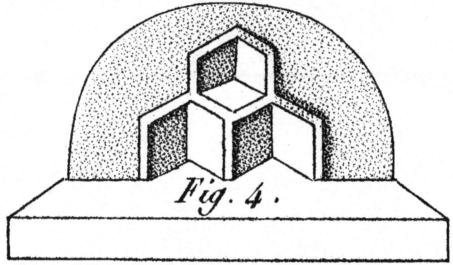

Volume 2 Plate VIIA Fig 4—Two parallel and lateral and two oblique sides formed upon the raised edges

But the fluting of the second row, the base of which was situated between the oblique faces of the bases of the first row, became hexagonal, two sides being in its base two parallel and lateral, and two oblique formed upon the raised edges (fig. 4).

The interior conformation of the cavities appeared to be derived naturally from the respective position of their outlines. It seemed that the bees, gifted with admirable delicacy of feeling, applied their teeth principally where the wax was the thickest, that is, in the parts where other workers had accumulated it, while working on the opposite side, which explains why the bottom of the cells is excavated in an angular shape behind the projections upon which the walls of the other corresponding cells are to be erected.

The bases of the cavities were thus divided into several parts which formed an angle, and the number and the shape of these parts depended upon the erection of the bases on the opposite side of the block, dividing the space; so that the largest fluting, opposite three others, was divided in three parts, while on the other side, those of the first row, opposite, were composed of two pieces only.

In consequence of the manner in which the flutings were opposed to each other, those of the second row and all subsequent ones, partially applied to three cavities, were composed of three equal pieces in rhomboid form. A glance at the figures makes it clear. I may here properly remark that each portion of the work of the bees appeared as a natural consequence of the preceding work, so that chance had no part in the admirable results which were witnessed.

Volume 2 Plate VIIB Fig 1—Block of wax.

I will now return to the thread of these operations, with all the details which were noticed.

Detailed Description of the Work of the Bees

(see the enlarged figures, beginning at the bottom, Plate VII, B).

We had reached the long desired moment; at last the bees were about to carve, under our eyes, and it was with some emotion that we saw them give the first chisel strokes upon the block which had just been erected on the lath.

It rose perpendicularly above it and differed only by its position from those that we had seen before. It was a minute, straight and vertical wall, five or six lines (about ½ in. or 1.3 cm) in length two lines in height (1/6 in. 4 mm) and half a line thick (1/24 in. or 1 mm) (Plate VII B. fig. 1 & 2).

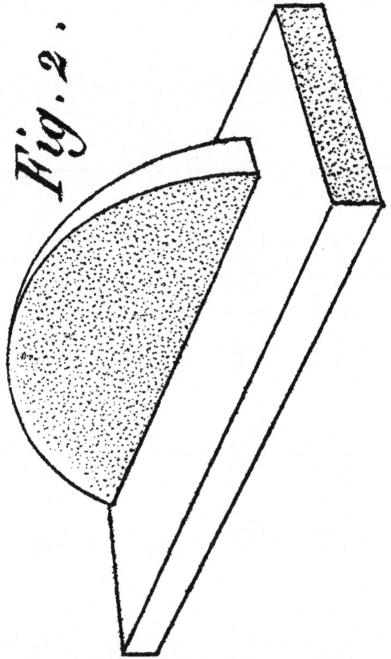

Fig. 2.

Volume 2 Plate VIIB Fig 2—Angle view of block.

Its edge was arched and its surface rough; it appeared much too light to suppose that bees should carve entire cells out of it; but it seemed sufficiently thick to form the wall out of which the cell bases are carved and which separates the two sides of the comb.

Volume 2 Plate VIIB Fig 3—Showing relationship of the two sides.

(This wall is shown by the zigzag lines in figure 3. Let us note that the work of bees is the reverse of what Mr. Buffon had imagined: he thought the bees built a big lump of wax in which they dug cavities by the pressure of their bodies. They build a lump, but it is so thin that it would hardly make the twenty-fourth part of the thickness of a comb: it is in this block, which is very small at first, that they build their cells as in relief, upon its edges they attach tubes five or six lines (about ½ in. or 1.3 cm) deep. We have used the word "block" for this first outline, although it gives the idea of a massive body, but as the cell bases are carved out of this wall of wax, we cannot give it another name yet).

We saw a little bee leave the cluster hanging between the combs, climb on the lath upon which the wax workers had laid the material which they had removed from under their rings, turn around the block, and after having examined both sides, begin work on our side of it. We will call this face of the block the anterior face, and we will consider the opposite side as the posterior face, no matter how we may view it later.

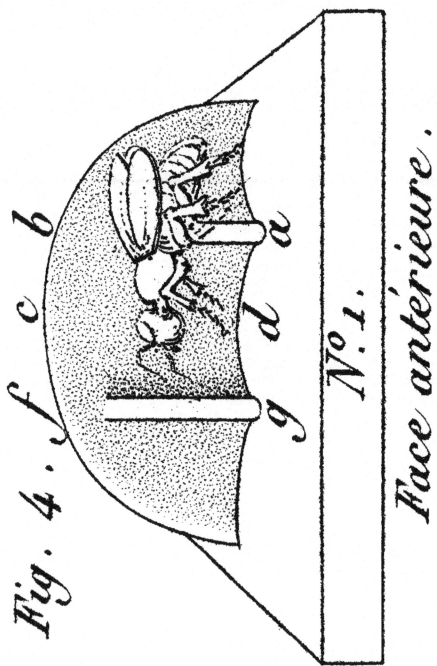

Volume 2 Plate VIIB Fig 4—Bees working the anterior side.

The worker, placed on the anterior face, fixed her position horizontally so that her head faced the middle of the block (fig. 4) and moved it briskly; her teeth worked in the wax but removed fragments of it only in a very narrow space, about equal to the diameter of an ordinary cell (abgf). So there remained at the right and the left of the cavity which she made, a certain space in which the block was still in the rough.

After having chewed and moistened the particles of wax, she deposited them in the edges of the cavity: after working a few instants, she walked away from the block: another bee took her place in the same attitude, and continued the work which had just been sketched by her, a third bee soon took the place of the second, deepened the cavity, accumulated wax to the right and left, raised the already sharp lateral edges of the cavity, and gave them a straighter shape (ab, gf). It was with her teeth and her anterior legs that she compressed and fixed the particles of wax in the required position.

More than twenty different bees took part in this same work: the cavity then had more depth at the base of the block than at its upper edge (adb, fig. 4): the depth of the cavity diminished from the lath up to the letter c: it resembled a fluting wider than long; its superior contour was less marked than its vertical edges. The horizontal diameter of the cavity was equal to that of an ordinary cell, but its length, in vertical direction, was only a line and three-fifths (about 1/8 in. or about 3 mm) or about two-thirds of its diameter. I will designate this cavity as № 1.

Volume 2 Plate VIIB Fig 5—Bees working the posterior side.

When the work reached this point, we saw a bee leaving the cluster formed by the workers walk around the block and select its posterior face as her labor aim; but a remarkable fact was that she did not begin at the center of the block as the others had done on the anterior face, she placed herself so that her teeth acted only upon one-half of this face (cdih, Fig 5), so that the middle (ab) of the cavity which she laid out, was opposite one of the edges which lined cavity № 1. At about the same time another bee began work to the right of this one, in that part of the block which she had left untouched and which was the right side of this posterior face (cdkl, fig. 5). So these bees carved two cavities, side by side, and we will call these № 2 and 3; after they had worked for some time, their places were taken by other workers which contributed in turn and separately in giving them the proper depth and shape.

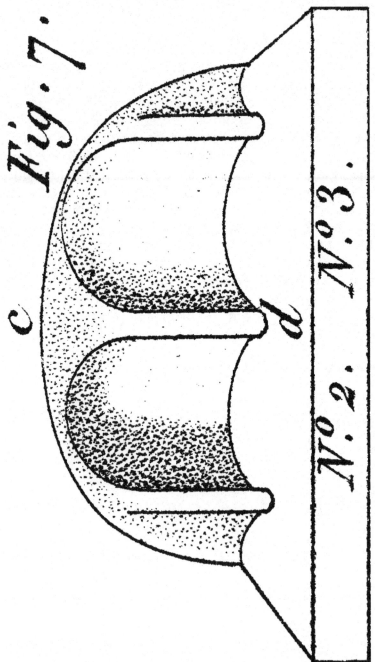

*Volume 2 Plate VIIB Fig 7—Gathering together of the wax
particles drawn from the interior. (Posterior).*

These two adjacent cavities were separated only by a common edge, formed from the gathering together of the wax particles drawn from the interior, and this edge (dc, fig. 7) was in the center of this face and corresponded with the center of the cavity made on the opposite side by other workers (dc, fig. 6).

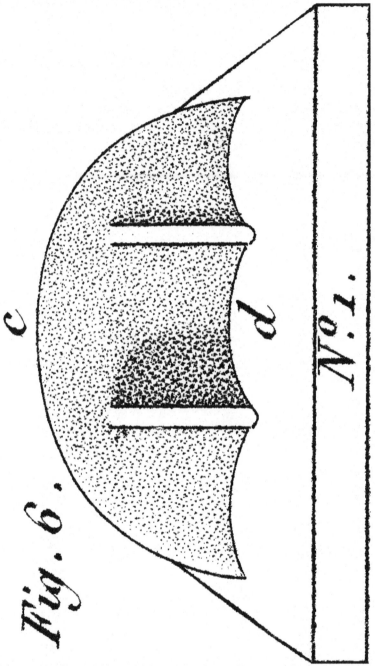

Volume 2 Plate VIIB Fig 6—Gathering together of the wax particles drawn from the interior. (Anterior).

Thus a part of each of the two cavities on the posterior side was opposite the anterior cavity; this could be verified by piercing both faces with pins (fig. 6 & 7).

These cavities were of the same diameter and were limited at right and left as with those of the anterior face, by small projecting borders which I call vertical arris, (arris=a ridge where two surfaces come together—transcriber) and which will serve as base for the vertical walls of the cells after the bases are carved.

The three outlined cavities did not have the full dimensions in every direction that they were to secure when completed; I have already said that they did not have the length of an ordinary cell; I mean the vertical diameter of those cavities (cd, fig. 6); but the block itself was not of a sufficient length to complete the diameter of the cell. So the bees continued to increase its size.

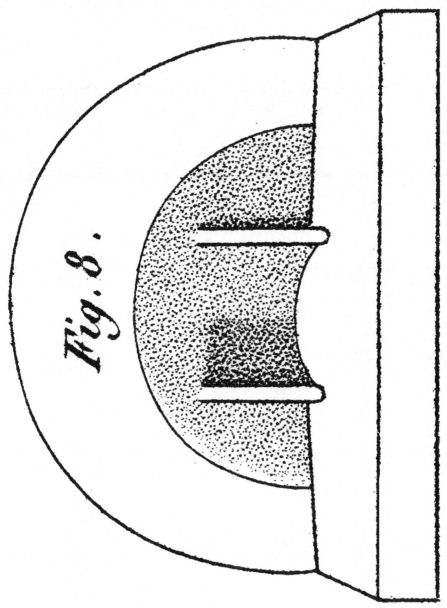

Volume 2 Plate VIIB Fig 8—Wax added increasing the size.

While they were still at work upon the excavations begun by their companions, we saw some wax workers remove scales of wax from their rings and apply them upon the edges so as to lengthen them; they increased its size nearly two lines (11/64th in. or 4mm) in every direction (fig. 8).

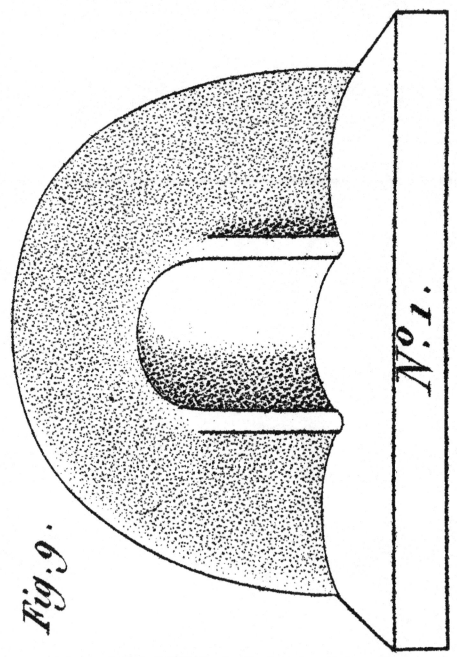

Volume 2 Plate VIIB Fig 9—Prolonging the cavities.

The small bees which appeared more especially charged with sculpturing the cells were able to continue their outlines; they prolonged the cavities upon the newly added material and lengthened also the edges which bordered them (fig. 9 & 10); but the raised edges were prolonged only at the right and left of the cavities and not at their upper extremity: they were also less prominent as they reached from the base, and we noticed that cavity № 1 was much more prolonged than cavities №s. 2 & 3; otherwise their shape was similar; they were similar elliptic, slightly lengthened, rounded at the top, arched inside, and had no angular shape; the first was a little longer than the diameter of an ordinary cell; but the others were shorter than this diameter in perceptible amount.

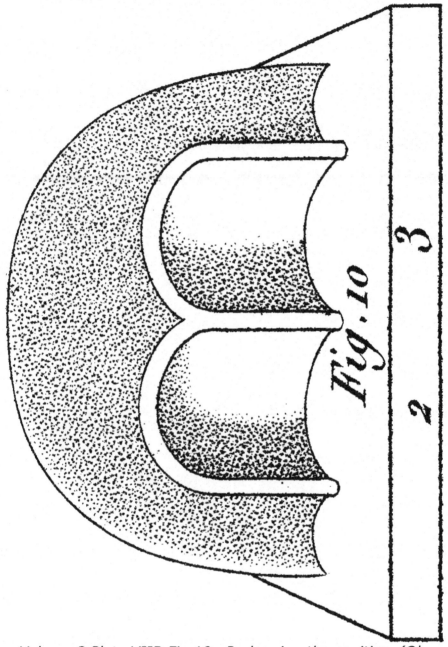

Volume 2 Plate VIIB Fig 10—Prolonging the cavities. (Obverse of 9).

This difference, the aim of which we already perceived, after our observations upon the formation of the cells of the first row, was not an imperfection.

I have said that each of these cavities was rounded at its upper extremity; the bees soon put edges upon them in this part as they had done on the vertical sides, but they did not purpose to give them an arched edge.

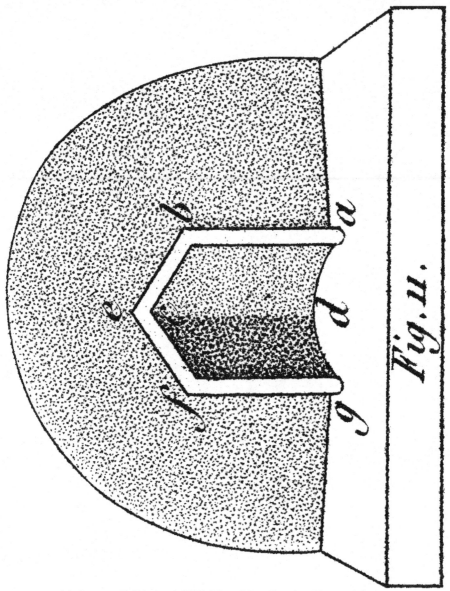

Volume 2 Plate VIIB Fig 11—Projecting ridges

The arch on the border of each of these cavities was divided into two equal ribs, and it was in this direction that the bees erected projecting ridges (fig. 11 & 12); we noticed that they formed an obtuse angle and this appeared equal to those of the rhombs of pyramidal cell bases; we could then conjecture that this angle would be part of a rhomb.

We noticed that the bees accumulated much wax on the upper edge of the cavity № 1, and it was at the top of this accumulation that the two oblique edges joined. But, on the contrary, the two ridges which terminated the posterior cells at the top were not raised on a projection, but they followed the concavity of the fluting.

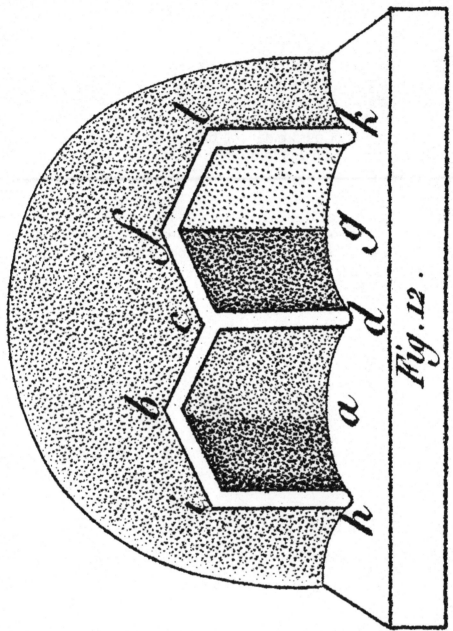

Volume 2 Plate VIIB Fig 12—Projecting ridges (obverse of Fig 11).

(See these bases, facing, in figures 11 and 12, and side-wise in figures 15 and 16; figures 13 and 14 represent the cavities before their upper edge was changed to angular edges, as in figures 9 and 10.

Figures 15 and 16 show the block at the time when the upper edge is changed into a ridge. In these figures the rough portion of the block should extend as far in the others).

At this time, each of the cavities was bordered by four ridges, two of them lateral, perpendicular to the lath, and two shorter ones oblique, joined to the former by one of their extremities and united together at the other extremities: the lath itself bordering them at their base (fig. 11 and 12, 15 and 16).

Now it became more difficult to follow the operations of the bees, because they often interposed their head between the eye of the observer and the bottom of the cell; but we noticed that the partition upon which their teeth worked had become transparent enough to enable us to see through it what passed on the other face; we could thus see very distinctly the end of the teeth of the bee working at carving on the opposite face and follow all her movements. We made this still more perceptible, by placing the hive so that the light would strike more fully upon the cavities which we desired to see outlined.

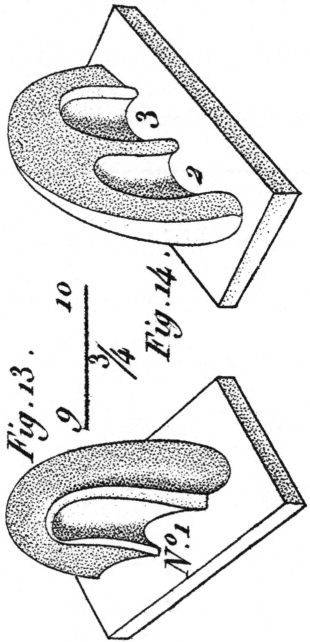

Volume 2 Plate VIIB Fig 13 & 14—Cavities before their upper edges were changed to angular edges, Fig 9 & 10 sideways.

Volume 2 Plate VIIB Fig 15 & 16—Cavities after their upper edges were changed to angular edges, Fig 11 & 12 sideways.

Volume 2 Plate VIII—Architecture of the Bees.

We saw, as a shadow, the contour of the cells on the opposite face, as the thick ridge did not permit the free passage of daylight and we soon recognized clearly that the height of the cell bases, № 2 and 3 was less than that of cell № 1, and that their vertical ridges were shorter (Plate VIII, fig. 17 and 18). The dotted lines here design the shadows of the arris on the opposite face. See the denoting letters.

One perceived through cavity № 1, (cd, fig. 17), the shadow of the vertical ridge which separated cavities № 2 and 3, but as the ridge forming this division was between the two shorter cells its shadow did not appear in the full length of cell № 1.

The shadow terminated at two-thirds of the length of the anterior cell, started from the base of the block (c, fig. 17); there it appeared to divide into two branches (cbef) which extended obliquely, one to the right, the other to the left of the center and appeared to terminate immediately behind the upper extremity of the vertical ridges (ab gf) of cavity № 1.

These oblique branches of the vertical shadow were none other than those of the oblique ridges (cb cf, fig. 18), making the edges of cavities № 2 and 3 in their highest part; the one belonged to the first and the other to the second of these cavities.

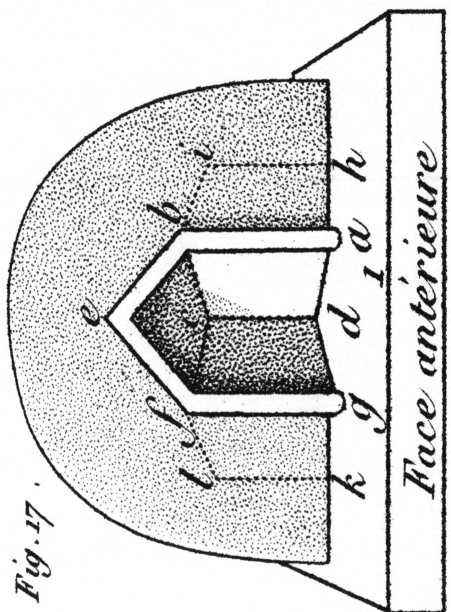

Volume 2 Plate VIII Fig 17—Dotted lines showing arris on opposite face (Fig 18).

Through the portion still in the rough of the mass, one could also see, but less distinctly, the rest of the contours of these same cavities extending to the right and left of the anterior base, designated by Nº 1 (ab, ij: gf, kl, fig. 17).

These oblique branches of the vertical shadow were none other than those of the oblique ridges (cb cf, fig. 18), making the edges of cavities Nº 2 and 3 in their highest part; the one belonged to the first and the other to the second of these cavities.

These oblique branches of the vertical shadow were none other than those of the oblique ridges (cb cf, fig. 18), making the edges of cavities Nº 2 and 3 in their highest part; the one belonged to the first and the other to the second of these cavities.

Through the portion still in the rough of the mass, one could also see, but less distinctly, the rest of the contours of these same cavities extending to the right and left of the anterior base, designated by Nº 1 (ab, ij: gf, kl, fig. 17).

It is quite evident that the bases of cells 2 and 3 were partly backed against that of cell Nº 1. They terminated in an obtuse point opposite the upper extremity of the vertical ridges of this isolated cavity (b, f, fig 17); from this the result was that the anterior cavity was longer than the other two, with the same proportionate difference that existed between its total length and that of its vertical ridges.

When one examined the block from the opposite side (fig. 18) one could see the shadow of the edges of cavity Nº 1, and this appeared to reach a the top beyond the contour of the cavities Nº 2 and 3.

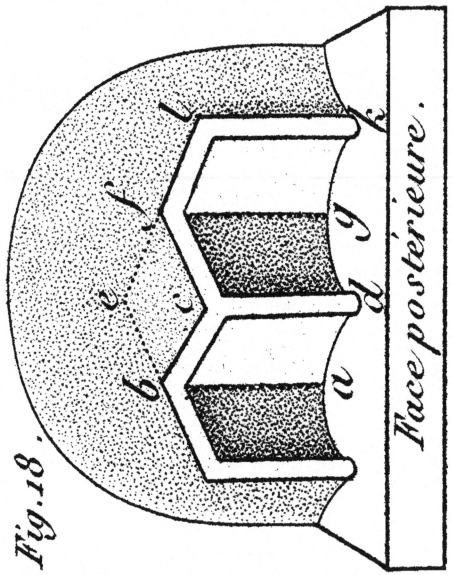

Volume 2 Plate VIII Fig 18—Dotted lines showing arris on opposite face (Fig 17).

One perceived at the base of each of the latter cavities the shadow of one of the vertical ridges (ab, gf) which bordered the cavity of the anterior face, shadows which ran from the top to the bottom of the twin cavities of the posterior, face, and appeared to divide them into two equal parts. But this was only the result caused by the reciprocal position of the ridges of the two faces.

While following the work of the bees that were busy deepening the cavities which they had outlined, we perceived that the dark lines were gradually replaced by cavities or angular furrows, and that the entire effort of the workers was directed opposite those ridges which we could see as shadows through the thinned block; the bees were digging on both faces behind the ridges of the opposite face.

Thus those which were working on the anterior face carved in the direction of the shadow of the posterior ridges which exhibited the figure of a Y, the branches of which were directed forward from the main stem (fig 17). The intermediate ridge formed the stem of the Y, and the two oblique ridges (bc, cf) belonging to the posterior cells, represented the two branches of that letter.

The bees were not only working to thin out the back of these projecting ridges, they also scraped and smoothed the space between the shadow these ridges and the ridges of the cavities upon which they were working.

Their work was directed along the shadow of the vertical ridge (cd) and afterwards in the direction of the oblique shadows (bc, df) made by the oblique ridges on the opposite side (ab, be: ef, fg) and the ridges of the posterior face first row; it was composed of two trapezes and one rhomb (fig. 19).

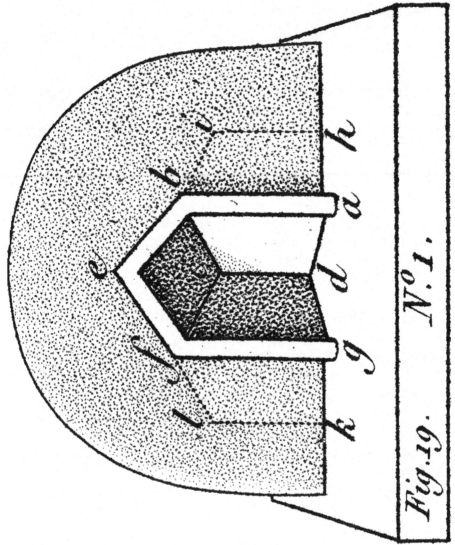

Volume 2 Plate VIII Fig 19—Dotted lines showing arris on opposite face.

    This cavity, first shown in a semi-elliptic form (fig. 9, Plate VII) and later bordered with four ridges (fig. 11), being divided in two-thirds of its length by a furrow (cd, fig. 17), which occupied its center, and the two surfaces (abcd: cdfg) adjacent to the furrow having been flattened and thinned down to the depth of the furrow itself, they furnished two planes inclined towards each other; but as this furrow did not reach the full length of the cavity, these planes were limited only by the vertical ridges (ab, gf) of this face and by the supporting lath itself. Their upper extremity, (df, cb) was not yet finished, or at least it was in the part of the cell not yet smoothed; but the bees, working to shape the furrows (bc, cf, fig. 19), corresponding to the oblique ridges bearing the same letters on the posterior face, gave these inclined planes an oblique termination; and as they were joined on the other three sides with parallel ridges and with the lath, these planes became equal trapezes (ab, cd: cd, fg) and were situated to the right and left of the principal furrow.

But the space remaining between the two oblique furrows and the upper extremity of the cavity (bef), being limited on one side by the sides of the obtuse angle (bcf) formed by these oblique furrows, and on the other by the sides of the obtuse angle (bef), formed by the upper edges of the cavity, and these sides and angles being equal, it produced a rhomboid (bcef) similar to those of which the pyramidal bases are composed.

This place, by its inclination, formed an angle with each of the trapezes, and consequently also, with the two trapezes united, a solid angle (fig. 19) the summit of which was placed at the junction of the three furrows or similarly, behind the bifurcation of the opposite ridges (c, fig. 19 and 20¾); but this solid angle was not a pyramidal base, it was a base composed of two trapezes and one rhomb.

Volume 2 Plate VIII Fig 19 3/4—Fig 19 at ¾ view.

Volume 2 Plate VIII Fig 20 3/4—Fig 20 at ¾ view.

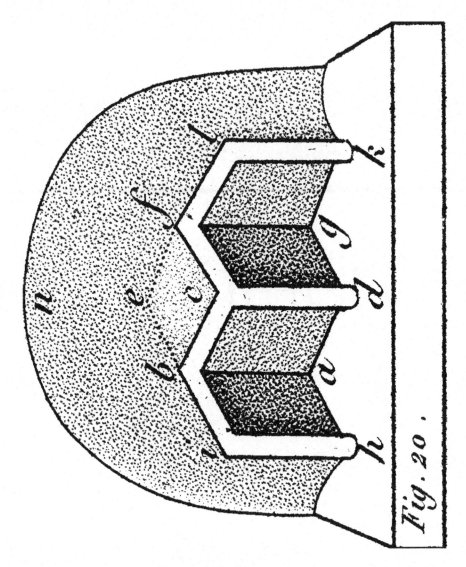

Volume 2 Plate VIII Fig 20—Dotted lines showing arris on opposite face.

This is the manner in which the bees work to form the base of the first anterior cell of the first row.

We have shown that they carved behind the projecting ridges, on the posterior face, two adjacent cavities separated only by a ridge (fig. 10); that they had determined the length and shape of the cavities by establishing two oblique ridges on their upper edge (fig 12), and carved a furrow of the whole length of these cavities (fig. 18).

Thus they had divided them into two equal parts, and when the pieces to the right and left of the furrow were smoothed by their labor these two pieces together made an angular plane (fig. 20).

They were of equal size, and as one of them was backed by one of the trapezes of the anterior cell, and as it was limited by the ridges, the shadow of which might have served as pattern for the bees working on the opposite side, it resulted that these two pieces, similar and equal to those of the anterior face, were themselves equal and similar to each other. The bases of the cells of the posterior face, in the first row, were then composed of two trapezes, such as we had already described, and this composition was a natural consequence of the method of the bees at the beginning of their work.

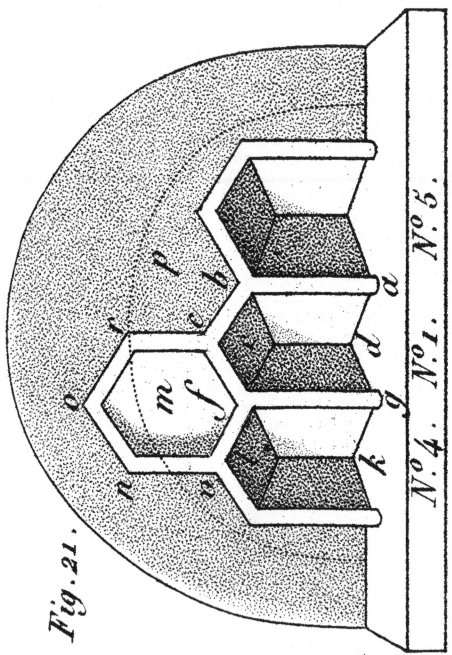

Volume 2 Plate VIII Fig 21—Starting the 2ⁿᵈ row.

The three bases of cells which I have just described were the first built; but while they carved the furrows which separated them, others having lengthened the block in every direction, they were enabled to carve other cavities. They began their carving behind the vertical ridges of cells 2 and 3, and to the side of cavity № 1, then on the posterior face, behind the opposite ridges: so that the trapezes were backed by other trapezes of similar shape and size (fig. 21 and 22). Usually, they dug out a face while others were making ridges on the opposite. So they formed cavities behind the lateral edges of the last built cells. Thus several bases, alternating on the two faces of the block, presented a first row of contiguous cells the tubes of which were not yet lengthened.

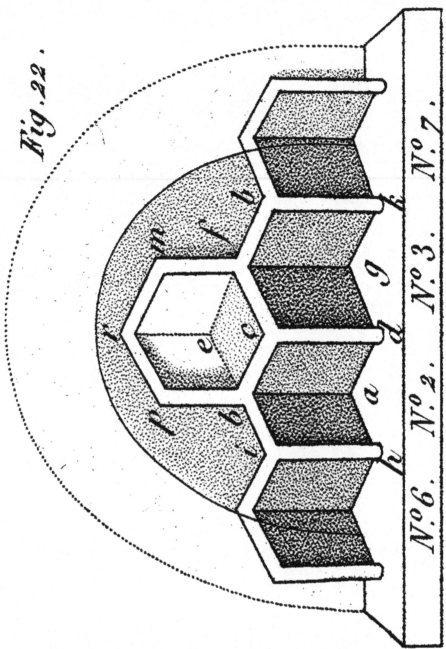

Volume 2 Plate VIII Fig 22—Starting 2nd row from opposite side from Fig 21.

The three bases of cells which I have just described were the first built; but while they carved the furrows which separated them, others having lengthened the block in every direction, they were enabled to carve other cavities. They began their carving behind the vertical ridges of cells 2 and 3, and to the side of cavity № 1, then on the posterior face, behind the opposite ridges: so that the trapezes were backed by other trapezes of similar shape and size (fig. 21 and 22). Usually, they dug out a face while others were making ridges on the opposite. So they formed cavities behind the lateral edges of the last built cells. Thus several bases, alternating on the two faces of the block, presented a first row of contiguous cells the tubes of which were not yet lengthened.

While these bees were polishing and perfecting these bases, other workers began the outlines of a second row of cells above the first, and partly behind the rhomb of the anterior cells; for their work follows a combined progress. We cannot say: *"When the bees had finished this cell they began new ones"*; but we can say: *"While some workers advance a certain piece, others outline adjacent cells."* Moreover, the work made upon one face of the comb is part of what is needed on the opposite face: it is a reciprocal relation, a mutual connection of the parts rendering them subservient to one another. It is therefore undoubted that a slight irregularity of their work on one side will affect the shape of the cells on the other side in a similar way.

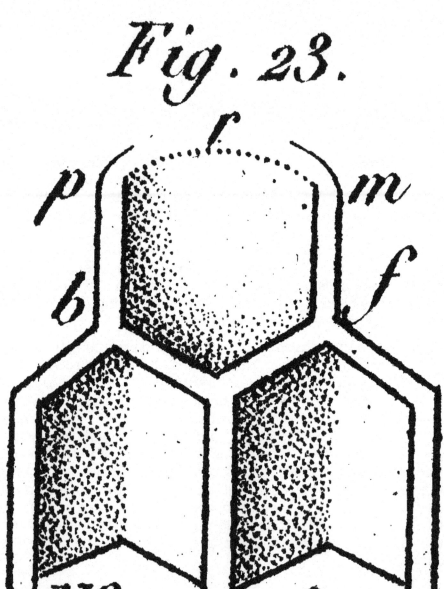

Volume 2 Plate VIII Fig 23—Closeup of start of 2ⁿᵈ Row.

Section III: Construction of the cells of the 2nd row.

The bottoms of the anterior cells of the first row, composed of two trapezes and one rhomb, were larger, as we noted, than those of the cells opposite or back of them, since the latter were composed of only two trapezes; so there was more space between the upper edge of the posterior cells and the edge of the block than there was above the anterior cavities; this space was great enough for the base of an ordinary cell (fig. 20 and 22); but there was not room for complete bottom above the anterior cells (fig. 19). The rough space between and above the posterior cavities in the opening of the angle of their oblique edges, extended much beyond their points (from bc up to n, fig. 20: or bc up to r, fig.22). It was in that spot that several bees began the sketch of a new cell (fig.22).

The first bee excavated a vertical fluting (fm, bp) in the space between the oblique edges (fc cb) of two neighboring cells and made edges for this new cavity, by accumulating the wax from this cavity to the right and to the left. In figures 23 and 27 the cell in question has been isolated so that we may better follow its development. The letters are the same as on figure 22. The contour (fmbp, fig. 23) shows the beginning of its outline. Its vertical ridges (fmbp) were exactly above the points of the two inferior cells № 2 and 3. These ridges started from these points and ascended vertically along the cavity up to a short distance from the edge of the block, which did not extend any farther than needed for the building of the entire base of the cell: the fluting was still terminated by a curved outline (prm, fig. 23).

But other bees established two rectilinear margins on its curvature, which united as two chords in the center of the arch, formed the obtuse angle (mrp, fig. 22). This cavity was then bordered by six ridges; the two lower ones (fc cb) belonging to the cells of the first row, № 2 and 3 between which the lower edge of this cell was placed; the lateral ridges (fm bp) parallel to each other ascending vertically, lastly the two upper ridges (rm pr) terminated the contour, joining one another and also joining the others at their lower extremity. These six ridges, equal in length, formed the hexagonal contour of the cell; but this contour was not uniform in its projection; it was higher at the angles (cpm) and depressed at the points (bfr) as may be seen more plainly in fig. 28, which displays the same cell at an angle.

The lower part, still unfinished (fcbe, fig. 23) of the space comprised between the six ridges was backed by the rhomb of cell № 1, since cells 2 and 3, above which the hexagon was formed, were themselves backed partly by this cell. The rhomb, inclined from the horizontal, but whose main diagonal was horizontal shown on the side of cell № 1 (c, fig. 21), exhibited its lower side. After the bees had outlined and made edges on the bottom of the hexagonal cell, they busied themselves in smoothing down the other face of this rhomboidal piece, and lined it with the furrows (fe and eb) which corresponded to the ridges of the same name on the anterior face.

This piece was then a rhomb, and this rhomb (fcbe, fig. 22) seen from above, was the first and upper piece of the pyramidal base.

It occupied one-third of the surface of the cavity, for the obtuse angle (feb) being in the center, and its edges resting upon the two edges (fc and cb), which formed one-third of the circumference, it is easily conceived that the entire bottom of the cell was to be three times that of this rhomb. In fact there was above the rhomb, inside of the hexagon, enough space to admit of two rhombs similar to this one, but turned differently.

This part of the base of the cell remained in the same condition until the work upon the opposite face was far enough advanced to allow the bees to build a ridge on the reverse face of the cell in a vertical direction (er, fig 21): (which could take place only after they had outlined the two cavities opposite the hexagonal cell). But after this ridge was established on the anterior face, behind the piece to be divided, one bee busied herself in making the base of the hexagonal cavity in that direction and made a furrow in the still unfinished space (er, Fig 22), from the upper edge of the rhomb, to the upper edge of the hexagon; when the two parts of this were finished, we saw that she had perfected two additional rhombs (ferm and erbp) equal to the rhomb (fcbe). Thus the six edges of the hexagonal contour enclosed three rhombs of equal size; or a pyramidal base complete: the first of them having been built on the lower edge of the block. It is easy to understand that, during this operation, other cells were outlined to the right and left, upon the adjacent cells of the first row, and there is no need of any further explanation in this regard since the work is similar to that which we have just described.

The block was still further enlarged by the wax producers and there was still more space above the cells of the first row for the construction of new cells (fig. 21). The space between the cells and the drawn line shows, on fig.22, that this space was not yet filled during the building of the posterior cell of the second row, but it was filled when they built the anterior hexagonal cell.

A bee placed herself on the anterior face, so as to work in the unfinished space between the points of two cells of the first row, designated by numbers 1 and 4, between their oblique edges (fe fv). This bee immediately carved a furrow above the vertical edge that separated them, in a space equal to the diameter of an ordinary cell, but this space was already limited below by the cells of the first row. The bee gave to this cavity a fluting shape, its edges were made by two vertical ridges (er vn), and its upper edge, first made in a circle (fig. 25) was later changed by two other workers into straight ridges (on ov, fig. 21); making an obtuse angle; thus the cavity became hexagonal as with the opposite side, which was backed by it.

The dividing of this cell, (fig. 21 and 25) did not appear to cause the bees any trouble: the pieces which composed it were already partly shaped on the posterior face; on that side, two contiguous cells had between them a ridge (fm, fig. 22), which was to serve as guide: its shadow divided into two equal parts the inferior portion of the hexagon cavity. One could also see the shadow of the oblique ridges of those two posterior cells, from the center m of the cell, one to the right and the other to the left, running towards vertical ridges at r and n (fig. 21).

This cavity appeared to be divided into three equal parts by the shadow of the posterior ridges. What we discerned in shadows was soon made real by the work of the bees; the shadows were converted into furrows opposite the ridges; the interval and the edge of the cell were smoothed until they showed distinct rhombs; but the bees, while shaping the vertical furrow divided the inferior part of the cavity, and the two first rhombs of the pyramidal base were formed to the right and left; then by following the oblique ridges of the posterior cells, they formed a third rhomb situated in the upper part of the cavity, and inclined similarly to the one of cavity № 1.

This rhomb (onrm, fig. 21) was not opposite any outlined cell on the posterior face; it was backed by still crude material, comprised between the upper sides (rm mn) of two cells of the second row; so this space was to be later a part of the posterior face of a cell of the third row.

The result of the work of the bees, within the hexagonal cavity, was another pyramidal base; it differed in no way from the bases of the same row on the posterior face, which backed it, except in the position of the rhombs.

From this it is easy to conceive the manner of building of additional cells; they are always located between the upper and oblique sides of the neighboring cells; above their points the bees will build vertical ridges which will be the right and left borders of the new cavity; then the contour will be made by erecting two other ridges horizontally, on the upper edge of the fluting, which will produce an hexagonal contour.

The inferior part of these cavities will always correspond with the walls of the opposite cells; that is why all the cells of that side will be divided by two rhombs in the lower part and one rhomb in the upper. (of course it is the reverse in combs built downwards; so we must invert the figures in order to follow the natural order, as the work must be the same and the result similar: the building of pyramidal bases).

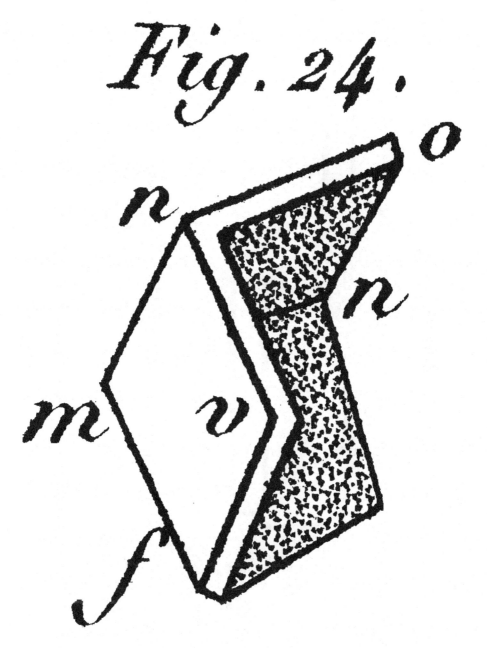

Volume 2 Plate VIII Fig 24—Furrow at base is oblique.

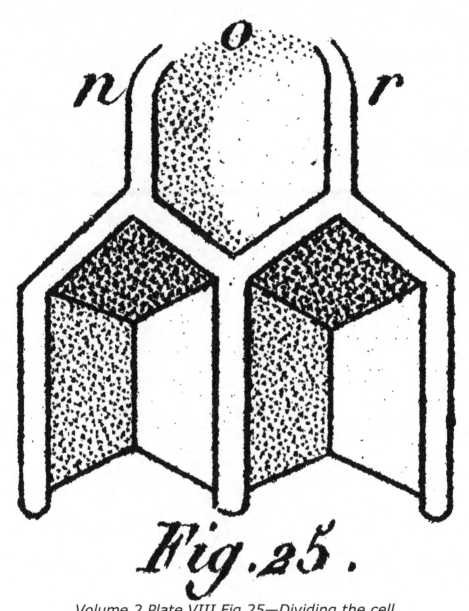

Volume 2 Plate VIII Fig 25—Dividing the cell.

The posterior cells are all formed on the model of those which we have described; one rhomb in the lower part and two rhombs in the upper. The anterior hexagonal cells are all situated a little higher than the posterior ones, for their lower part corresponds with the upper rhombs of the opposite cells.

Volume 2 Plate VIII Fig 26—Closeup of 1ˢᵗ cell of 2ⁿᵈ row.

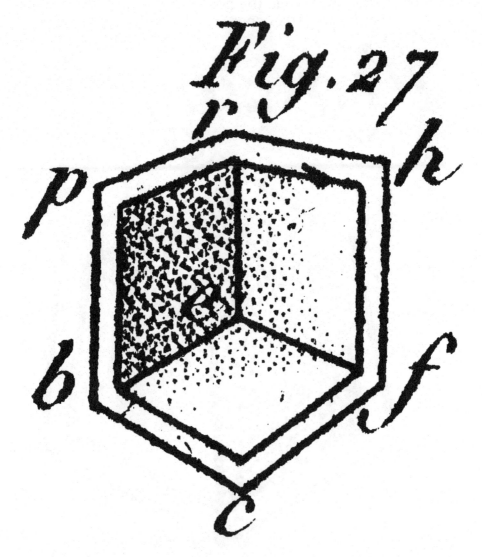

Volume 2 Plate VIII Fig 27—Closeup of first cell of second row (obverse of Fig 26).

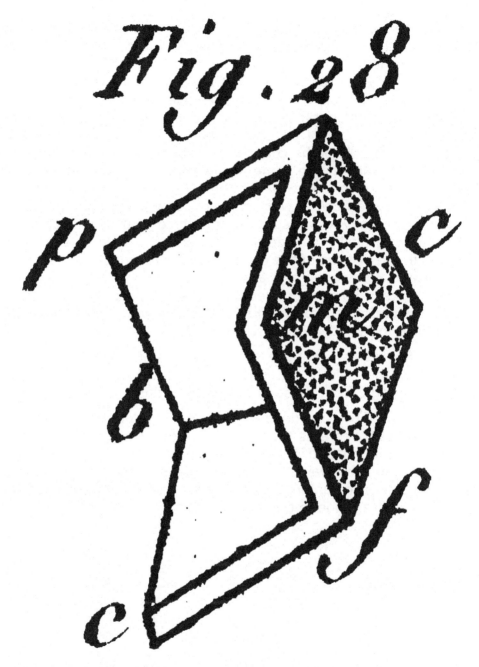

Volume 2 Plate VIII Fig 28—Showing Fig 27 rotated to show 3 dimensions.

We still have to make a few remarks concerning the difference between the pyramidal bases and the bases of the first row: the latter are composed, as we have shown, of two trapezes and a rhomb, or two trapezes only, which ascent perpendicularly from the lath, so the position differs from those of the pieces of pyramidal bases; as the three pieces of a pyramidal base start from the top of the pyramid towards the edge which outlines the contour of its base, they are all three inclined forward in the same proportion.   We have taken for granted, in our former explanations, that the furrow at the base of a cell was vertical. It was simply to show that it appeared to ascend vertically, when seen from its face. But when we cut the block vertically, we see that the furrow is oblique, since it starts from the base of the cavity to reach its edge; fig. 24, 28 represent a posterior and anterior pyramidal base; none of their edges or furrows are vertical. It is not the same with the trapezes of the base of the first row; they are actually vertical no matter on which side we view them.

The result is that the union of the latter with the oblique rhomb of the cells of the anterior face must be in a slightly different angle from those of a pyramidal base.

Each of the six ridges which form the edges of a pyramidal base is to serve as the basis for one of the six sides of a cell. The four sides of those of the first row (fig. 32) are also fixed in the same way around their bases. The prisms which are a result of the union of the sides are fastened to the edges of the cavities made in the block.

Volume 2 Plate VIII Fig 29—Surface of the new comb.

Fig. 30.

Volume 2 Plate VIII Fig 30—Surface of the new comb, side view.

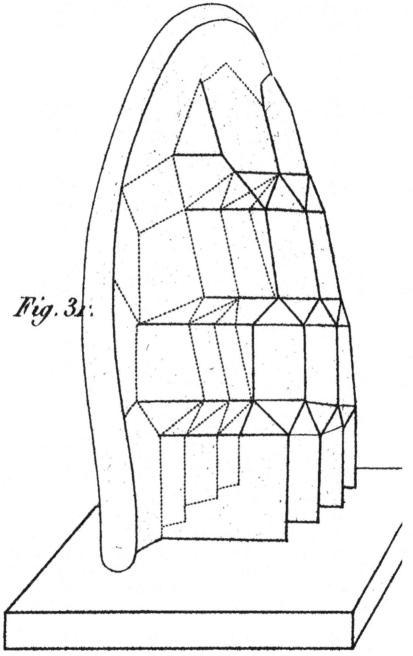

Fig. 31.

Volume 2 Plate VIII Fig 31—Surface of the new comb, see through view.

At first sight it would seem that there is nothing plainer than the adding of wax upon the edges of the contour of a cell base, but owing to the unevenness of this rim, which we have noticed, and which produces three projections and three recesses for the pyramidal bases, a projection for each of the bases of the anterior cells of the first row, and the recess for the posterior ones; on account of this unevenness the bees must begin by filling out what is lacking, by adding more wax on the shallower edges than they put on the projecting ones; in this way all the edges of the cells offer a uniform surface from the beginning and before the cells have acquired their proper dimensions.   But the surface of a new comb is not entirely plane, for there is a progressive decrease in the work of the bees.   The walls of the cells are prolonged in an order corresponding with the completion of the bases to which the cells belong (fig. 30), and the length of the tubes is so regulated that there is no gap or conspicuous irregularity among them. Thus the surface of a new comb is lenticular (fig. 29, 30, 31); the thickness of it decreasing to the edges, because the lately outlined cells are shorter than the older ones.   This progression continues in the comb while it is increased in size; but as soon as the bees lack space for its prolongation, it loses this lenticular shape and becomes parallel.   The bees form all the cells of the same depth by bringing the newest to the depth of the first built; the comb has then reached the shape that it is to preserve; but it is not yet fully completed; we will show later the termination of the work.

How can we explain the combination of their operations; why does instinct lead them to give a different form and different dimensions to the bottom of the first rows of either side, which have so great an influence on the remainder of the comb?   How can the bees working on the face of a comb determine the space to be excavated for the invariable mutual relation of the bases?   We should clear up this question, as the remainder of the problem depends upon it.

We do not see the bees visiting the two surfaces alternately, to compare the respective positions of the cavities which they outline; nature did not instruct them to take measurements which would appear to us indispensable for the construction of symmetrical work: there insects content themselves with feeling the part to be hollowed out with their antennae, and appear by this means sufficiently apprised, to execute a very complicated work, in which all seems to be combined with great exactness.

Not a parcel of wax is removed before their antennae have felt (palpated) the surface to be sculptured. Bees do not trust to their eyes for any of their operations; but with the help of their antennae, they can build, in darkness, those combs which are deservedly regarded as the most admirable production of insects. This organ is so flexible an instrument that it lends itself to the examination of the most delicate parts of the most distorted pieces; it may be used by them as compasses in measurement of the smallest objects, such as the edge of a cell.

Bees, therefore, appear to be regulated in their work by some local circumstance; we notice that while sketching the bottoms of the first cells, before there was any ridge on the reverse, they sometimes cause such a ridge to appear on the opposite surface, by the simple pressure of their legs upon the wax still soft and flexible, or by the efforts made with their teeth to excavate the interior of the block. Sometimes it occasioned a breach of the partition, which was soon repaired, but a slight protuberance always remains on the opposite surface, which may serve as a guide for the bees working upon that side. They place themselves to the right and left of this ridge to begin a new excavation, and heap up a part of the materials between the two flutings resulting from their work.

This ridge, converted into a real rectilinear rib, becomes a guide for the bees to recognize the direction to be followed in making the vertical furrow of the anterior cell.

We have often conceived, when seeing these insects follow so accurately the reverse of the ridges to excavate the corresponding furrows, that they perceive the greater or less thickness of the partition, from its flexibility, elasticity, or from some other physical property of beeswax: whatever may be the case, it is certain that they give the bases of the cells a uniform thickness, without having any mechanical means of measuring them; for the same reason, they may perceive very distinctly whether there is a ridge behind the partition, and excavate into it until they have reached the point which must not be exceeded.

I do not wish to present these explanations with more positiveness than as a simple hypothesis. I desired to show the linking of the operations of the bees, but I have not undertaken to discover the secret causes of their actions.

I believe however that they may be explained without resorting to extraordinary causes. The length of the cavities, their respective positions and the thickness of the block once determined, the inclination of the oblique sides of the trapezes of the first row, to which that of the lozenges of the second is subordinate, is established of itself, without any need of instruments for measuring angles or without calculation on the part of the bees.

What we need to understand is the manner in which they establish the relation between the unequal cells of the first row. One of the contributing causes for securing these dimensions, upon which so many important conditions depend, is the manner in which the block is enlarged.

Its original height determines about the vertical diameter of the posterior cavities, which is equal to two-thirds that of a common cell. But they cannot complete the bottom of the anterior cell until the block is enlarged, which on that account is extended more than necessary for finishing the cell, but just enough to give sufficient space for the entire base of a posterior cell of the second row; for the rhomb making part of it is already comprised in the interval of the cells formed of trapezes. The bees adding to the block two-thirds of the diameter of a cell, are enabled to construct, on the anterior face, the bottoms of cells of the second row, a part of which is already intercepted between the upper edges of the first cells; but there will not be room yet for the construction of a third row, until the block shall be enlarged anew.

The bees cannot deviate from the prescribed rule, unless particular circumstances alter the bases of their work, for the block is always lengthened in uniform quantity; and what is admirable, this is done by the wax producers, the depositories of its first elements, who do not have the faculty of sculpturing the cells.

Thus in dividing the functions between the wax producers and the small bees, the author of nature appears to have distrusted the exclusive lights of instinct.

What simplicity and depth in the means, what linking of causes and effects! It is a diminutive image of this harmony which strikes us in the great works of creation.

Such processes could not be foreseen. One does not divine the ways of Nature, it lays out methods that confound our science, and it is only by studying it carefully that we may succeed in unveiling some of its mysteries.

From the facts just described, should we not draw the conclusion that the geometry which shines in the work of the bees is rather the result of their operations than the principle that causes them?

Our readers will doubtless share the pleasure which we experienced when we received the following communication in which one perceives a singular connection between the geometrical solution supplied by a skilful mathematician and the work of the bees, such as we have exhibited from our observations.

The bases of the cells of the first row, which determine the inclination of the rhombs of the entire comb, represent two sides of a prism cut so as to from three angles equal to the rhomboidal plan which they intercept. One might believe that the bees succeed in constructing their cells by the sole knowledge that they have of the required section of the prism, and the solution supplied by Mr. Le Sage shows it to be more simple than one had thought.

We find great satisfaction in recalling here the labors which are too little known, of a savant who is beloved of his countrymen, and we are authorized to state that the project of publishing his principal works has not been overlooked by Professor Prevost, of Geneva, who mentioned it in the preface of his "Notice upon the life and writings of Le Sage," 1 vol. in-18 at J. J. Paschoud, Paris and Geneva

Article Communicated by Mr. P. Préfvose, Professor at Geneva.

In 1781, Mr. Lhuillier sent to Mr. de Castillon a memoir upon the "minimum of wax of the bees", which was read at the Academy of Berlin and inserted in his Memoirs for the same year. This learned mathematician gives in it, in a few words, the history of the researches made upon this subject, by Maraldi, Réaumur, Koenig, etc., and treats the subject by a more simple method than had yet been done in previous works, since he reduces the problem to a few elementary propositions.

In this memoir he gives honorable mention to Mr. Le Sage. He mentions him also in a later work and gives more details on the mathematical process through which this philosopher solved the problem relating to the shape of the base of the cells constructed by the bees. He informs us, that le Sage was, to his knowledge, the first to treat this matter in an elementary way; a method easily applicable to all the problems which do not exceed the second degree; a method which had been kindly communicated to Mr. Lhuillier ten years previous to the time when he published his own.

The memoir of Mr. Lhuillier contains not only the solution of the problem relative to the construction of the rhomboidal bases, so as to obtain, for a given cell, the least expense of wax, but also that of the problem relative to the *"minimum minimorum,"* or to the shape of the cell of equal capacity that would cost the least, as well as other remarks regarding this subject. It ends with a memorandum from Mr. de Castillon, relative to the actual dimension of the cells of the bees.

This memoir and the Latin work following that which I have mentioned, having been published for a long time and being consequently within reach of those who occupy themselves with these matters, it is sufficient to refer to them. But it may give them pleasure to find here an outline of the first elementary work which has been undertaken to solve the problem of the rhomboidal bases of the cells. A paper, written in Mr. Le Sage's own hand and of very ancient date, presents this work in a very simple form. It was drawn from one of his portfolios in which he had gathered the material for a bulletin which is mentioned in the account of his life. We shall transcribe it here without change, up to the second note which we will replace by an explanation

Notice of G. Le Sage on the base of the cells:

"Given the mutual inclination of the two planes, for instance 120 degrees; cut into them with a third plane, in such a way that the three resulting angles be equal.

"This is a problem which even a very shallow artisan could solve with very simple instruments: for the only thing needed is to find the center of a proposed straight line; which even insects may do with their legs (a). This solves the famous problem of the minimum, *of which we are astonished to find the solution in the base of the bee's cell, and which consists in using the least possible quantity of wax, without diminishing the size of the cell; and for which they have needlessly used all the apparatus of the calculation of the infinite (b)."*

For geometrical explanations

"Problem. Given (Plate XI, fig 2) the width of AB of the face of a regular hexagonal prism; add to one of its edges or withdraw from it, the length

AX, equal $\sqrt{\dfrac{AB^2}{8}}$

"Solution. Cut AB in two equal parts at C. Draw AD to equal AC. Draw CD; cut the line in equal parts at E. Draw AE from A to X, upon AD or its prolongation.

Demonstration: $(AE)^2 = \frac{1}{2}(AC)^2 = \frac{1}{2}\left(\dfrac{AB}{2}\right)^2 = \frac{1}{2} \times \dfrac{(AB)^2}{4} = \dfrac{(AB)^2}{8}$

(b) "for the geometrical explanations"

This is the heading of the second note which we have suppressed. It was intended to demonstrate algebraically that the problem relating to the bases of cells amounts to the geometrical problem solved in the first note. Several reasons have induced us to substitute for this algebraical note a few detailed explanations. One may find, in the above mentioned works of Lhuillier (especially in the Berlin Memoirs for 1781, marginal note page 284), the method of Le Sage and his learned disciple, to determine, with the help of algebra, the minimum of expense in the construction of the bases.

Supposing the hexagonal cell to be a straight prism, the question is to cut the ridge conveniently at the desired spot. For this purpose, the rhomboidal base must be a minimum. A simple equation of the second degree, leads to the following formula: The distance from the intersecting point to the hexagonal base is equal to the half-side of this base, divided by the root of two, or similarly to the side divided by the root of eight.

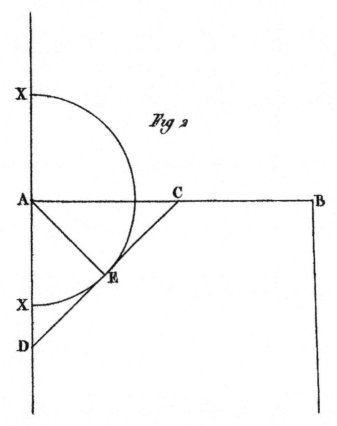

Volume 2 Plate XI Fig 2—Geometry of the cell.

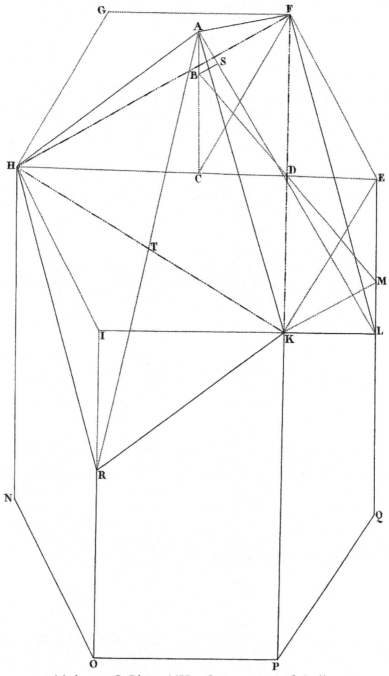

Volume 2 Plate XII—Geometry of Cells.

Chapter V: Modifications in the Architecture of Bees

The researches relative to the organization and development of animal productions, may not be in spite of their importance, the most interesting in the eyes of the naturalist philosopher. Those which embrace the degrees, the resources and limits of this faculty which serves as judgment for so numerous a class of beings, offer a still wider and more fertile field for his meditations.

The vulgar, commonly believe that sensations and physical needs exercise an absolute empire over animals: unquestionably they have influence upon them in many circumstances; but it would be as difficult to explain the conduct of creatures subjected to instinct by the sole attraction of pleasure or fear of pain as it would be unfair to ascribe the virtues of feelings and reasoning beings to personal views alone, though it has often been asserted that self-interest was the only motive of our actions.

If there is a direct connection between the organization and the habits of living beings, this connection is so enigmatic in its characters that we cannot analyze it. We may notice, in physiology, a few salient points, such as the long beaks or webbed feet of some birds, by which we discern the reckoning from this to the cunning of animals the recesses of their instinct; even if we should reason from their customary behavior, we might be drawn into error, for many of them have ingenious resources in difficult circumstances: they leave their usual routine and appear to act according to the situation in which they find themselves; that is indeed one of the most curious phenomenon's of natural history.

Invariable laws, concerning the actions of animals, appear to us a subject of admiration, for the mind becomes easily accustomed to the ideas of order, and readily accepts a uniform plan; but in the designs of the author of nature, there is a flexibility, a freedom which bears the imprint of supreme power; the most opposite conditions are united without jar or confusion: can we conceive that being subject to a common law and gifted with some intellect, should be able to swerve from the letter and act accordingly? That they should be able to change their processes and modify the prescribed rules when necessary? How can we imagine that there may be exceptions to the great laws of nature, and that animals be able to act, in some circumstances as if they understood the intentions of the law-maker? Those are phenomena which no theory can explain; but we must not get false views concerning the nature of animals; do not our prejudices blind us as to the distance from their faculties to ours? This would require profound investigations and it is in that direction that the ultimate labors of the zoologists should tend. To acquit ourselves in part of our own debt in this regard, we will describe some anomalies which we have noticed in the behavior of the bees.

Some anomalies in the behavior of the bees.

I will not yet develop the consequences which seem to result from these; it will be only after making known the bulk of their operations that I will take the liberty of making a few remarks on the true place which these insects occupy in the order of life.

Everything connected with the fabrication and use of combs had been skillfully combined; cells turned downwards like those of wasps would not have suited bees, since they have to store fluid: each comb presents innumerable small honey-pots laid horizontally; they are provided on both sides; perhaps their shape, and the affinity between the wax and the honey, prevent the latter from escaping; the combs are on parallel planes and are separated from one another by lanes only a few lines in width. It was after measuring these fairly regular distances and average thickness of the combs that I conceived the invention of book-hives, which I always used with success.

Parallelism of the combs

The parallelism of the combs is not one of the least difficult subjects of explanation nor would it be explainable, did we conceive that their foundation was laid simultaneously by a number of workers. Experience teaches us, to the contrary, that one cannot see the bees begin different blocks of wax here and there at the same time. A single worker deposits materials in an apparently suitable direction; she departs; another re-places her; the block rises; the bees sculpture its opposite faces alternately; but scarcely are some rows of cells con-structed when we perceive two other blocks similar to the first, established parallel to the first, which widen and length on either side. These blocks soon become combs, for bees work with astonishing speed: shortly after, we notice two other still parallel and built in relative progression according to the date of their origin; the first one, being the oldest, exceeds those parallel to its two faces by some rows of cells, and the latter exceeds those following by a similar quantity; thus the two faces of a comb are in great part concealed by those next to it.

I shall not try to explain how bees take such accurate measurements and know the direction parallel to that of the first comb. But one perceives clearly that if they were permit-ted to place different blocks in the roof of their hive at the same time, these outlines would be neither properly spaced nor built parallel to one another.

Bees have no discipline and know no subordination.

We see an example of the same method in the manner of outlining the cells; it is invariably a single bee that selects and determines the place of the first cavity; this one, being established, serves to direct the ulterior labors. Did each of several workers sketch a cell at the same time, the symmetry of the cells resulting from this operation would be left to chance; for these insects have no discipline and know no subordination.

This impulse for comb building is successive.

A great number of bees work upon the same comb, in-deed, but they are not guided by a simultaneous impulse, as might be conceived if one did not observe their operations from the outset. This impulse is successive; a single bee begins each partial operation, and several other successively join their efforts with hers to the same end; each appears to act individ-ually in a certain direction, directed by the bees which preceded her or by the state in which she finds the work which she is to continue; and the bee that commences a new operation is led to it by the effect of a harmony which rules the progression of the work. But if anything in the conduct of bees could give the idea of almost unanimous consent (which we present as a doubtful thing) it is the inaction of the rest of the colony while a single bee determines the position of the comb. Immediately, others assist her and add to the height of the block; then they again cease acting and a single individual of a different profession, if the word may be allowed in speaking of insects, traces the first outline of the base of a cell which, by its peculiar shape prepares a different kind of work; it is a base or a fundamental plan for establishing the entire edifice. A subtle sense of feeling shows to the bees, across the partition, the situation of the margins of the cavity, and it is from this that they direct their efforts for the division of the base of the new cells: but it is not only by the means of the ridges that they discover the direction to be followed; we have ascertained that they profit by diverse circumstances to guide themselves in those excavations. The bee which forms the first cell is a remarkable exception; she works in a rough mass, and thus has nothing to point out the way, instinct being her sole conductor.

The workers outlining the cavities of the second row, on the contrary can take advantage of the edges and angles previously made on the same face, and use them as a basis or point of departure for subsequent operations. I shall soon give a singular example of the art with which they take advantage of these when they have no other resource, but I shall speak first of the ordinary labor of the workers: I had seen them sculpt only upwards; I explained all their maneuvers when they are working in that direction, but the explanation of their behavior and the results which they attain then might belong to a special case.

So it was necessary to learn whether they always act in the same manner and pass through the same proceedings: they sculpt upwards with much less speed than downwards; but this circumstance was favorable to the observing of the diverse labors which the formation of the cells requires; otherwise it would have been impossible to follow the detail of their proceedings; yet the tardiness of the bees in this occurrence had its inconveniences; their work was sometimes interrupted for several hours; the wax was wanting when needed or it was not sculpted soon as deposited, or several blocks were deposited on the same lath.   Their work was evidently relaxed or impeded, and it was only through the number of small combs which they built that we were enabled to overlook the irregularities of their operations and form an accurate opinion of their architecture; so it was important to learn whether the process which we had seen them follow was the same in ordinary circumstances; it was to clear this doubt that I had a hive constructed of a new shape (Volume 2 Plate I, fig. 5b & 5c).

Fig. 5.

Volume 2 Plate I Fig 5b—Hive to Observe Comb Building.

Experiment to observe bees building comb downwards.

In order to fill my requirements, the top of this hive must be composed of several pieces, removable without disturbing the bees; it was also necessary that each part be separable and removable each time that we desired to ascertain the progress of their work. A ceiling, composed of glass and wooden slips placed alternately in a horizontal plane, was used for this purpose. A screw at each end of the slips permitted us to raise the combs above the top of the hive, so that we might examine them and return them conveniently without deranging the bees; in this way we could remove such of them as we wished to preserve and compel the bees to build others.

Volume 2 Plate I Fig 5c—Huber's hive to Observe Comb Building (Cheshire).

When they were established in their new home, they built combs along the wood laths following the direction of the intersecting line between the slips and the laths.

The first block established by them gave nothing new; we removed it and the bees built another at once; they again established it on the edge of the lath; we gave them time to carve their first cells: then by turning the screws upon which the work rested, the latter was brought up and allowed us to observe the formation of the new outlines; they showed flutings similar to those seen in the combs built upwards; we again lowered the comb and the bees continued their work. A few minutes later, the comb was again observed, the outlines had been advanced, the faces of the cells on both sides were unlike each other; they showed vertical trapezes; but only the anterior cells had a rhomb at their lower extremity; we then saw the bees proceed with the cells of the second row and became convinced that the march of their operations was in every point similar to what we had witnessed in the upward building.

Fig. 2.

Volume 2 Plate IX Fig. 2.—Lath with combs above and below and imprints on the lath as they build upwards.

We compelled the bees to begin a great number of small combs, the outlines of which more or less advanced, showed us that they were built upon the same principles and with the same gradations as those that had been built upwards.

It is clear, in my opinion, therefore, that the particular configuration of the first cells, on both sides, determines invariably the shape of the pyramidal bases of all the subsequent cells.

One could not have foreseen that the bees, in beginning their masonry, could have taken other measurements and a different method from that which they follow for the rest of the comb. This already proves that these insects do not act altogether mechanically; however, as it might be taken for granted that there is a necessity in this order of work, I will cite a frequent example of an altogether different action.

When I compelled the bees to work upwards, they laid blocks and built combs upon the horizontal part of the laths; but they were not always so docile. I have often seen them use wax from under their rings to stretch and extend some old combs into the space in which I desired them to build new ones (Plate IX, fig. 2 shows the lath with combs above and below).

The manner in which they do this deserved attention. To extend a comb placed under a lath and bring it up into the space above it, they begin by lengthening forward the upper edges of the cells of the first row, perpendicularly to the comb, and so that their extremities will project a little beyond the lath; after they have thus staked the ground, and fixed the points to work from, they pile wax on the vertical edge of the lath and with this wax they shape curves from the two parallel ridges of a cell and transform them into the walls of a cell. Thus they succeed in outlining regular hexagons on the vertical side of the lath, each with six ridges which will serve as bases to the cells they will erect at that spot; these cells are flat bottomed since they are built on the edge of the lath (Plate IX, fig. 2), but their diameter is equal to that of cells which are built upon a block of wax; if the lath is thicker than required for a single row of cells, the bees continue with additional ridges above those previously traced, until they reach the upper edge of the lath; when they build upon its surface a block which they sculpt in accord with the hexagons outlined on the wood; they will then give the first row of cells the ordinary shape of cells of the first row, and three rhombs to all subsequently built cells.

Volume 2 Plate IX Fig. 3.—Lath with combs showing progress of multiple combs and merging them.

We thus perceive that bees may shape cells upon wood and give them hexagon contours without pyramidal bases; thus they deviate from their usual routine, but not in the measurement of the cells and the shape of their walls, which they outline upon the wood with a symmetry that guides them in their ulterior work. But they do this by taking advantage of the previously built cells to form their ridges and give the curves a proper base. These flat bottom cells are less regular than the ordinary cells; we see in them some cells the contours of which are not angular, or the dimensions of which are not exact; but in all of them we notice the hexagons more or less marked.

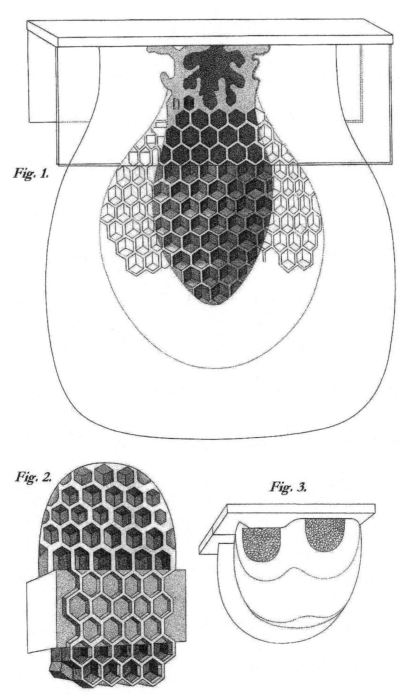

Fig. 1.

Fig. 2.

Fig. 3.

Volume 2 Plate IX—Some comb anomalies.

After seeing the bees build upwards and downwards, it was natural to investigate whether we could compel them to build their combs in some other direction. We tried to confuse them by placing them in a hive with the upper and lower sides entirely glazed, so that they had no place of support except on the side walls of the dwelling.

They clustered in one of the angles of the hive, in an impenetrable mass; we were compelled to disturb them in order to see their work and found that they had built combs perpendicular to one of the walls: they were just as regular as those which they usually built under a horizontal ceiling. This was a remarkable result, since the bees, habitually sculpting downwards, were compelled to place their foundations on a plane which is unusual to them. But the cells of the first row were similar to those which they construct ordinarily, with the only difference that the ridges were built in a different direction: the other cells were none the less fit for the common uses and distributed on both faces, with the bottoms alternately corresponding with the same symmetry.

I put these bees under still greater trial: having observed that they try to build their combs, in the shortest way, toward the opposite side of the hive, I covered the latter with a panel of glass, in order to find whether they would be content with a surface which they do not usually trust, unless their cluster can hang in the close vicinity to a substance less slippery than glass. I know that they prefer fastening their combs to wood, and that they accept glass only when they have been deprived of any other substance to strengthen their constructions. I had no doubt however that they would fasten the comb to this pane, taking chances to later strengthen it by securing more stable attachments, but I was far from suspecting what they would do.

As soon as the board was covered with this smooth slippery surface, they deviated from the straight line which they had hitherto followed, and continued their work by bending their comb at right angle so that the forward edge would reach one of the walls left uncovered.

Varying this experiment in several ways, I saw the bees constantly change the direction of their combs whenever I approximated a surface too smooth to admit of their clustering at the ceiling or on the sides of the hive; They have always selected the direction which would bring them to the wooden sides; I thus compelled them to curve their combs in the strangest shapes by placing a pane at a certain distance in front of their edges.

These results indicate an admirable instinct; they denote even more than instinct; for glass is not a substance against which bees may be warned by nature; there is nothing as polished as glass or resembling glass in their natural abodes, the interior of trees. The most singular part of their work was that they did not wait until they arrived at the surface of the glass to change the direction of the combs, they selected the suitable spot beforehand; did they anticipate the inconvenience that might result from any other mode of construction? The manner in which they made an angle in the comb was no less interesting; they necessarily had to alter the ordinary fashion of their work and dimensions of the cells; therefore those on the convex side were enlarged to two or three times the diameter of the others on the opposite face. Can we understand how so many insects occupied at once on both sides would concur in giving them the same curvature, from one end to the other; how they could decide to build small cells on one face, while upon the other face they built cells of so exaggerated dimensions; and is it not still more wonderful that they should have the art of making cells of such great discrepancy correspond between them? The bottom of the cells being common to both sides, the tubes alone assumed a taper form. Perhaps no other insect has ever supplied a more decisive proof of the resources of instinct, when compelled to deviate from the ordinary courses.

But let us observe these bees in natural circumstances, for it is not even necessary to test their instinct in order to see them modify the order of their architecture: by comparing what nature has required of them with the means employed by them in unexpected cases, we will better judge of the extent of their faculties.

Since the cells of bees are to serve as cradles to individuals of different sizes, the caliber of those tubes must be proportioned to the intention of their use. Thus the workers which were to build drone cells, were to follow a larger pattern than when they build ordinary worker cells; but they gave them the same shape, their bases are also composed of three rhombs, their prisms of six walls, and their angles are equal to those other small cells. The diameter of worker cells is 2-2/5 lines (.200 inch or 5.08mm), that of the drone cells is 3-1/3 lines (.277 inch 7.06mm); those dimensions are so fairly constant that some authors believed that they might be used as invariable patterns of measurement.

The drone cells rarely occupy the higher part of the combs; it is usually in the middle or in the lateral parts that they are found, and they are not isolated; they are built together and correspond with one another on the two faces of the comb.

Transition cells.

No observations have been made of the art with which they manage to construct alternately large and small cells without too flagrant inequalities in their work. The manner in which the drones cells are surrounded can alone explain how the transition is effected: when they are to sculpt drone cells below worker cells, they build several rows of intermediate cells, whose diameter augments progressively until gaining that necessary for drone cells; for the same reason when the bees wish to return to worker size they change by progressive gradation down to the size of cells of that class.

We usually see three or four rows of intermediate cells; the first drone cells still participate in the irregularity of the ridges which adjoin them, some bases corresponding to four cells instead of three. Their furrows are always in the line of the ridges, but one of the sides of the base, instead of being immediately opposite to the center of the cell on the reverse, divides it unequally, which alters the shape of the bottom, so that it no longer presents three uniform rhombs, but consists of pieces more or less irregular (See the appendix which follows).

The farther removed from the transition cells the more regular are found the male cells, so we often seen several consecutive rows without defects; the irregularity is resumed on their opposite confines and does not disappear until beyond several rows of ill-fashioned worker cells.

When building drone cells, the bees establish a heavier block of wax thicker than they make for the cells of workers: they also give it more height; the irregularity is resumed on the opposite confines and does not preserve the same order and symmetry while working upon a larger scale.

Irregularities have often been noticed in the cells of bees. Réaumur, Bonnet and several other naturalists cite examples of this as so many defects. What would have been their astonishment had they observed that some of these anomalies were calculated, that there is, so to speak, a mobile harmony in the structure of the combs: if, through some imperfection of their organs or of their instruments, the bees made some uneven or ill shaped cells, they would still show talent in repairing them, in compensating them by other irregularities; it is much more astonishing that they know enough to quit the ordinary route when circumstances demand that they build drones cells, and that they are able to vary the dimensions and the shape of each piece to return to a regular order; that after having built thirty or forty rows of drone cells, they quit the regular order again to return to the starting point by successive reductions.

How can these insects get through such difficult requirements, such complicated structures, change from the small to large, form the large to the small; from a regular plan to fantastic shapes and from these back again to a symmetrical figure? No known system can explain it.

Instinct capable of modification.

Since bees are every year obligated to construct cells of different sizes, we can attribute this trait to instinct, but it is an instinct capable of modification. What circumstance is it which prompts them to change the plan of the cells? Is it alteration in their senses, a change in the temperature, more abundant food or more suitable than what they find during the rest of the season? Not by any means; it seems to be the laying of the queen which determines the kind of cells to be built: as long as she lays none but worker eggs, you do not see the bees build drone cells; but if she finds no room available for the latter kind of eggs, the workers seem to be informed of it at once and we see them immediately gradually changing the shape of the cells, and at length producing cells for the masculine cradles.

Honey storage cells during a flow are larger.

There is another circumstance under which bees enlarge the dimensions of the cells; it is when a considerable crop of honey presents itself; not only do they give the cells a much larger diameter than common, but they prolong their tubes as far as space admits. In times of great harvest, we see irregular combs, the cells of which are an inch to an inch and a half in depth (2.5 to 4 cm).

There are times that bees will shorten a cell.

On the other hand, bees are sometimes induced to shorten their cells. When wishing to lengthen an old comb, the cells of which have received their full dimensions, they gradually reduce the thickness of its edges, by gnawing down the walls of the cells, until they have been restored the original lenticular shape; they then add wax to the edges of the pyramidal bases, as we have seen them doing in ordinary work: it is a certain fact that they never lengthen the cells of a comb in any direction without having first thinned out its rim, which is diminished in a sufficient space to remove any angular projection.

The edge is removed when changing the depth.

This law which obliges the bees to partly demolish the cells on the edges before giving them additional length, deserved more profound investigation than we are able to give it; for even if we can conceive the instinct which leads them to a particular industry, how can we account for that which induces them to undo a part of what they have executed with the utmost care? We must acknowledge that such phenomena will long be a stumbling block for all hypotheses that try to explain instinct.

When they construct a new comb there is a regular gradation in all the parts next to the edge, to which they appear to be accustomed and which may be necessary in the formation of new cells. But those edge cells are prolonged later like the cells of the rest of the surface, so that they no longer preserve the decreasing gradation observed in new combs. Thus it is evidently for the purpose of restoring the comb to its primitive form that they reduce the depth of the cells proportionally to their distance from the edge. Note: This reinforced edge that Huber refers to is obvious in its absence when you are extracting and having cut the thicker outside edge off the cells are very fragile. The bees quickly reinforce the edge again.— Transcriber.

Anomalies appear to be part of a plan.

All the anomalies exhibited in the labor of bees, are so well appropriated to the object proposed, that they seem to be a part of the plan under which they act, concurring to the general order.

The greatness of views and means of the ordaining wisdom is such that it does not reach its aim through minute exactness, it goes from one irregularity to another which compensate each other: the measurements are lofty, the apparent errors are managed by a sublime geometry, and order results from diversity. This is not the only example that science has divulged to us of preordained irregularities which astonish our ignorance and secure admiration from our most enlightened minds; for the more we study the general laws as well as the special laws, the better we see the perfection of this vast system.

Appendix on the Architecture of Bees

By P. Huber, Son of F. Huber

Having been called upon to review the facts which I have described, I have acquired a little information which had not been transmitted to my father by his faithful secretary; among these facts are found a few peculiarities which I now will present upon the method of comb enlargement, upon the principle and cause of their irregularity and upon the shape of the transition cells in drone combs.

It was not possible to give a complete idea of the enlarging of the combs, in the description of the bees' work, cell after cell. When we consider the matter in its ensemble we discover a few modifications which were not perceptible in very small parts of the comb and upon which we had not arrested our attention, so as not to complicate our statement.

We have stated that the work of bees was ordinarily conducted downwards: one might believe that it is always so, but this fact, which is applicable to a part of the cells, does not extend to the entire surface of the comb, its shape preventing this. Circumstances sometimes permit us to watch the bees while they are building combs, without disturbing the natural order of their work; those circumstances are rare and do not give us all the advantages found in inverting the order of their work, but they give us a more correct idea of the whole.

For this purpose, it is necessary that the bees, hanging in a cluster at one side of the hive, should work upon the edge, or in a way, outside of this cluster; after having built one comb they establish a second one, then a third, nearer and nearer to the observer who follows their work through the transparent wall of the hive.

The original base, upon which the bees begin, is composed of three or four cells, sometimes more; after being continued of that breadth for two or three inches, it begins to be enlarged at about three-fourths of this length.

Were the bees to work only downwards, it would form but a narrow strip of a uniform diameter, only a few bees could work upon it at the same time; but it is necessary that the work should proceed rapidly, and that they be able to sculpt at the same time in all directions; the preliminary lengthening of this little strip and its widening at its inferior end enable a large number of bees to work upon the edge, and the entire orbit of the comb is extended in every direction under the work of their shears.

The bees at the lower edge of the comb lengthen it downwards, those on the sides widen it to the right and left; those above the main bulging portion extend it upwards; the wider it extends below, the more necessity there is of its rising directly to reach the vault of the hive.

Thence results a fact which we had not yet mentioned; that the cells of the first row are not the first built throughout the hive; so the primitive cells are only those which are constructed at the upper part before the comb is widened. This small base is sufficient to trace out the pyramidal bases of the entire comb; but although the subsequently built cells of the upper line are built either upwards or obliquely they are of about the same shape as the primary cells; they are composed of vertical plates, with or without rhomb, according to the side from which they are viewed. They fit against pyramidal cells as well as against the ceiling of the hive; there is more irregularity and confusion in them than in ordinary primitive cells but the strength and general order lose in no way thereby.

The same thing occurs when the lateral edges of their combs reach the vertical wall; the bees build the bases of the last cells perpendicularly to this surface, so that they are similar to those of the first row, with the only difference that they are situated horizontally instead of vertically; and when the wall is of glass, one sees the base of all those cells in the shape of a zigzag in its center, as with the first cells built.

Bees work in all directions simultaneously.

Thus bees work in all directions; their processes are uniform in every case. But we should be unable to recognize the original small waxen block, did we not take notice that it now appears as a flat ribbon which runs around the edge of the entire comb. It is in this edge that the bees sculpt new cells and deposit scales of wax; its width is of two or three lines and it is apparently of more compact build than the rest of the comb. The bees work at the same time over all parts of this ribbon when they have abundance of wax.

We must notice, however, that even when their work progresses in all parts, it does not advance in the same proportion; they work more quickly downwards than horizontally, and more slowly upwards than in any other direction; thence ensues the ellipse or lens shape which the comb assumes while it is being enlarged; thence also the greater length than breadth, it being more pointed at its inferior extremity and narrower at the top than in the middle. The shape of the combs, therefore, is fairly regular; their outline usually offers no asperity; and there is a singular harmony in the lengthening of all the cells. We have previously stated that the length of their prisms is in proportion to their age; but investigating with more attention, we recognized that in a new comb, their length is proportioned to their distance from the edge. Thus the first rows are not those of which the cells are the deepest, the cells there are shallower than in the middle of the comb; but when the comb acquires a certain weight the bees hasten to prolong those cells so essential to the solidity of the whole; sometimes they even make them deeper than those that follow.

Cells are sloped.

The prisms are not perfectly horizontal, their orifice being almost always a little higher than the base, which enables us to recognize the original position of a comb, though detached. Hence the axis of a cell is not perpendicular to the wall which separates the two faces of a comb; this rule, hitherto overlooked, is an insuperable bar to geometrical calculations regarding the shape of the cells, for these prisms are more or less inclined upon their bases, sometimes deviating from the horizontal above 20°, ordinarily 4° or 5°.

Fig. 1.

Fig. 2.   *Fig. 3.*   *Fig. 4.*   *Fig. 5.*   *Fig. 6.*

Fig. 7.   *Fig. 8.*   *Fig. 9.*

Volume 2 Plate X—Transition Cells.

However, whatever be their irregularities they are less prominent that those of the bases, and frequently where the latter are irregular, the cells preserve the hexagonal form, as we will show.

Symmetry is in the totality rather than the details.

Bees in general observe a tendency to symmetry, perhaps not so much in the small details as in the totality of their operations; it sometimes happens, however, that the combs assume a singular shape; but if we followed in details the work of these insects, we could nearly always assign reasons for these apparent anomalies; the bees are compelled to adapt themselves to localities, one irregularity produces another, and they usually originate in the arrangements which we make them adopt. The inconstancy of the temperature, by causing frequent interruptions in their operations, affects the symmetry of the combs; for we have always remarked that interrupted work is less perfect than continuous labor.

We have sometimes accidently given too little space between supports intended to bear the combs, and thus caused the bees to follow a particular direction. At first they did not seem to notice the incorrectness of the dimensions and built their combs on those laths placed too closely together; but they very soon appeared to suspect the error, and gradually changing the line of their work, they returned to the customary distances; this operations giving their comb a more or less curved form. New combs, built parallel to the first, necessarily had the like deformity, which was imparted to the following combs successively. However the bees seek as much as possible to bring them back to the regular form; often a comb is convex above only; lower down the defect is rectified and the surfaces of the lower part are brought to a straight figure.

We have seen their love for symmetry in other circumstances much more striking. From a series of previous irregularities, the bees of one of our hives, instead of establishing one block upon the lath, as usual, built two, the one opposite the most advanced part of the built comb, the other opposite the least advanced portion; the two combs built upon the same lath being of irregular shape, owing to the irregularity of the previous comb, could neither meet at their ends nor be extended without being in each other's way; the bees adopted a very effectual plan. They curved the edges of these two combs and brought their edges together so perfectly that they could continue them jointly. The part above this junction was irregular but as the combs were prolonged downwards, their surface became more and more level, until it became perfectly uniform.

We saw another work exceedingly regular in its whole, although of a very peculiar shape. The bees had commenced their comb at the lower edge of a vertical strip of glass; it was lengthened several inches upon a base of only four or five cells, without any other support than the wax fastened to the edge of the glass; but as its weight increased, the bees built several rows of cells upwards upon one of the vertical edges of this glass, and these cells, which were fastened to those of the comb, increased its solidity: one might have considered them as a continuation of the same comb, since their edges were regular; but their walls were fastened upon the glass, which served as a base for them; the bees appeared satisfied with five rows of those cells upon the glass; then wishing to give them still more strength, they attempted to fasten it to a wooden lath located at the upper end of the glass strip; for that purpose it was necessary for them to continue the work in that direction, but they constructed only two ascending branches, to the right and left of the flat-base cells (Plate IX, fig. 1), and these, when reaching their destination, were divided into two branches, in Y shape, along the junction point of the wood with the glass.

After the comb had acquired a certain extent in its lower part, the bees prolonged it upwards to the lath; for this purpose they changed the direction of its edges so as to establish it behind the glass strip which they wished to avoid; they built it far enough away from it to give their cells the proper depth, and after succeeding in this they carried their masonry parallel with the glass. The comb was built up to the ceiling of the hive and filled all the space that it was possible to occupy, with the exception of the interval between the flat-base cells and the ascending branches; but although this comb was not of the ordinary shape, its symmetry was perfect; the braces built for strengthening it were exactly alike and at equal distances from the center; there was not an extra cell on either side and the projection of their lateral sides was uniform in every part.

Fig.1.

Volume 2 Plate IX Fig. 1.—Two ascending branches, to the right and left of flat-base cells on glass.

Irregularities found in the building of drone combs.

We may readily judge, by those various works, of the spirit of union which regulates the bees; we will now detail the irregularities found in the building of drone combs.

In the previous chapter we stated that the drone cells are surrounded with several rows of cells of average size. A comb is rarely commenced with drone cells, the first rows being formed of very regular small cells; but the openings soon cease corresponding exactly with one another, and the bases are less symmetrical; it would be impossible for the bees to build irregular cells in regular shapes; that is why we often see between those cells some masses of wax occupying the intervals. By thickening the sides and giving the contours a more nearly circular shape, the bees sometimes succeed in uniting cells of different diameter, for they have more than one method of compensating the irregularities of the cells.

Fig.1.

Volume 2 Plate X Fig 1—Transition comb.

Bases offer more pronounced irregularities.

But although the surfaces of the cells always show hexagon outlines with only slight modification, the bases offer much more pronounced irregularities, which announce a determinate plan and explain their progressive enlargement.

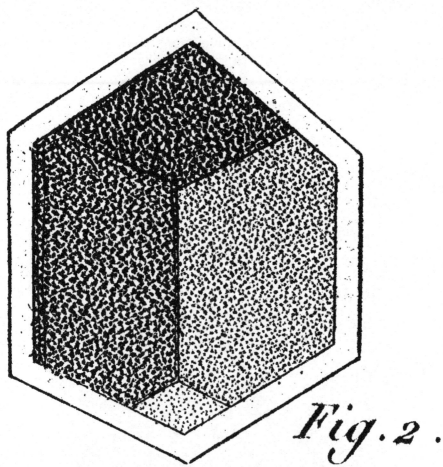

Volume 2 Plate X Fig 2—Cell with two rhombs.

Examining a comb through a vertical line in its middle we observe that the cells next to this line are enlarged without much alteration of shape; but the bases of the adjacent cells are no longer composed of three equal rhombs; each instead of corresponding with three others, corresponds with four cells on the opposite face, while their orifices are not less hexagonal;

but their base is composed of four pieces, two of which are hexagonal and two rhomboidal (Plate X, fig. 1). The size and shape of these pieces vary; these cells, which are somewhat larger than the third part of three opposite cells, comprehend a portion of the bottom of the fourth cell in their circumference. Under the last regular pyramidal bottoms are found those having a base in four parts, three large and one small, the latter a rhomb.

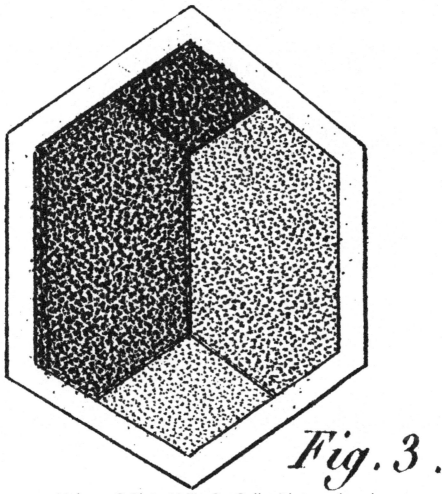

Volume 2 Plate X Fig 3—Cell with two rhombs.

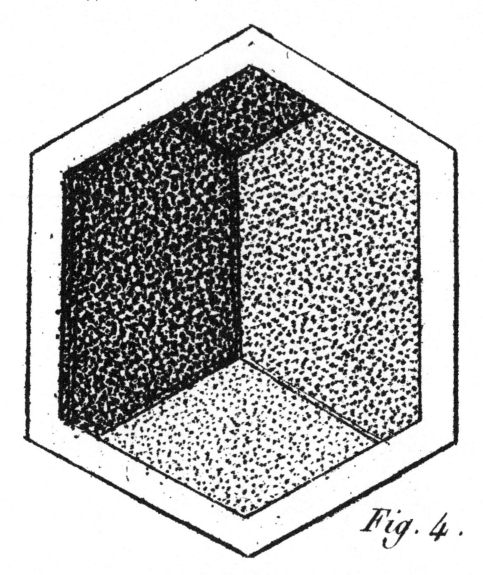

Vol 2 Plate X Fig 4—Cell with two rhombs obverse of Fig 2.

Thus it is by encroaching slightly upon the cells of the opposite face that the bees succeed in giving their cells the larger dimensions; the graduation of the transition cells being reciprocal on both faces of the comb, it follows that the hexagonal circumference on each cell embraces four cells.

After the bees have reached any degree whatever of this progression, they may stop there and preserve it in several consecutive rows; they seem to continue longest at the medium, when we find a great many cells with the bottom regularly made of four pieces; they could build the entire comb upon this plan, were not their aim to resume the pyramidal form they have left. When they diminish the diameter of their cells, they return by similar gradations, in inverted order.

In order to gain an idea an idea of the modifications that are possible in the cells, we should carry a hexagonal contour over other contours of similar shape, but a little smaller and arranged like those of the bees.

We could secure the same regularity with perfectly equal tetrahedral outlines; but in order that the bees may be able to return to pyramidal cells of a different dimension, it becomes necessary that the diameter of the intermediary corresponding cells be a little larger on each face of the comb alternately.

As to the manner in which the bees construct them, it is easy to understand that they build the vertical ridges of their cells long enough to go beyond the center of the opposite cells, afterwards outlining the hexagon, etc. The lower oblique ridges, cross the ridges of the opposite face and form a supernumerary rhomb. The bees smooth down the spaces between the ridges of the two faces, and the base of the cell then has four pieces instead of three. The shape of those pieces varies according to the greater or less analogy of the opposite ridges with those of common cells. It would be very difficult to measure the inclination of the tetrahedral bases; but they appear to me to be little shallower than the pyramidal bases. It must be so, for the two rhombs being smaller, the intermediary line which forms the bottom of the cell and which begins at their extremities, will be less sunk and so the cell will be shallower.

In general, it appears that the shape of the prisms of the cells is more essential than that of their bases, for we have seen cells with tetrahedral bases more or less regular, the walls of which were hexagonal, and also cells built upon either glass or wood without wax base, but with six sided walls. These observations concur with the previous ones to show that the shape of the pieces which form the bottom of the cells depends upon the manner in which this is cut by the contours of the cells of both faces; or in other words upon the direction of the ridges upon which the walls were erected.

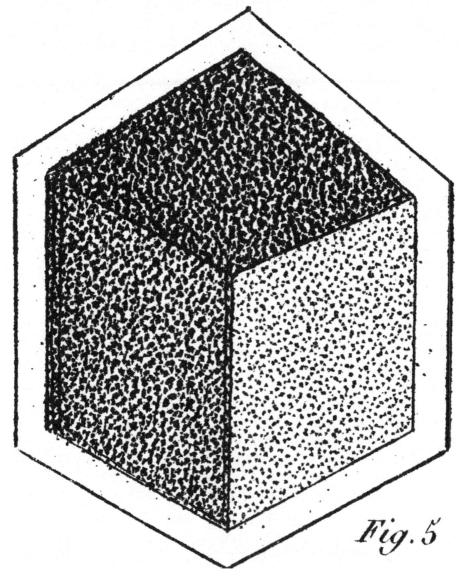

Fig. 5

Volume 2 Plate X Fig 5—Pyramidal bases which are separated from one another by technical base cells.

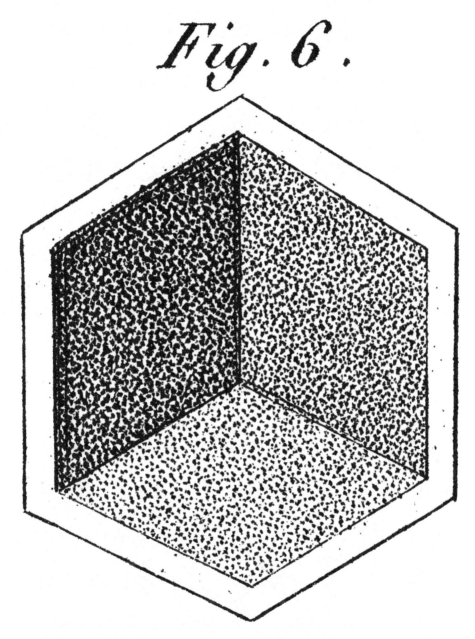

Fig. 6 .

Volume 2 Plate X Fig 6—Pyramidal bases which are separat-
ed from one another by technical base cells.

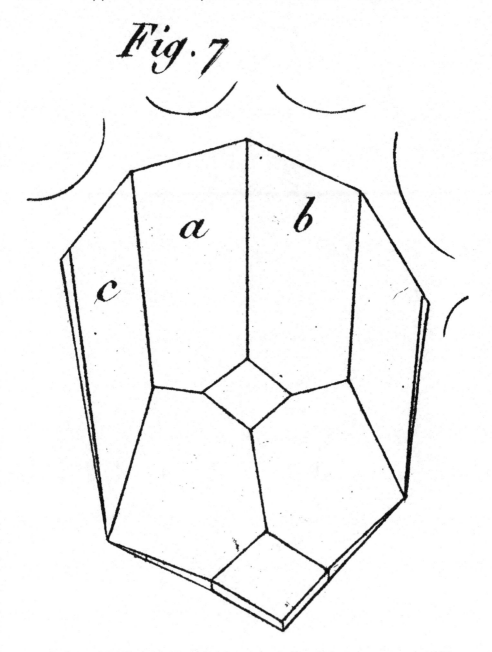

Volume 2 Plate X Fig 7—Bevel-shaped, bases so as to fit upon each other.

Fig. 8.

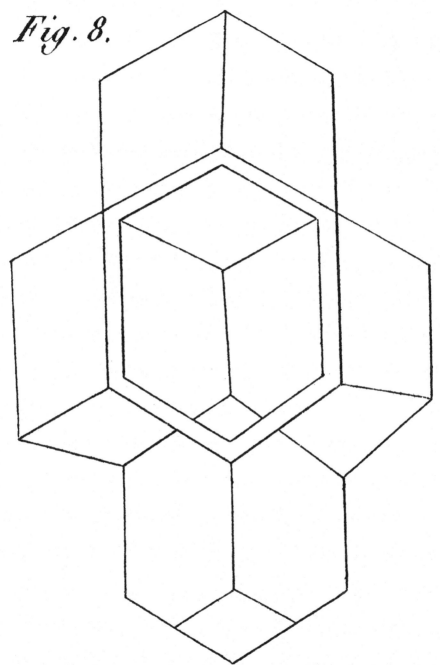

Volume 2 Plate X Fig 8—Showing transition and other side.

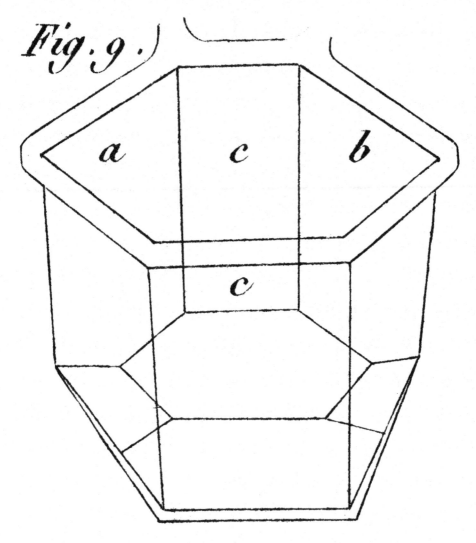

Fig.9.

*Volume 2 Plate X Fig 9—See through perspective of transi-
tion cell.*

    The shape of the walls of the tetrahedral cells differs ac-
cording to the bases to which they belong: those that correspond with one of the faces of the rhomb and a part of the
hexagonal face are bevel-shaped, so as to fit upon each other
(Plate X, ab fig. 7 and 9), while the two walls which correspond
with the large side of the hexagon are rectangular parallelo-
grams (c fig 9).

Note Well: **The pyramidal bases which are separated from one another by technical base cells, do not have their lozenges situated similarly; it is a consequence of what we have stated (fig. 5 and 6).**

These observations show us how flexible is the instinct of the bees, how well it yields to the local conditions, to the circumstances and requirements of the family. Necessity, in the work of these insects, as in all that pertains to the habits of animals, must be limited to a small number of essential points, all others being subordinated to the circumstances.

The conduct of bees depends upon judgment.

The limits of their industry are assuredly less narrow than at first supposed; and the reader will admit, with us, that the conduct of bees depends also in some measure upon what might be called the judgment of the insect; this judgment, doubtless, is rather a matter of tact than formal reasoning; but its subtleness resembles choice, rather than habit or habitual mechanism independent of the will of the insect.

Certain facts produce no longer upon us, the impression of novelty; we see them without trying to discover their causes and their aims; but can we foresee what will excite our curiosity? Is anything indifferent to the naturalist? If he avoids the unconcern which is the effect of habit, as well as the belief, that all that deserves attention has already been observed, he soon finds interest in subjects that seemed to call for it the least.

In the course of our researches, we have often thought ourselves at the end of our labor; we perceived no more questions to solve, no more doubts to clear; but the bandage over our eyes fell of itself at last. A simple fact, seen every day without attention, would at last strike us, and we wondered why it should be less interesting than other peculiarities upon which we had spent much time. It was a new country open to us, and we were imperceptibly drawn into a new road, the existence of which we had not even suspected.

After several implements had given us the opportunity of studying the shaping of the combs and the modifications of the architecture of bees, we thought that new researches up on this subject would be useless; we were in error: the combs of bees are not completed when the bases and sides of the cells are built.

Combs are not completed when the shape is finished.

In the origin of the material of the cells is of dull white color, semi-transparent, soft, smooth without gloss; but it loses most of these qualities in a few days or rather it acquires new ones; a more or less distinct yellow tint spreads upon the interior of the cells, their edges become much thicker than they were at first and appear less regular, and these shapes which did not appear able to resist the slightest pressure acquire a consistency of which they did not seem susceptible.

We noticed that finished combs were of greater weight, in equal quantity, than those that were unfinished; the latter broke under the least touch; but the perfected combs bent instead of breaking; their orifices appeared sticky; the white cells could be melted in water at a lower temperature than the colored ones. All these observations indicated a noticeable difference in the composition of the combs and it was evident that those which were not new contained a material differing from beeswax.

Combs are coated in propolis which gives resilience.

In examining the orifices of the yellow cells, we perceived that their circumference was coated with a reddish unctuous, odoriferous varnish, and we recognized, as we thought, the resin called *propolis*. Afterwards it appeared not to be restricted to the orifices, that reddish threads were sometimes found on their inner walls, upon the rhombs or trapezes; this solder, placed at the points of contact of different pieces, and at the summit of their angles, appeared to help in strengthening the cells; one would sometimes notice one or two reddish zones around the axis of the longest cells: when the bees are short of wax, they are sometimes compelled to interrupt their work; when a more ample supply enables them to laborate the material, they resume the work; it is probably during this interruption that they varnish the edges of the cell, and when the latter have been lengthened, they retain traces of the material with which they had been coated.

These peculiarities had evidently not struck any of the naturalists who wrote upon bees; they knew that propolis was used to coat the inside of the hive; but they were not aware of this resin being used in the building of the cells; this was worth verifying. I made sure of it by comparative experiments, using the ordinary reagents.

The propolis taken from the walls of the hive and from the edges of the red-colored cells, submitted to the action of ether, alcohol or oil of turpentine, imparted a golden color to these liquids. The brown matter of the cells was dissolved by them, even when cold. The orifices of cells, in either alcohol or turpentine, retained the cell shape and their yellow tint after losing the varnish that coated them. Those placed in ether also lost the red varnish, they became bleached shortly after and disappeared when the wax was dissolved.

The coloring matter of the cells orifices, exposed to a mild heat, became soft and could be drawn into threads; the propolis of the walls did likewise. Nitrous acid, at a low heat, poured on both whitened the yellow wax in a few minutes, but the varnish of the orifices and masses of propolis underwent no alterations.

Other orifices, put into boiling water, displayed a curious peculiarity; after the wax in them was melted the varnish remained entire above it, on the cake which it formed, without losing its hexagonal contour, while its diameter seemed a little enlarged.

Fixed caustic alkali which changes wax into a kind of soap, has no effect upon propolis; we tried its action upon very old cells which had already served as cradles to a number of larvae, the cocoons with which they were lined hiding the varnish and the wax upon which they had been molded. The primary effect of the alkaline wash was to dissolve the wax by combining with it, separating it from the silky cocoons; then it bleached the cocoons, which are naturally of brown color and gave them the appearance of gauze: they retained the shape of the cells; the reddish threads then appeared, for they were not dissolved, and remained upon the outer edges of the cocoons, just in the way that they had been placed by the bees in the furrows formed by the junction of the different pieces which composed the cells. These threads of propolis were finally separated from the cocoons, but they were not altered by remaining several months in the solution.

The yellow coating is neither propolis nor wax.

From these experiments it is evident that the substance which gives a dark red color to the edges of the cells and to the lines of intersection of their walls, has the greater analogy to propolis; it is clear also that the yellow color of the cells has no relation to the varnish covering the joints of their different pieces.

Notwithstanding my confidence in such conclusions, I felt that they would be indisputable only after I had found the bees in the act. It was then necessary to follow them in their harvest of propolis and make sure of their use of it; but these researches were difficult.

Propolis has similar properties to those of gum-resin and has long been suspected of belonging to the vegetable kingdom. But for many years I fruitlessly endeavored to find the bees on the trees producing an analogous substance; but none of my investigations directed me to those upon which the bees gathered this harvest: though we saw multitudes returning laden with it.

Experiments proving the origin of propolis.

Being fatigued with the uselessness of my attempts, I devised a very simple expedient, from which I could obtain some light. The question was to secure such plants as would be likely to supply propolis, and place them within their reach; this plan succeeded; the first plants that I placed near my hives displayed to me in a short that that which I might have never found out, without this scheme.

The resin from poplar buds is gathered by bees.

In the beginning of July, some branches of the wild poplar, which had been cut since spring, before the growth of their leaves with very large buds, coated both on the outside and inside with a viscous, reddish and odoriferous sap, were brought to me; I planted them in vessels before my hives, in the way of the bees going out to the field, so that they would be sure to notice them. In less than a quarter of an hour a bee took advantage of this chance; she alighted upon one of the branches, on one of the largest buds, separated its involucra with her teeth, pressing out its parts, drew out threads of the viscous matter; then taking with one of the legs of the second pair what she held in her jaws, she brought forward one of the posterior legs and placed into the pollen basket of this leg the little pellet of propolis that she had just gathered; this done, she opened the bud in another spot, removed more threads of the same material, took them with the legs of the second pair and gently laid them in the other basket. She then flew to the hive; in a few minutes a second bee alighted upon these same branches and loaded up propolis in the same manner.

We made the same experiment upon recently cut poplar limbs, the young shoots of which were filled with propolis; they did not appear to attract the bees; but their sap was neither as thick nor as red as that which we had first offered to them, the buds of which had been preserved since spring.

Since the bees harvested this reddish and viscous substance from the buds of the common poplar, all that was needed was to identify this substance with propolis; no doubt of this remained after an experiment which we then made.

Propolis comes from poplar buds.

We took dry propolis from the walls of an old hive, we broke it up and soaked it in ether; this liquid assumed a yellow tint in each of nine consecutive experiments; but at the last it was very slightly colored; we evaporated it and there remained at the bottom of the vessel a residue of grayish white color. This residue, after having been steeped in distilled water, was examined with a microscope and distinctly showed vegetable debris, such as epidermis, portions of membrane, some opaque, and others transparent, but no trachea.

Ether gave a similar reaction on poplar buds, it was colored with yellow several times over, and the residues, steeped in distilled water, showed through the microscope similar debris, but less thoroughly dissected than those found in propolis.

Thus the identity of the two substances was no longer in doubt and we had but to discover the manner n which the bees applied it to use; we desired especially to witness the perfecting of the cells, but it was out of the question to see them work without some lucky expedient. We hoped to follow them more easily in a hive where they would build their combs upwards, because in such case some of the cells rest against the glass and their cavities are open for the eyes of the observer.

How bees distribute propolis.

So we peopled a hive so prepared as to fulfill our views. The bees, building upwards, soon reached the glass, but unable to quit their habitations on account of supervening rains, they were three weeks without bringing home any propolis. Their combs remained perfectly white until the beginning of July, when the atmosphere became more favorable for our observations. Serene weather and high temperature engaged them to forage; and they returned from the fields laden with this resinous gum resembling transparent jelly; with the color and luster of the garnet it was easily distinguished from the farinaceous pellets then brought home by other bees. The workers bearing propolis joined the clusters hanging from the ceiling of the hive, we saw them travel through the outside of these clusters; after reaching the supports of the combs, they appeared to rest, sometimes they stopped on the walls, waiting for their companions to relieve them of their burden. We actually saw two or three approach them and carry the propolis away with their teeth. The upper part of the hive exhibited the most animated spectacle, thither a host of bees resorted from all quarters, the distribution and application of the propolis being then their predominant occupation; some conveyed between their teeth the material which they had secured from the purveyors and deposited it upon the frames and supports of the combs; others hastened to spread it out like a varnish before it hardened, or formed it into strings proportioned to the interstices of the walls of the hives to be puttied up. Nothing could be more diversified than their operations; but we were most interested in the art which they used in applying propolis on the inside of the cells. Those which appeared to be charged with this task were easily distinguished from the multitude of workers because their heads were turned towards the horizontal pane. Upon reaching it, they deposited the propolis in the middle of the interval separating the combs. Then we saw them apply this substance in the real place of its destination; taking advantage of the points of support which its viscosity supplied, they appeared to hang to it with the claws of their posterior legs, seemingly swinging themselves under the pane of glass; the effect of this motion was to carry their body backwards and forward and at each motion we saw the lump of propolis come nearer to the cells; the bees used their anterior legs to sweep together that which had been detached and to unite these fragments upon the surface of the glass; the latter recovered its transparency when all the propolis was brought to the mouth of the cells. A few bees entered the cells located against the glass; it was there that I expected to see them at leisure: they brought no propolis, but they cleaned and polished the cell with their teeth worked in the angular corners, making them thicker, smoothed the rough edges; while the antennae appeared to feel the way; these organs located in front of their jaws evidently enable them to notice such projecting molecules as must be removed.

After one of these workers had smoothed down the wax in the angle of a cell, she emerged from the cell backwards and having approached a heap of propolis, she drew out a thread of it with her teeth; this being broken off by a quick motion of the head, it was taken in the claws of the forefeet and the bee re-entered the cell which she had just prepared. She did not hesitate but immediately placed it in the angle of the two parts that she had just smoothed, but she probably found it too long for the space required, for she cut away a piece of it; both of her front feet were used to fit it and stretch it between the two walls; and her teeth worked to imbed it in the angular furrow to be lined. After these diverse operations, the thread of propolis evidently appeared too large for her taste; she raked it over with the same instruments and at each time removed a parcel of it: when the work was completed, we admired the accuracy with which it was adjusted between the two walls of the cell. The worker did not stop there, turning to another part of the cell, she worked with her jaws upon the edges of the two other trapezes and we understood that she was preparing a spot to be covered with another thread of propolis. No doubt she was about to help herself out of the heap from which she had taken it previously; but contrary to our expectation she availed herself of the portion of the thread cut off from the first bit, arranged it in the appointed space and gave it all the solidity and finish of which it was susceptible. Other bees finished the work began by this one, all the cell walls were soon encircled with threads of propolis, while some were also put on the orifices; but we could not seize the moment when they were varnished, though it may be easily conceived how it was done.

While these observations made known to us the art used by the bees in coating the walls of their cells, we had no explanation of the yellow coloring of their interior. In some of the chemical experiments already mentioned, the coloring pigment of the cells had not been acted upon in the same way as the propolis which coated them; since it appeared to have no analogy with it, it was necessary to ascertain the differences by additional experiments.

Experiments showing the yellow color of wax is not propolis.

1st Experiment: Showing the yellow color does not dissolve in alcohol but propolis does.

We picked out a few cells of a comb, the walls of which were of jonquil color; their edges were coated with propolis; we removed carefully the latter from each wall and steeped these yellow cell walls in alcohol; it remained thus in a dark place for three weeks. The alcohol was not colored and the walls of the cells retained their yellow tint. Other cells of jonquil color, from which the propolis had not been removed, were treated in the same manner and gave more and more color to the alcohol. This propolis was soon entirely dissolved, but at the end of the experiment the yellow color of the walls had seemingly become more striking.

2nd Experiment: Showing the yellow color fades in sunlight and propolis does not.

I enclosed some of the yellow colored cell walls between two strips of glass and exposed them to the light of the sun: a few days were sufficient to bleach them entirely; I placed in the same manner some colored cells coated with propolis, and kept them in the sun for two summer months. The wax soon lost its yellow color, but this long test in no way altered the color of the propolis.

3rd Experiment: Showing that the yellow color is dissolved in nitrous acid and propolis is not.

I took some yellow cells, coated with propolis upon their orifices and around their edges; I steeped them in nitrous acid, and boiled this solvent for a few minutes: when the nitrous gas began to form, I removed the vial and allowed it to cool. I then saw that the yellow color had disappeared, that the wax was bleached, but the propolis had retained its color; a prolonged test of this kind gave no other result.

4th Experiment: Showing the yellow color will dissolve in ether as does propolis.

I steeped cells of yellow wax devoid of propolis in ether; the liquid first acquired a slight yellow tint, then it became darker and wax was entirely discolored. I allowed the ether to evaporate, expecting the coloring substance to remain at the bottom of the capsule, but after evaporation of the liquid I found only the small quantity of white wax which had been dissolved.

Cells of white wax, the orifices and walls of which were coated with propolis were steeped in the same solvent. The ether acquired a fine yellow tint which became more and more intense, and no propolis remained upon the different parts of the cells. I uncorked the vial, and after the ether was evaporated, I found at the bottom a reddish propolis varnish upon which one could notice some of the white wax which the ether had dissolved.

The yellow color has no analogy with propolis.

These experiments demonstrate that the substance which colors the wax has no analogy with propolis. My observations have indicated that this tint is not a property of wax; the new cells are formed of white wax; this tint becomes altered in a short time; sometimes two or three days are sufficient to turn white combs into yellow. I knew nothing of the cause of this change, and I thought, as other naturalists did, that this alteration might be effected by the heat of the hives or by the vapors of their atmosphere, or by the emanations of the honey or of the wax, and the presence of these substances in the hives. However, these ideas could not withstand a thorough examination; I had often seen new combs remaining unaltered for several months, although used by the bees in the ordinary way. By comparing the combs of several swarms newly hived, we found some of which one side was white while the other face was of a jonquil color: we could sometimes find, on the same side of a comb, a space in which the cells were of a lively yellow, while those adjacent had lost none of their whiteness. We could even ascertain the exact limit of this coloration; a single cell having several yellow faces, while others were white, sometimes even one cell was party-colored in white and yellow. This distribution of colors could not be explained through the causes which we suspected of having influence. Honey and pollen would have uniformly tinted all the faces of a cell, up to the height of the liquid or of the coloring substance; the vapors of the hive likewise could have only a general influence upon the color of the combs; but it was necessary to ascertain more directly that these things had nothing to do with the observed effect.

Experiment showing bees add yellow color to the wax.

It was first necessary to make sure whether cells that were kept from the contact of bees would preserve their whiteness; for this purpose, I used a hive with a division in the middle through which the bees could not pass. In this I enclosed a portion of comb of complete whiteness; it was exposed for a month to heat, moisture and all their atmospheric vapors, without alteration of color from any of those causes. Meanwhile the combs exposed to the contact of the bees yellowed more and more, but this coloring was partial and distributed irregularly, as in a striped manner; everything indicating that it was not due to exposure in the interior of the hives for more or less time, but to some direct action on the part of the bees.

Observations of bees polishing comb with liquid from their trunk.

We are not sure of the manner in which they give this tint to the combs. We have attributed it to two different maneuvers; first, the bees which appear to be resting upon the combs, or upon the glass or wood of the hive rub the tip of their mandibles against the object which they are supposed to varnish, moving their head back and forth; their jaws spread apart and come together successively, after each motion of the head; their front legs repeatedly rub with some speed the surface upon which they stand; the bee which is thus occupied walks right and left and continues this maneuver for a long time; the wall of the surface of the comb, to which they apply themselves, appears to change color, though we have not ascertained positively that it was in consequence of this work. We have noticed that there is always a little yellow substance in the cavity of the bees' teeth: but was this a substance which they were removing or which they were applying upon the wax? It appeared probable that it was being deposited, though while they rubbed both wood and glass in the same way, the glass did not secure any color, but the wood assumed a very pronounced tint.

The second process that we witnessed was performed with the trunk; this instrument acted like a slim and soft brush; it swept to the right and left the surface of the glass and appeared to leave upon it a few drops of a transparent liquid.

At each change of direction we could see a bright and silvery liquid, flowing from the middle of the trunk and of the two longest palpi which surround it; this liquid was distributed from the end of the trunk upon the parts of cells for which it was intended; it was also deposited upon the glass, but not so as to tarnish it; for the opacity which glass sometimes acquires is not due to this cause; this happens only when the bees spread upon it parcels of wax which have been deposited upon its surface.

We shall not affirm which of these operations is the source of the yellowness of wax, but we incline to refer it to the first, because we often thought the color of certain cells altered, after the bees had rubbed them with their teeth and forelegs.

Observation that bees reinforce comb with propolis mixed with wax.

The bees do not restrict themselves to painting and varnishing the cells; they also give greater solidity to the edifice itself, by means of mortar which they know how to compose for that purpose.

The ancients, who had much studied these insects, knew some of the properties of propolis; they informed us that the bees mixed it with wax in several circumstances; they gave the name of *metis* or *pissoceron* to this substance, thus indicating its amalgamation with beeswax.

A test which I made with the propolis that coats the inside of beehives, indicated to me how well they had studied the subject, and that, although we may often reject their assertions, it would be a mistake to do so without previous examinations.

Through my reported experiments, I had learned that ether dissolves propolis, and that it removes but a fraction of the wax submitted to its action: so I took some fragments of this mortar from the walls of an old hive and steeped them in ether. Decanting it several times, I concluded that all the propolis was dissolved, when it ceased to color; the residue remaining in the vial was only the white wax which had been mixed by the bees with the gum-resin.

Pliny believed that these insects used a mixture of wax and propolis in constructing the braces and bases of combs. Réaumur, on the contrary, thought it only pure wax. Perhaps the facts that I am about to relate may enable us to reconcile the opinions of these two great naturalists.

Bees tear down the foundations of the new comb and reinforce it with a mixture of propolis and wax.

Shortly after the bees had finished the new combs, a manifest disorder and apparent agitation prevailed in the hive. The bees appeared directed by a sort of fury against their own combs; the cells of the first row, the structure of which we so greatly admired, were scarcely recognizable; thick and massive walls, heavy and shapeless pillars were substituted for the slight partitions which the bees had previously built with such regularity at the beginning; the substance of them had changed along with the form, being apparently composed of wax and propolis. From the perseverance of the workers in these devastations, we suspected that they intended some useful alteration in their architecture.

Our attention was drawn to the least damaged cells; some were still untouched, but the bees soon rushed precipitately upon them, destroyed the vertical walls of the cells, broke up the wax and cast aside the fragments. But we noticed that the trapezes of the bases of the first row were untouched;

they did not tear down at the same time the corresponding cells on both faces of the comb; they labored alternately upon each of its faces, leaving to it a part of its natural supports, otherwise the combs would have fallen down, which was not their object; they wished, on the contrary, to provide a more solid base, and prevent their fall, by making these joints with a substance the tenacity of which infinitely surpasses that of beeswax.

The propolis which they used in this occasion had been deposited in a mass over a cleft of the hive, and had hardened in drying, which perhaps rendered it more suitable for the purpose intended than fresh propolis would have been.

Bees add secretions to propolis.

These insects had some difficulty in removing it from the wall, on account of its hardness; we thought that they were impregnating it with the same frothy matter from the tongue, which they used to make wax more ductile, and that this process served to soften and detach it. Mr. de Réaumur had observed something similar in a like occasion.

Observing bees mixing wax with propolis.

We distinctly observed these bees mixing fragments of old wax with the propolis, kneading the two substances together to amalgamate them. They used this in rebuilding the cells that had been destroyed; but they did not follow the ordinary rules of their architecture; economy was entirely set aside; they were occupied alone with the solidity of their edifice; night intervening prevented us from following their maneuvers, but the following day we were able to judge of the result which confirmed what we have just mentioned.

These observations teach us that there is an epoch in the labor of bees, when the upper braces of their combs are constructed simply of wax, as Réaumur believed, and that after all the requisite conditions have been attained; the base is converted to a mixture of wax and propolis, as published by Pliny, so many centuries before us. (The change made in the structure of the cells of the first row does not take place at a particular time.   It depends perhaps upon the several circumstances which are not always together. We sometimes see the bees satisfied by bordering the edges of the upper cells with propolis without altering their shape and without adding to their thickness.)

Bees reinforce combs after they are built.

This trait in the conduct of bees explains the apparent contradiction, in the writings of these two naturalists. The first row of cells, built to serve as a base for the subsequent cells, was temporarily established, to carry the edifice as long as the magazines were not quite full: but those light plates of wax would have been insufficient to sustain a weight of several pounds. The bees appear to anticipate the eventual inconvenience: so they soon destroy the too frail walls of the first row, leaving untouched the trapezes of their bases, and substitute, in the place of these light walls, strong pillars, heavy walls of a viscous and compact substance.

But this is not the utmost extent of their foresight. When they have enough wax, they make their combs of the breadth necessary to reach with their edges the vertical walls of the hive. They know how to solder them against the wood or glass by structures approaching more or less the shape of cells, as circumstances admit. But if the supply of wax falls before they have been able to give a sufficient diameter to the combs whose edges are still rounded, these combs, being only fastened at the top, leave large voids between their oblique edges and the hive walls; they might break down by the weight of the honey, did not the bees provide against it, by building great pieces of wax, mixed with propolis, between their edges and the hive walls; these pieces are of irregular form, strangely hollowed out and their cavities are not symmetrical. The following happening, in which the instinct of bees is still better displayed, is a development of their particular art in solidifying their magazines.

Instinct of bees in solidifying their magazines.

During the winter, a comb of my bell-shaped glass hive, not having been sufficiently fastened in the building, fell between the other combs, still retaining its position parallel with the rest: the bees were unable to fill the vacuity between its upper edge and the ceiling, because they do not build combs of old wax and no new wax could be then obtained. Note: Huber was mistaken in stating that bees do not build combs of old wax; they do not usually do it, but when circumstances of warmth are favorable, they can build quite a large amount of comb from old wax. In this instance it is probably that the conditions were unfavorable. The sentence which follows shows that bees do build combs from old wax.—Translator. In a more favorable season they would not have hesitated to graft a new comb upon the old one; but as their provision of honey could not then be spared to supply the elaboration of this substance, they provided the stability of the comb by another process.

They took wax from the bottom of other combs, and even from their faces by gnawing the orifices of the longest cells; they then gathered together in great numbers on the edges of the fallen comb between it and the adjoining combs; they constructed there a number of irregular braces, pillars, buttresses, joists, arranged with art and adapted to localities.

They did not confine themselves to repairing this accident in their masonry, they apparently thought of those that might happen and profited by the warning which the fall of one comb had given them, by strengthening the others so as to prevent a second similar event.

The remaining combs had not been displaced, they appeared solid upon their bases, so we were greatly surprised to see the bees strengthen their principal fastenings with old wax, rendering them much thicker than before, and fabricated a number of new braces to unite them more closely together and more strongly to the walls of their home. All this passed in the middle of January, at a time when bees commonly keep themselves in the upper part of their hive, where such work is no longer seasonable.

I may restrain myself from reflections and commentaries, but I acknowledge that I could not suppress a sentiment of admiration for an action in which the brightest foresight was displayed.

*Comb that fell (from a letter from Huber to Revue Interna-
tionale d'Apiculture, May 1830)*

CHAPTER VII: ON A NEW ENEMY OF THE BEES

Among the labors of insects, those that concern the defense of their habitations are perhaps not the least worthy of the attention of man who is so often called on to provide himself against the enterprises of his enemies. If we compare the measures of security taken by these little animals against aggression, with our own tactics, if we establish a parallel between their policy and ours, we can better appreciate the relative height of their horizon. No other branch of their industry could be used with better success to indicate this gradation than natural protection; an impulse which is common to all species. In such circumstances, nature unfolds the most unexpected resources; in this it leaves the greatest freedom to the beings which it rules; for the chances of war are the object of one of those general laws concurring to the maintenance of universal order; without those alternatives of success and reverse, how could the equilibrium be maintained between the species? One of them would annihilate all those that are inferior to it in strength; nevertheless the most timid have subsisted since the origin of things: their tactics, their industry, their fecundity, or other circumstances peculiar to each kind, enable them to escape the extinction which seems to menace them.

Among the bees, as with the greater number of the hymenopters, the ordinary means of resistance are those poisoned darts with which they wound their enemies; the fate of war would be in their favor, on account of the greatness of their numbers, were not several of their antagonists still better armed than themselves; if others had not the art of evading their vigilance by surrounding themselves with a tissue that shelters them from their stings, and if there were not others still that profit by the weakness of some ill-peopled hive to gain a surreptitious entrance to it.

Traditional enemies of the bees.

Wasps, hornets, moths, and mice have been known from all time by their ravages among hives; and as I have nothing to add to what everyone knows on this matter, I shall confine myself to pointing out a new enemy of the bees, whose ravages I have already described in a special memoir (Brit. Lib. Nº 213 and 214).

A new enemy.

Towards the close of summer after the bees have stored up a part of their crop, we sometimes hear a surprising noise near their habitations; a multitude of workers issue during the night and escape in the air; the tumult frequently continues during several hours, and when we examine the effect of so great an agitation, in the morning, we see numbers of dead bees before the hive: for the most part it contains no more honey and sometimes is entirely deserted.

In 1804, many of my farmer neighbors came to consult me on an occurrence of this kind; but I could not yet give them any explanations; notwithstanding my long practice concerning bees, I had never seen anything similar.

On visiting the scene, I found the phenomenon still subsisting and that it had been very accurately depicted; but the peasants attributed it to the introduction of bats into the hives, and I disagreed in crediting this supposition. Those flying mammals are satisfied with seizing nocturnal insects in their flight, which are never wanting in summer. Bats do not eat honey; why therefore should they attack bees in their hive for the purpose of pillaging their stores?

Death's head moths.

If it was not the bats which attacked the bees, it might be some other animal. Therefore, having put my people in ambush, they soon brought to me, not bats, but sphinx atropos, great moths, better known under the name of *Death's head moths*. These sphinxes flew in great numbers about the hives and one was caught as it was about to enter in one of the least populous; its intention evidently was to penetrate within their home and live at the expense of the bees. From all quarters I learned of similar ravages committed by bats, as supposed. Cultivators who expected a plentiful harvest, found their hives as light as in the first days of spring, though they had recently been noticed well provisioned; at length the gigantic moth, which had caused the desertion of the bees, was surprised in several hives.

Such repeated proofs were required to convince me that a lepidopter, an insect without a sting, without any shield, and deprived of all other means of defense, could contend victoriously against thousand of bees; but these moths were so common during that year that it was easy to be convinced of the fact.

Entrance reducer prevented them entrance.

As the enterprises of the sphinx were constantly more disastrous to the bees, we resolved to contract their entrances to prevent the enemy's access. We manufactured a sort of grating, out of tin, the openings of which were only large enough to admit the bees and we established it at the entrance of the hive; this process was completely successful, quite was restored and the damage ceased.

Bees, given time use the same solution.

The same precautions had not been universally taken; but we perceived that the bees, left to themselves, provided for their own security; without help. They barricaded themselves, by means of a thick wall made of wax and propolis, fitted behind the entrance of the hive, and sometimes in the entrance itself; it obstructed it entirely, but it was perforated by passages for one or two workers at a time.

Here the operations of man and bees completely met; the works which they had established at the entrance of their habitations were of varied forms; here, as I have just mentioned, was a single wall, whose openings were in arcades disposed in the higher part of masonry; there several bulwarks behind each other recalled the bastions of our citadels; passages, masked by walls in front, opened upon the faces of the second row and did not correspond with the openings of the first; sometimes a series of intersecting arcades gave free egress to the bees, without permitting the entrance of their enemies; for these fortifications were massive, their substance being firm and solid.

But only as a response to the attack.

The bees did not construct those casemated gates, without urgent necessity, so it is not a demonstration of general prudence prepared in advance to obviate inconveniences which the insect can neither know nor anticipate; it is when the danger is there, pressing and immediate, that the bee, compelled to seek an assured preservation, employs this last resource; it is curious to see so well armed an insect, supported by the advantage of numbers, conscious of its powerlessness, protecting itself by an admirable combination against the insufficiency of its arms and courage. So the art of war among bees is not restricted to attacking their enemies, they know also how to construct ramparts for shelter against their enterprises; from the role of simple soldiers, they pass to that of engineers; but it is not against the sphinx only that they must guard; weak hives are sometimes attacked by strange bees attracted by the odor of the honey and the hope of easy pillage.

The same solution for robbing bees.

The besieged bees being unable to defend themselves against such invasion, sometimes have recourse to a measure similar to that employed against the sphinx atropos; they also raise walls and leave but narrow openings through which a single bee can pass at a time; these are easily guarded.

Bees will enlarge it again during a nectar flow.

But the time comes when these narrow passages are no longer sufficient for themselves; when the harvest is very abundant, the hive excessively populous, and the time comes of forming new colonies, they demolish these gates which they had erected at the hour of danger, and which now restrain their impetuosity; these safeguards have become inconvenient, and they discard them until new alarms demand their reconstruction.

Sphinxes come only in certain years.

The entrances built in 1804 were destroyed in the spring of 1805; the sphinxes did not appear that year, neither where they seen in the year following, but in the autumn of 1807 they were seen in great numbers. Immediately the bees barricaded themselves and prevented the threatening disasters. In May 1808, before the departure of swarms, they demolished these fortifications, whose narrow passages did not give sufficiently free passage to their multitude.

It is to be noticed that, when the entrance of their hive is naturally narrow, or when care has been taken to contract it soon enough to prevent the devastation of their enemies, the bees dispense with walling it.

Bees' instinct adjusts according to circumstances

This timeliness in their conduct can be explained only by admitting the development of their instinct according to the exigencies of the circumstances.

But how can a sphinx alarm such warlike colonies? Can this moth, the dread of superstitious people, also exercise a secret influence upon the bees and have the power of paralyzing their courage? Does it perhaps emit some emanation pernicious to these insects?

Is the sound of the sphinx dreadful to the bees?

Other sphinxes subsist upon the nectar of flowers only; they have a long slender, flexible, spirally coiled trunk, and seek their food soon after sunset, but the atropos awakens later, it does not fly about the hive until night is farther advanced; it is armed with a very short, very large proboscis endowed with much strength; when it is seized some unknown organ emits an acute, stridulous sound. May not this sound, to which the vulgar attach sinister ideas, be also dreadful to the bees? May not its resemblance to the piping of the queens in captivity, which has the faculty of suspending the vigilance of the workers, explain the disorder observed in their hive on the approach of the sphinx? This is only a conjecture, founded on the analogy of sounds, to which I attach no importance. However, should the sphinx raise this piercing cry during its assaults, and should the bees then yield to it without resistance, this conjecture would acquire some weight.

Mr. de Réaumur attributed the sound produced by the death's head sphinx to the friction of the trunk against its sheaths, but we have ascertained that this takes place without the use of the trunk. Though many naturalists have sought its source, nothing satisfactory is yet known on the subject. It appears certain that the sphinx emits this sound at will, and particularly when affected by the apprehension of some danger.

The introduction of so large and so tangible a lepidopter as the sphinx atropos in a well populated hive, and the extraordinary consequences thence resulting, are phenomena the more difficult to explain, that the organization of this insect offers no indication of its being screened from the stings of the bees.

We should have desired to observe this singular contest in our glass hives, but no opportunity has hitherto presented. However, to solve some of my doubts, I made a few experiments on the manner in which the sphinx is received in the nest of bumblebees (muscorum).

Experiment introducing a sphinx moth into a hive.

The first that I brought to them did not appear to be affected by the odor of honey, of which their cells were full; it first remained quiet in a corner of the box; but as it approached the nest and its inhabitants, it soon became the object, not of dread, but of the wrath of the workers, they assailed it successively with fury, and gave it many stings; it sought to escape and ran with speed; at last, by a violent motion, it pushed away the glass which covered the apparatus and succeeded in escaping. It appeared to suffer but little of its wounds, remained quiet all night, and was still wonderfully well several days after.

I was unwilling to repeat this cruel experiment; captivity or some other circumstance evidently reduced this insect to too great a disadvantage to the bumble bees. Yet after this attempt, it became still more difficult for me to conceive how it could introduce itself into the hives of common bees, whose stings are so much more dangerous, as well as their numbers incomparably greater. Was the light of the torch an obstacle to the development of the sphinx's means of attack? Possibly the success of its enterprises results from the faculty of seeing during the night, as with other moths of the same genus.

Experiment offering honey to sphinxes.

Another fruitless experiment was that of offering honey to these insects: I left two sphinxes beside a comb for a whole week, without their touching it: we vainly unfolded their proboscis, dipped it in the honey; this experiment which succeed perfectly with day butterflies, had no success with the sphinx atropos.

I might have entertained doubts of their fondness for this food, had I not proof of their avidity for it when in the natural state. A recent observation came to support of the facts already related. When dissecting a large sphinx caught in the open air, we found its abdomen entirely filled with honey; the anterior cavity which occupies three-fourths of its abdomen was filled like a barrel; it might have filled a large tablespoon; this honey, of perfect purity, had the same consistency and the same taste as that of the bees. What appeared very singular was that this substance was not enclosed in a particular intestine, but occupied the space ordinarily reserved for air in the body of these insects. It is know that their abdomen is divided into a certain number of lodges, the walls of which being exceedingly thin, have vertical membranes; all of these membranes had disappeared; I could not affirm whether they had been ruptured by the quantity of honey with which the sphinx had gorged, or by our opening of its upper rings; one thing is certain, that in opening other sphinxes in the same manner, we always found these lodges well preserved though entirely empty.

These facts belong to the natural history of the sphinx, not to that of bees. Let us return to the means of preserving the latter from one of their most dangerous enemies.

Huber's entrance reducer design.

I have already proposed to use, for this purpose, three different entrances according to the season. A horizontal strip pierced in its length with three sizes of openings and placed as a slide between two stakes, may fulfill this purpose. These entrances must be proportioned to the requirements of the bees and fulfill the gradations which they establish themselves, when they seek to protect themselves from their enemies by similar means.

As they destroy their fortifications, in the spring, before the issue of the swarms, we should imitate them by leaving the hive entrance free: they have few enemies to fear at that time, their hive is well populated and can defend itself. After the issue of the swarms one should reduce the entrance, since the hive is weakened and strange bees and moths may enter. This proceeding is pointed out by the bees themselves when threatened with robbing. Each of the openings, left by them in the wax wall which is to protect them against outside dangers, can allow the passage of only one bee at a time. They are in proportion to the size of the insects that the bees dread.

In the middle of July, these entrances are enlarged by the bees to such an extent as to permit two or three workers to pass through them, and to allow the free egress of the males which are of larger size than the workers. At his epoch, therefore, we must change the slide before the entrance so as to permit the use of the larger openings, which must be cut in the upper part, with their convexity downwards.

Lastly the crop being in full swing, in the months of August and September, the bees must not be too much impeded; those whose example we follow opened a third passage in the lower part of the wax wall; it was shaped like a very low vault; we should imitate this construction In the third row of holes; by this means the sphinx will be unable to enter the hive and the bees will issue freely. If the slide be made of tin instead of wood, it will exclude mice, one of the most dangerous enemies of the bees.

When man takes possession of animals, he destroys in some measure the equilibrium which natural circumstances establish between rival species, and more or less diminishes their energy or vigilance; it is only by studying the peculiarities of their instinct that he may recognize certain features which subjection has lessened, which their new position has made less common, and in his turn he should partly compensate the advantages of which they have been deprived: he must do sill more, if he wished to augment their products, since he has to contend with nature which assigns limits to multiplication of individuals; but this art demands a very profound knowledge of the resources which providence has placed within their reach; for it is from them alone that we shall learn the art of governing them.

Chapter VIII: On the Respiration of Bees

(Translation of this chapter is one entrusted to Graham-Burtt—Translator)

Part I: Introduction.

Translators note: It may add to the interest of the following chapter to recall the fact that Huber lived during the period when the foundations of modern scientific knowledge were being laid. Lavoisier in France, Priestley in England, and Scheele in Sweden had, within his life time, made their discoveries as to the nature of the atmosphere, the laws governing combustion and their application to living beings. Thus though his work on this subject may seem elementary to us in reality he was amongst the most advanced scientists of his age and was applying the newly discovered laws to his own particular hobby.

Do bees require air?

The air, though in time it destroys all, has nevertheless a healthful influence on living organisms. Even plants absorb it in their own way, and, like animals, owe to it the vital force of their existence. To all that has life it is an indispensable element; is the bee an exception to this universal law?

It is well known that all animals from the quadruped to the mollusk decompose air, combining its respirable part with the carbon which is so abundant in nature, and breathing it out in the new form which it has received while in the lungs or gills: and that the heat necessary to life is generated by this process of combustion.

These laws are so widespread that they would not seem to admit of any exception. However one set of circumstances, as yet unconsidered, seem irreconcilable with them.

If a colony of insects could continue to live successfully and without any inconvenience to their well being, in an enclosed space, where air could only circulate with great difficulty, the scientist would be confronted with a new problem.

Now this is precisely the strange condition presented by the bees. Their hive, the dimensions of which do not exceed one or two cubic feet, contains a multitude of individuals all living, active and industrious.

Air does not naturally circulate with only one small opening.

The entrance, always very small, and often obstructed by the crowd of bees which come and go during the laborious days of summer, is the only opening by which air can be introduced, yet it suffices for their needs. Moreover the hive, coated on the inside with wax and propolis by the bees themselves, and on the outside plastered with lime by the care of their owner, does not furnish any of the conditions necessary for the establishment of a natural current of air. Public halls offer, in proportion, far less obstruction to ventilation than a hive of bees, for air cannot circulate in a place which possesses only a single opening, and this moreover not favorably situated for the purpose. The following experiment will show that even were the opening much larger, the air would not penetrate from the outside except by artificial means.

Experiment showing even a larger entrance does not provide enough air.

Take a box of bell-glass of the size of a hive and place it, with the opening at the bottom, on a board in which is cut a groove wider than a hive entrances. Introduce under this glass a lighted candle. In a few minute the flame will flicker, become bluish and die out. Air does not enter the vessel fast enough to sustain combustion, since there is no means of setting up a through current. The effect on any living things shut up in large numbers in such a glass would be analogous to that on the lighted candle.

Why then is not the same result shown in a hive inhabited by bees? Why do they not perish, when a candle flame cannot continue to burn? Are they so unlike all else in nature? Do they breathe differently from other animals, or do they not breathe at all?

I could not admit a deduction so opposed to general laws. I therefore wished to find out if these questions appeared of equal interest to persons more enlightened than myself.

I first put the problem to Mr. Charles Bonnet, who struck by its singularity, warmly encouraged me to investigate it. But his death having unfortunately deprived me of the satisfaction which I found in sending him my results. I approached an eminent scientist whose approval was alone sufficient to incite me to new efforts. Mr. de Saussure listened with interest to the details of my experiments and his conversation gave me greater confidence and eagerness to continue the work which I had undertaken.

Huber gets assistance from Mr. Senebier.

But, inexperienced as I was in the analysis of gases, I should have had difficulty in attaining my end if I had not been aided, as I have said elsewhere, by Mr. Senebier, who kindly took an active part in my experiments, and gave a part of his time to the actual scientific tests which my investigations needed. Mr. Senebier as the colleague of Spallanzani, who was researching on the breathing of insects, had the advantage which I had not of knowing the similarity which was shown between his records and mine. Note: "Memorandum on Respiration" by Spallanzani, 4 volumes, 8 vo., obtainable from J. J. Paschoud, publisher, Geneva and Paris.

Part II: Experiments on the Respiration of Bees.

Proceeding systematically in our researches, we began by observing the effect of different gases on adult bees. We repeated the same tests on larvae and nymphs and came to the conclusion that it was necessary to examine with greater care than heretofore the external organs of respiration.

The first tentative experiments were designed to discover whether the bees are differently formed in this respect from other animals. If they are not under the necessity of breathing, they should be able to withstand a vacuum. They should be able to live as well I hermetically sealed jars as in ordinary air: in short their relation to the atmosphere ought to make little or no difference to their existence.

1st Experiment: Showing air is indispensable to bees.

We introduce some bees into a receptacle connected with a vacuum pump. The first few strokes of the pump did not appear to make any appreciable difference to them. They walked and flew for some time, but when the mercury in the pressure gauge had dropped to within a quarter of an inch of the level they fell on their sides and remained motionless. They were however only rendered senseless, and on air being readmitted they were soon completely restored. The experiments which followed also showed without doubt that a certain amount of air is indispensable to these insects.

2nd Experiment: Showing bees consume oxygen.

I wished to ascertain the effect on bees of keeping them in an enclosed space, and to note at the same time whether any alterations took place in the air which they had been in contact. We took three sixteen ounce flasks which contained ordinary air and introduced 250 worker bees into the first, the same number into the second, and 150 drones into the third. The first and third were carefully sealed. The second, destined to serve, as a basis for comparison, was only closed in such a way as to prevent the escape of the bees inside.

The experiment began at midday. At first there appeared to be no difference between the bees in the sealed flasks and those in the unsealed one. Some seemed to show signs of impatience with their captivity, but without giving any sign of discomfort. At a quarter past twelve those in the sealed flask began to show signs of suffering. Their rings contracted and dilated with greater rapidity, they breathed more heavily, and seemed to undergo a great change for they licked up moisture from the sides of the flask.

At half past twelve the cluster, until then hanging around a straw smeared with honey, suddenly gave way, and the bees composing it fell to the bottom of the flask and were not able to rise again. At a quarter to one they were all asphyxiated. We then took them out of their prison into fresh air, and a few minutes afterwards they regained the use of their powers. The drones suffered the most tragic results from the confinement to which we had condemned them, as none of them came back to life. The bees shut up on the second flask with free access to the air had not suffered at all.

We next examined the state of the air in the sealed flasks and found it greatly altered. Other bees introduced into it were quickly suffocated. A lighted candle would not burn in it and a sample shaken with water showed a decrease in volume of 14%. It precipitated chalk from lime water, lettuce seeds would not germinate in it, and lastly, tests with nitrous oxide showed the total absence of oxygen.

Note: Endiometric tests:
Ordinary air 1 part, nitrous oxide, 1 part, residue 0.99.
Air consumed by workers 1 part, nitrous oxide 1 part, residue 1.93.
Air consumed by drones 1 part, nitrous oxide 1 part, residue 1.85.

3rd Experiment: Further proving the need for oxygen.

In order to learn whether the absence of the last named gas, oxygen, was the cause of the collapse of the bees, and whether I ought to attribute their return to life when restored to liberty to its presence, I made the following experiment. We took a ten ounce jar and poured into it nine ounces of water; the tenth part was reserved for the bees, and a layer of cork separated them from the liquid: the bees were therefore in ordinary air, and we had only to seal the opening.

In this experiment as in the preceding one the air was consumed by the bees who were quickly suffocated. We then opened the lower part of the jar under water and introduced one ounce of oxygen.

Note: The method employed for measuring the consumption of oxygen was the one used by Priestley of absorbing the remaining oxygen with vitreous oxide and measuring the loss in volume.

The result was very satisfactory. Hardly had the oxygen reached the part of the jar occupied by the bees when we noticed slight movements in their proboscis and antennae: next the rings of the abdomen resumed their normal functions, and a further dose of the life-giving fluid completely restored the insects to the full use of their powers.

4th Experiment: Showing that oxygen extended their lives.

When other bees were placed in an atmosphere of pure oxygen they lived eight times as long as in ordinary air, a very striking result. However in the end they also died of suffocation, all the oxygen having been converted into carbonic acid gas (CO_2).

Note: Endiometric tests:
Ordinary air 1 part, nitrous oxide 1 part, residue 0.99.
Oxygen 1 part, nitrous oxide 3 parts, residue 1.98.
Oxygen consumed by bees 1 part, nitrous oxide 1 part, residue 1.58.

5th Experiment: CO_2 did not sustain them.

In carbonic acid gas (CO_2) prepared from chalk, they immediately lost the use of their powers, but regained them at once in the air.

6th Experiment: Nitrogen alone did not sustain them.

In nitrogen prepared from a mixture of sulfur and moistened from filings, the bees perished at once and did not recover.

7th Experiment: Hydrogen alone did not sustain them.

The same result followed their introduction into hydrogen prepared from zinc.

8th & 9th Experiments: Hydrogen and oxygen 3:1, sustained them for a while, nitrogen and oxygen 3:1, did not sustain them.

We introduced bees into an artificial atmosphere composed of three parts of hydrogen and one of vital air, two gases together having a volume equal to six ounces of water. During the first fifteen minutes there was no change in the state of the bees, but after that their powers began to fail and at the end of an hour they were without movement or life. Lastly in a mixture of three parts nitrogen with one part of oxygen the bees perished immediately.

Perhaps it was superfluous to search for further proofs that bees breathe: but before leaving the subject we wished to assure ourselves of the effects which the same gases would have on them in a state of torpor.

10th Experiment: Torpid bees do not breathe.

We shut some bees in a glass receptacle surrounded by crushed ice. A thermometer placed in the same vessel fell from 140° R (the temperature of the surrounding air) to 6° R (about 45° F or 7.5° C), when the bees became numb. They were then lifted out of the receptacles to be shut in tubes filled with gases which had had such disastrous effects in the preceding experiments. They were left for three hours and when they were taken out they came to enjoy the full use of their faculties.

This experiment was very conclusive. It was not the contact of the poisonous gasses which caused the death of the bees in the previous experiments, for in this case they had suffered no harm, but the introduction of the gases into their breathing tubes. This was proved by the preservation of their life in the midst of these gases when subjection to cold had arrested their vital functions.

11th Experiment: Showing the consumption of oxygen and the formation of CO_2 by eggs larvae and nymphs.

We repeated with the eggs, larvae and nymphs of bees the same tests as those applied to the adults. The results were entirely analogous; showing the consumption of oxygen and the formation of carbonic acid gas. The larvae consumed more than the eggs and the nymphs more than the larvae, and the nymphs were the only ones which succumbed.

12th Experiment: Larvae breathe.

Two larvae placed in nitrogen and carbonic acid gas (CO_2) lived several seconds longer than adult bees had done.

13th Experiment: Nymphs breathe.

Nymphs subjected to the same tests did not survive more than a few seconds.

Note: Endiometric tests:
Ordinary air 1 part, nitrous oxide 1 part, residue 1.08.
Air shut up with eggs 1 part, residue 1.08.
Air shut up with larvae 1 part. residue .
Air shut up with nymphs 1 part. residue 1.31.
Air shut up with empty cells 1 part. residue 1.04.

Air shut up with royal jelly 1 part. residue 1.09.

14th Experiment: Breathing of bees in all their stages is subject to the same laws.

Eggs placed in air which had been altered by the breathing of bees did not develop, but larvae and nymphs numbed by cold were not affected when kept for some hours in these harmful gases.

These experiments proved that the breathing of bees in all their stages is subject to the same laws. It should be borne in mind that Swammerdam had discovered three pairs of breathing orifices in the thorax, and seven on the abdomen of nymphs.

It therefore seemed to me of some importance to ascertain whether the same organs were also to be found in the adult insects, and my experiments in this direction yielded results which I am about to give. I employed the well known method of immersion in water, but to avoid the complication which might arise through numbness, I used water slightly warmed.

15th Experiment: Head of the bee not involved in breathing.

I will give here only the principal results of my experiments. When only the head of a bee was immersed in water or mercury for a period of half an hour she did not seem to be affected.

16th Experiment: Thorax of the bee is involved in breathing.

If on the contrary the head only was left outside the liquid the insect unrolled her tongue and quickly became suffocated.

17th Experiment: Abdomen is not sufficient for breathing.

If the head and thorax were immersed leaving the abdomen in the air, the bee struggled several seconds, but very soon ceased to show signs of life.

18th Experiment: The breathing apparatus is found in the thorax.

As the head and abdomen seem insufficient to supply bees with the air they need the breathing apparatus should be found in the thorax. This was demonstrated by immersing the head and the abdomen at the same time, and leaving only the thorax out of water. The bee bore this uncomfortable attitude fairly patiently, and when released took to flight.

19th Experiment: Immersed bees suffocate quickly

When wholly immersed in water, a bee quickly suffo- cates, but it is then that the workings of the orifices or stigmata can best be seen. Four air bubbles appear, two between the neck and the base of the wings, the third on the neck at the base of the proboscis and the fourth at the opposite extremity of the thorax just above its junction with the abdomen. These bubbles do not immediately rise to the surface of the water for the bee seems to wish to retain them, as they are partially drawn in again several times. They only escape at last when they have grown large enough to overcome the resistance caused by the breathing organ, or alternatively by the adher- ence of the air to the walls of the orifice. The two last named bubbles show the existence of stigmata which had escaped the attention of Swammerdam.

10th Experiment: One of the several orifices is suffi- cient to maintain respiration

In other experiments we submerged each of the orifices in turn, leaving the others outside the water. We discovered that one only of the orifices is sufficient to maintain respiration, and we noticed that in each case the other orifices did not release bubbles, which in my opinion shows the existence of intercommunication.

21st Experiment: Bees produce CO_2

The same test repeated with lime water proved that the formation of carbonic acid gas (CO_2) in the preceding experi- ments was in a great measure due to the respiration of the bees, for the bubbles escaping from the bodies made the liquid milky by precipitating the chalk.

Part III: Experiments on the Ventilation of Hives

We had thought to explain the existence of bees in their hive by supposing them equipped in such a manner as to have no need of breathing. As however we are now convinced of the fallacy of this hypothesis, the difficulty remains, for it is impossible to believe that the air could keep itself pure enough to maintain life in so confined a space. Moreover the number of bees may rise even to 25,000—30,000 or more.

However as we could only determine by experiment whether the air had or had not been altered, we judged it necessary to analyze it, and for this purpose we made the following preparations.

1st Experiment: The air nearly as pure as that of the atmosphere

We prepared a large cylindrical receptacle to serve as a hive. In it we placed a swarm and gave it time to establish itself and build several combs so that conditions might be those of a normal colony. We then connected up a flask with a tap arranged in such a way as to permit the introduction of air from the cylinder. This air, displaced by the fall of water or mercury contained in the flask, mounted into it when the communicating taps were opened, and these were closed again with all the necessary precautions. The mercury or water used in this experiment was received in a funnel which conducted it into a basin situated at the bottom of the hive so that the bees did not suffer any inconvenience.

The air of the hive, taken at different times of the day, was analyzed by Mr. Senebier by means of nitrous oxide. The results were very different from those we had expected, for he found the air nearly as pure as that of the atmosphere. In the evening he found a slight alteration but this was not appreciable and could be explained in other ways.

Note: Endiometric tests:
Ordinary air 1 part, nitrous oxide 1 part, residue 1.05.
Air taken from the hive at 9 a.m. residue 1.10.
At 10 a.m. 1.12, at 2 p.m. 1.13, 6 p.m. 1.16.
At 11 a.m. 1.13 at 3 p.m. 1.13, 7 p.m. 1.15.
Midday 1.13, at 4 p.m. 1.13, at 8 p.m. 1.16.

1 p.m. 1.13, at 5 p.m. 1.13.

In another experiment a flask was connected with the hive for a period of six hours and when the air was analyzed it was found as pure as that of the atmosphere.

Note: Endiometric tests:
Ordinary air 1 part, nitrous oxide 1 part residue 1.02.
Air from the hive, 1.05
Air from the hive, 1.06.

Have the bees then either in themselves or in their hive any means of supplying oxygen?   One of our experiments showed that neither wax nor pollen produced it.

Empty cells of 82 grains in weight, also the same quantity filled with pollen were shut for 12 hours in a six ounce flask at the temperature of the hive and did not make the air any richer in oxygen. It even seemed slightly poorer.

Not yet satisfied that I had found any solution to my problem I decided to try an experiment which seemed more promising. I thought that if the bees had in their hive any source of oxygen capable of supplying their needs, it should be a matter of indifference whether the door of the hive were open or closed, which we could try by sealing them in their hive and testing the air inside. This test would overcome all objections which could be raised to the preceding experiments: for by separating bees from their fellows, their larvae and their hive we might have indirectly exercised an influence on them.

2nd Experiment: Bees have not in their hive any means of supplying oxygen

It was only necessary to shut the bees in a hive with transparent walls which would permit observation of what passed inside. For this experiment I made use of my swarm living in the cylinder.

Immense activity reigned in their busy world. Approaching within ten steps we could hear a loud hum. For carrying out the experiment we chose a rainy day so that all the bees might be in the hive. The experiment commenced at 3 p.m. We closed the entrance carefully and, not without misgivings, watched the effects. In a quarter of an hour the bees began to show signs of discomfort. Until then they had appeared to ignore their imprisonment, but now all work was suspended and the hive entirely changed its aspect. Soon we heard an extraordinary noise. All the bees, both those covering the surfaces of the combs and those which were clustered beneath, stopped work and beat the air vigorously with their wings became less continuous and less rapid. At thirty-seven minutes past three they had entirely lost their powers and could no longer cling on with their legs. This state was quickly followed by collapse.

The number of bees on the floor of the hive rapidly increased until there were thousands of both workers and drones. There did not remain a single one on the combs. Three minutes later the whole colony was apparently suffocated. The hive suddenly became cooler, and from 28° R (about 95° F or 35° C) the temperature dropped to that of the outside air.

We hoped to restore life and warmth to the suffocated bees by giving them pure air again. We opened the door of the hive and also the tap fixed to the flask. The effect of the current of air thus established was striking. In a few minutes the bees recommenced breathing. The rings of the abdomen resumed their normal play, the bees simultaneously started to beat their wings, a very remarkable circumstance, which we had noticed as we have said when the lack of air first began to make itself felt in the hive.

Soon the bees climbed up onto their combs, the temperature rose to normal, and by four p.m. order was re-established.

This experiment shows without doubt that bees have not in their hive any means of supplying oxygen, which therefore comes to them from the outside.

Part IV: Researches on the Method of Renewing the Air in the Hives.

Renewal of the air inside hives is absolutely necessary to the existence of bees and certainly takes place. Fresh air must come from outside as the bees perish so soon as the entrance is hermetically sealed. How does this come about?

We thought at first that the natural heat of the bees might have enough influence to establish a current between the inside and outside air by upsetting the equilibrium between them. However we soon gave up this idea as we called to mind the experiment in which we had placed a lighted candle under a bell-jar. The bell-jar had an opening larger than that of a beehive but the candle went out for lack of air though the temperature of the jar was raise d as high as 50° R (144° F or 63° C).

There remained only one hypothesis to explain the purity of the air contained in the hive, namely to admit that the bees possess the extraordinary faculty of being able to draw fresh air into the hive and at the same time to expel that used up by their breathing.

We had therefore to find out whether their activities offer any special circumstances which would explain this phenomenon. Not finding any satisfactory explanation, our attention was again drawn to the possible connection between the circulation of the air and the fanning of the wings being pronounced enough to produce a continual hum from the interior of the hive. We surmised that the motion of the wings being pronounced enough to produce a definite sound, might also be sufficient to replace the air used up in breathing.

But could so apparently slight a thing dispose of the waste air resulting from the respirations of the bees? At first sight it seems difficult to believe, but on considering how continuous and energetic is the fanning of the bees it seems to offer a simple and satisfactory explanation of the problem. Anyone who places his hand near a bee when in the action of fanning will notice that she sets up an appreciable current, her wings moving so rapidly that one can scarcely distinguish them. United at their edges by little hooks the two wings on each side make a very effective fan, the more so as they are slightly concave. The movement of the wings is through an angle of

90° which can be easily verified as they move so rapidly that they can be seen in all positions practically simultaneously.

The bees brace themselves firmly against the floor of the hive: the first pair of legs are stretched out in front, the second are spread to the right and left of the body, while the third, very close to one another, and immediately beneath the abdomen, enable the insect to raise and lower itself.

During the summer a certain number of bees may always be seen beating their wings in this manner in front of the hive door, and others can be observed within, most commonly stationed on the floor of the hive. All those thus occupied, whether inside or out face towards the interior of the hive.

It is evident that the bees place themselves in order so that they may fan with greater effect: they form themselves into rows, often converging towards the door. This however is not necessarily the case owing probably to the necessity of the fanners giving place to the foraging bees whose rapid coming and going might knock them over at every moment were they not ranged in rows.

Sometimes as many as 20 bees or more are fanning within the hive. At other times their number is more limited. Each bee fans for more or less time. We have watched individuals at work for as much as 25 minutes during which time they did not stop at all though several times they seemed to take breath ceasing the vibration of their wings for a fraction of a second. As soon as any cease to fan, others replace them, so that there is never any interruption in the hum of a well inhabited hive.

If in winter they are obliged to fan near the center of the cluster, doubtless the perform this important function between the irregular combs whose surfaces leave between them enough space to permit the movement of the wings for there must be a space of at least half an inch to allow free movement.

A further question is whether ventilation is necessary for bees in their wild state as for those in hives. Dwelling as they

do in hollow trees and in holes in rocks, their different circumstances might give rise to variations in their method of renewing the air of the hive. Consequently we sought to imitate
natural conditions by placing bees in a hive five feet high. It
was glazed the whole height so that it was easy to see on all
sides the cone shaped cluster which hung from the combs at
the top of the hive. The door was placed at the bottom as in
ordinary hives.

We saw that there were only a few bees fanning near the
entrance, the majority being always on the side of the hive and
that the one nearest the cluster. They were spaced only a
short distance from one another in the same path as that of the
foragers returning from the field.

This ventilation by the bees or the humming which is the
indication of it, manifests itself not only in the heat of summer,
but throughout the year. It even appears at times to be more
marked in the middle of the winter than when the temperature
is more moderate. An action which so continuously occupies a
certain number of bees must have a very marked effect on the
atmosphere. The equilibrium once being upset, a current
should be established and the air thus renewed.

**Experiment demonstrating the existence of a current
of air at the door of the hive.**

But so remarkable a result cannot come about without
some outward sign, and nothing is easier than to show this.
For this purpose we fixed a small indicator (lit: anemometer) in
front of the hive entrance. It must be very light—of paper,
feathers or cotton wool, and this should show us whether there
is any appreciable current of air passing in or out of the hive
door and if so what is its strength?

For this experiment we chose a calm day and a time
when the bees were all in their hive, taking the precaution to
fix a screen at some distance from the entrance in order not to
be confused by any chance current from outside.

The indicators were scarcely in place when they began to
move. Sometimes they seemed to precipitate themselves
towards the door, and stop for a moment, sometimes they were

repelled with the same rapidity and held themselves in the air as much as one or two inches out of the perpendicular. The amount of motion appeared to be proportionate to the number of bees fanning. Sometimes there was less movement but they were never entirely stopped.

This experiment therefore demonstrates the existence of a current of air at the door of the hive: It shows that the air corrupted by the bees is at once replaced by external air, thus explaining the purity which we had previously noted.

It may possibly be objected that it is the custom of some beekeepers to close the doors of their hives during winter, apparently without harm. Assuredly if, by this method, entry of air were completely prevented it would be obvious that the bees could do without it. But this practice is only followed by skeppists and skeps are very difficult to close entirely as the air can penetrate through their joints.

For the rest we can affirm nothing of winter as we only made a single Experiment, though it certainly seemed sufficient to set our minds at rest on this point. It was again to Burnens that we entrusted the care of the experiment. He had by this time left us and sent the following letter on the subject.

Sir,

I have just carried out, at the request of Mr. Senebier, the experiment which we made in the summer.

I chose for it a skep which was well populated and one in which the bees seemed to be full of life and activity. After having fixed the edge of skep to its floor, I placed through the top a fairly strong wire ending in a hook from which I suspended a loop made in the end of a hair. This carried a small square of the thinnest paper I could find, which was placed level with the door of the hive at a distance of about an inch from it.

As soon as the apparatus was in position, I noticed that my indicator began to move. To measure the movement I had placed at the junction of the hair and the paper a small horizontal rule graduated in lines (The twelfth part of an inch or about 2 mm) of the Paris foot. The paper moved backwards and forwards a number of times, and the greatest movements were an inch out of perpendicular.

I tried putting the paper at a great distance from the opening, but the oscillations no longer took place, and the apparatus remained motionless.

Following your suggestion I made an opening in the upper part of the skep and ran in some honey. Very soon afterwards the bees started humming. Then the hum became louder, and several bees emerged. I watched the apparatus carefully, and saw that the movement of the paper was more frequent than before the introduction of the honey, and that it had a greater intensity: for when I fixed the hair fifteen lines (1 ¼ inches or 32 mm) from the entrance, the paper was definitely moved to and fro several times. I endeavored to see whether the movement would take place at a greater distance, but the paper remained motionless.

All that remains is for me to report on the temperature. I had an alcohol thermometer which registered a shade temperature of 5 ¼ ° R (just over 43 ¾ ° F or 6.6 ° C). There was bright sunshine, and the experiment was made at 3 p.m.

If you wish for any further work be so good as to tell me of it and I will fulfill your behests with the greatest pleasure.

I have the honor to be Sir,

Your most humble and obedient servant,

F. BURNENS

Part V: Proofs Taken From the Results of a Mechanical Ventilator.

The preceding experiments left me no doubt as to the object of ventilation. One could no longer hold the theory that the air was produced by chemical changes in the hive. I had shown that the used air could not by its own change in weight set up the ventilation which is so essential to the bees. However not daring to trust entirely to my own judgment I wished again to consult Mr. Saussure before establishing a hypothesis which in many ways is of interest to scientists. This learned man was interested in the results of my experiments and being struck by the originality of the means employed by Nature to preserve bees from a certain death, suggested to me a test which would do away with all doubts on the matter.

He saw only one way of deciding whether the renewal of air in the hives could be attributed to natural ventilation, and this was to imitate the movements of bees by a mechanical action under conditions similar to those of an ordinary hive, all other possible sources of ventilation being cut off. He suggested that I should use a mechanical ventilator, the wings of which would vibrate at a speed fast enough to reproduce the movement of fanning bees. One of my friends (Mr. Schwepp, inventor of the process for making aerated waters.) a skillful mechanic and clever scientist, helped me make this instrument, and assisted also in the various experiments for which it was destined.

In place of a number of small ventilators we constructed a tin windmill having eighteen wings. We adapted this to fit a large cylindrical vessel of which the capacity was increased by an upper story (super) on which it was solidly fastened. An opening in the upper story of suitable size, which could be completely closed, served to introduce a candle into the bell jar. The ventilator was placed above the super and fixed in place. On one side of this box we had arranged another opening.

This part of the apparatus communicated with the upper vessel, but was arranged to prevent a direct draft, so that the ventilator should not itself blow out the candle. We suspended light substances in front of the opening of the box, and stared with the following experiment in which the mill was not put into action.

1st Experiment: Entrance open, no ventilation, one candle.

We introduced a candle into the bell jar, the hole corresponding to the door of the hive being left open. The flame did not long maintain its first brilliancy. It soon diminished, and at the end of 8 minutes. Went out, although the capacity of the vessel was about 3,228 cubic ins. (12 gallons or 53 liters). The upper part of the bell jar was warm, and the indicators gave no sign of any current of air.

2nd Experiment: Repeat of 1st experiment.

After having renewed the air which had been consumed, we repeated the experiment. The candle went out after the same length of time, showing that one opening only is not sufficient of circulation of air, unless it is put in motion by some outside agency.

3rd Experiment: Entrance open, simple ventilation, one candle.

Having again renewed the air of the vessel, we replaced the candle, and hung several indicators near the door. When these preparations were made we started the ventilator. At once two currents of air were established: the indicators showed this clearly swinging to and from the door, and the brilliancy of the light did not diminish at all during the course of the Experiment, which could be prolonged indefinitely. A thermometer placed at the lower part of the apparatus registered 40° R (122° F or 50° C) and the temperature in the upper part was evidently higher.

4th Experiment: Same as 3rd, but two candles.

I wished to see whether my ventilator would provide enough air for two lighted candles. They burnt for 15 minutes and then went out together. In another test where the mill had not been started they burned for 3 minutes only.

5th Experiment: Increase in openings decreased ventilation.

We tried increasing the number of openings in the side of the box, but were not successful. One of the two candles went out at the end of 8 minutes. The other kept alight as long as the ventilator was in motion. I had therefore *not* obtained a stronger current by multiplying the openings.

These experiments show that in a place with an opening only on one side, air can renew itself when there is some mechanical cause tending to displace it, and this seems to confirm our conjectures on the effect which the fanning of bees has on the hive.

Part VI: Immediate Causes of Ventilation.

We shall misconstrue Nature if we suppose that the real objects of any give actions are always those that appear on the surface. This line of thought, which is capable of great development, is one of those which best show the invisible power which governs the universe. The bees in beating the air with their wings little realize the object which they achieve. Perhaps some simple desire or need makes itself felt, and instinct prompts them to fan their wings which seem to have been given them for flying only. This is without doubt a natural reaction to the stimulus of some particular sensation, for one cannot credit them with the knowledge which would lead us to act were we in an analogous position. Nevertheless it is interesting to note the characteristics with which Nature endows them; lower orders though they may be, since they achieve the end which they set out to accomplish.

Excess heat is one cause.

The first idea which occurs to us is that the bees do not fan except to procure a sensation of freshness, and an experiment will easily convince us that this motive may be one of the actual causes of fanning. We opened the shutter of a glazed hive: the sun's rays beat on the combs covered with bees. Soon those which first felt the influence of the heat started to hum, while those still in the shade remained quiet. An observation which one can make any day confirms the results of this experiment: the cluster of bees one sees in front of the hive during the summer, feeling the heat of the sun, fan with the greatest energy, but if an intervening body shade a part of the cluster, the fanning ceases in the shaded part, while it continues in the which is in the sun.

The same fact may be noticed with insects similar to bees. The velvet coated bumble bees whose nest we kept on a window sill, ordinarily became very active when the sun heated the box which held them, and all beat their wings, making a loud humming.

Sometimes one hears the same noise in nests of wasps or hornets. Thus it seems a constant law that heat will cause bees or other insects to fan.

Heat is not the only cause.

But the remarkable point about bees is that they fan in the depth of the winter, and that this noise is often the sign by which one tells that they are alive during that season. Heat is therefore only a secondary cause which in summer augments this habit of the bees. It is necessary to seek other causes. We tried surrounding bees with various obnoxious gases and found that several of these stimulated them to fan. We separated a number of bees from their hive, leaving them some honey, and then placed some cotton wool soaked in methylated spirit near them while they took their food. The wool had to be placed quite close to their heads before they noticed it, but then the effect was striking. The bees at once moved away, returning again shortly to the honey. As soon as they had come back we recommenced the experiment. They moved away once more, but this time without rolling up their tongues, contenting themselves with beating their wings while feeding. Several times however the insects too close to the disagreeable odors moved away immediately and took to flight. Sometimes a bee turned her back to the honey, fanned until the odor was diminished, and then turned back to partake again of the repast we had provided.

These experiments succeeded best at the door of the hive, as the bees, held by the double attraction of honey and their home, were less disposed to escape by flight from the smell with which we were testing them. The humble bees, of which we have already spoken, act in the same manner when confronted by harmful odors, but a point which is very remarkable and emphasizes to a certain extent the importance of fanning, is that the drones and queens, though very sensitive to strong smells, do not know how to preserve themselves as do the workers.

Ventilation is therefore one of the labors of the hive undertaken only by the workers. The Almighty, in assigning to these insects a dwelling place into which air could only penetrate with difficulty, also gave them a means to overcome the disastrous effects which might result from the alteration of their atmosphere.

Of all the animal world the bees are perhaps the only creatures to which the care of so important a function is given, and incidentally this indicates the perfection of their organization. An indirect consequence of this ventilation is the high temperature which bees sustain without effort in their hives. It results from their breathing as is the case with all other living beings. This heat, which one writer has attributed to the fermentation of honey, is certainly derived from the gathering together of a number of bees in the same place. It is so absolutely essential to them and their brood that it should be independent of the temperature of the outside air.

The existence of bees is dependent on the continuity of their fanning.

The very existence of the bees is therefore in direct dependence on the continuity of their fanning. Though called to so many different labors, each of these insects must occupy itself constantly in the duty of maintaining the air at the necessary degree of purity. This function exercised by a number of individuals each in their turn, does not exempt any of them from the other work of the hive which has to be performed.

Thus the social organization of these insects permits them to fulfill in turn the different functions imposed on the entire population.

CHAPTER IX: ON THE SENSES OF BEES AND ESPECIALLY THAT OF SMELL

The infinite variety of habits exhibited by the different races of insects and animals, gives rise to the very natural idea that physical objects do not procure them sensations similar to those of man; their faculties not being the same, and their nature admitting not the light of reason, they must be directed by other agents. Perhaps the idea which we form of their senses, founded upon those which were given to ourselves is incorrect; senses of a more subtle kind or modified otherwise, may present objects under an aspect unknown to us, and cause impressions which are foreign to us; were they only better developed than ours, they would open a new field to our observations. Thus what man discovers with the help of enlarging glasses still belongs to eyesight, although the ancients had no idea of the objects which we can perceive since progress came in the art of optics.

Can we not admit that the intelligence which dispenses to each animal the organization suitable to its tastes and habits has the power to modify its senses beyond any knowledge that art gives us?

Cannot the same regulator who created for us those five grand avenues, whereby our mind gains its notions of the physical world, open up to beings less favored with judgment channels more secure, more direct, or more numerous, the branches of which extend in the entire domain assigned to them?

Has nature created other sensations for beings which differ from us?

Art enables us to determine regarding objects not so immediately within the sphere of the senses, where judgment is more particularly required; as physics and chemistry prove in a thousand examples; thermometers, solvents, and reagents by means of which we detect the most intimate nature of objects which elude our senses, as so many new organs. Thus there may be other means of viewing objects, those which we invent speak only to the mind; but when Nature establishes communications between the physical and the spiritual, it does so through sentiment or sensation, and it is not repugnant to admit the possibility of its having created other sensations for beings which differ from us in so many other respects.

Insects living in a republic, among which bees certainly occupy the highest rank, often exhibit traits inexplicable, even supposing these small beings to be endowed with the same senses as ourselves, which renders it so difficult to penetrate the secret impulse actuating them. However they possess sensations of a less subtle nature, and as it is advisable to gain as much knowledge of their powers as possible, it would be wrong to neglect the study of the outward displays that are within our reach, whereby we can judge at least of their appetites and their aversions.

Senses of the bees.

Sight, feeling, smell and taste are the senses most generally ascribed to bees; hitherto we have no proof that they enjoy the sense of hearing, although a custom very prevalent among the country people seems to support a contrary opinion; I allude to the practice of striking a sonorous instrument, at the time of the issue of a swarm, to prevent it from flying away; but in compensation, how great is the perfection of their organ of sight! How easily a bee recognizes her habitation amidst an apiary of numerous boxes all similar to its own? She returns to it in a straight line and with extreme speed, which indicates that she distinguishes it from the others from afar by marks escaping our notice. The bee departs and flies straight to the most flowery field; having ascertained her course, she is seen transversing it by a path as direct as the flight of a bullet escaping from the barrel of a musket: her harvest being made, she rises aloft to recognize her hive and returns with the rapidity of lightning. Note: Since Huber wrote the above, it has been ascertained that the so-called beeline is more or less wavy, probably owing to the currents of air and the breeze.—Translator.

Work in the hive is done in darkness.

Their sense of feeling is perhaps still more admirable, it is substituted for, and completely supplies the want of sight within the hive: the bee constructs her combs in darkness, pours her honey into the magazines, feeds the young, judges of their age and necessities, recognizes her queen, all by means of the antennae, the shape of which are much less adapted for *knowledge* than our hands; shall we not therefore grant to this sense modifications and perfections unknown in the touch of man?   Had we but two fingers to measure and compare so many diverse things, what subtlety would they not require to perform the same service?   Note: The three ocelli on the head of the bee are generally believed now to serve them in the darkness of the hive, at very short range—Translator.

Taste.

The sense of taste is perhaps the least perfect of all the senses of the bee; for this sense in general admits of selection in its object, but contrary to the received opinion the bee certainly displays little choice in the honey that it collects. Plants whose odor and savor appear to us most disagreeable do not repulse them. Poisonous flowers are not excluded from her choice, and it is said that the honey harvested in certain provinces of America is a rather violent poison; aside from this, bees do not despise the secretions of aphides under the form of honeydew, in spite of the impurity of its origin; we see them even quite tolerant concerning the quality of the water which they drink; that of ponds and of the foulest ditches is seemingly preferred to the most limpid stream and to dew itself.

Nothing therefore is more unequal than the quality of honey: that of one district does not have similar flavor to that of another; that of spring is unlike that of autumn; the honey of one hive does not always resemble that of the hive adjoining.

Thus it is true that the bee does not select her food; but if she is not particular as to the quality of the honey, she is not indifferent as to the quantity contained in flowers. They constantly resort where most is to be found; they issue from their hive much less in regard to the temperature than according to their expectation of a more plentiful or scanty harvest. When the basswood (tilia) or buckwheat are in bloom, they brave the rain they depart before sunrise, and return later than ordinary;

but this effervescence relaxes as soon as the flowers fade, and when the scythe has cut down those which adorned the meadows, the bees remain in the hive, however brilliant the sunshine. To what shall we ascribe the knowledge of the greater or less abundance of honey in the flowers of the country which bees appear to posses, without leaving their home? Does one sense, more subtle than the others, that smell, warn them of it?

There are odors repugnant to bees; others attract them; the smoke of tobacco and every other kind of smoke displeases them. Human industry turns to its benefit their aversion as well as their liking; but it is satisfied with reaching the desired aim and does not invade the domain of philosophical inquiry.

Led by other motives, we will endeavor to find how different odors affect the bees, to what degree they are attracted by some and repulsed by others; this is within our reach; perhaps someday the growth of progress will permit us to go beyond.

Of all odorous substances, honey is that which most powerfully attracts bees; other odors have the same faculty perhaps only as far as they suggest to them the presence of a liquid that which seems so valuable to them.

Experiments showing bees find honey by smell.

To ascertain whether it was the odor of honey and not the sight of flowers only which apprises bees of its presence, we must hide this substance where their eyes could not see it; for this purpose, we first placed honey near the apiary, in a window, where the shutters almost closed still allowed their passage if they chose; in less than a quarter of an hour, four bees, a butterfly and some house-flies insinuated themselves between the shutter and the window, and we found them feeding on it. Although this observation was sufficiently conclusive, I wished it better confirmed: we took boxes of different sizes, colors and forms, we adjusted to them small card valves corresponding with apertures in their covers; honey being put into them, they were placed two hundred paces from my apiary.

In half an hour bees were seen arriving, they carefully inspected the boxes, and soon discovering openings through which they could enter we saw them press against the valves and reach the honey.

One may thence judge of the extreme delicacy of smelling of these insects; not only was the honey quite concealed from view, but its emanations could not be much diffused, since it was covered and disguised in the experiment.

Flowers frequently exhibit an organization resembling our valves; the nectary of several classes is situated at the bottom of a tube, enclosed or concealed by the petals; nevertheless the bees find it; but its instinct, less refined than that of the bumblebee (Bremus), affords less resource; the latter, when unable to penetrate the flowers by their natural cavity, knows how to make an aperture at the base of the corolla, or even of the calyx, to insert its proboscis at the place where nature has located the reservoir of honey; by means of this stratagem and the length of its tongue, the bumblebee can obtain honey where the domestic bee would reach it with great difficulty. From the difference of the honey produced by these two insects, one might conjecture that they do not harvest it from the same flowers.

The honeybee, however, is as much attracted by the honey of the bumblebee as by her own. In a time of scarcity, we have seen them pillage, a nest of bumblebees which had been placed in an open box near an apiary; they had taken almost entire possession of it: a few bumblebees, remaining in spite of the disaster to the nest, still repaired to the fields and brought back the surplus of their needs to their ancient asylum; but the plundering bees, training them, accompanied them home and never quitted them until having obtained the fruits of their harvest; they licked them, held out their trunks, surrounded them and did not release them until they had obtained the saccharine fluid of which they were the depositaries: they did not try to kill the insect which thus afforded them their repast; the sting was never unsheathed, and the bumblebee itself was accustomed to these exactions, it yielded its honey and resumed its flight: this new-fashioned domestic economy lasted above three weeks; wasps, attracted by the same cause, did not become so familiar with the original proprietors of the nest; at night the bumblebees remained alone; they finally disappeared and the parasites did not return.

We have been assured that the same scene happens between robber bees and those of weak hives, which is less astonishing.

Bees have long memories.

Not only have the bees a very acute sense of smell, but to this advantage is added the recollection of sensations; here is an example. Honey had been placed in a window in autumn, bees came to it in multitudes; the honey was removed and the shutters closed during the winter; but when opened again, on return of spring, the bees came back, though no honey was there; doubtless they remembered that some had been there before; thus an interval of several months did not obliterate the impression received.

Let us now seek the site or the organ of this sense, whose existence has been so well proved.

Nostrils have not yet been recognized in insects, nor do we know in what part of the body these, or any organs corresponding to them are placed, in this class of beings. Probably odors reach the sensorium by a mechanism similar to the one given us; that is, the air is introduced into some opening at the termination of the olfactory nerves; hence we must ascertain whether the stigmata do not perform this function, whether the organ which we seek is situated in the head or some other part of the body.

1st Experiment: Sense of smell is not in the abdomen, the thorax, the head or the stigmata of the thorax.

A pencil dipped in turpentine, one of the substances most formidable to insects, was presented successfully to all parts of the body of a bee, but whether it was brought to the abdomen, the thorax, the head or the stigmata of the thorax, the bee which was busy eating did not seem to being the least affected.

2nd Experiment: Organ of smell, in these insects, resides in the mouth or in parts depending on it.

From the uselessness of the first test we concluded that it was necessary to bring the pencil successively to all parts of the head: so we took a very fine pencil, to avoid touching more than one spot each time. The bee, busy with her meal, held her trunk protruding forward; we brought the pencil near the eyes, the antennae, the trunk in vain; it was otherwise when we placed it near the cavity of the mouth, above the insertion of the proboscis.

At that instant the bee receded, left the honey, and beat its wings while walking with much agitation; she would have taken flight had not the pencil been withdrawn; she resumed her eating and we again presented the turpentine, still placing it near her mouth; the bee then turned away from the honey, clung to the table and fanned herself during some minutes. A similar test, with oil of marjoram produced the same effect, but in a more speedy and constant manner.

This experiment seems to indicate, therefore, that the organ of smell, in these insects, resides in the mouth or in parts depending on it.

Bees not occupied in feeding appeared more sensible of this odor, they perceived it at a greater distance, and speedily took flight, whereas, when their trunk was dipped in honey, several parts of the body might be touched without disturbing them from this occupation.

Were they absorbed by their love for honey and distracted by its smell, or were their organs less exposed? This could be ascertained in two ways, either by covering all parts of the body with varnish, leaving only the sensitive organ bar, or by cementing up the part wherein the seat of this sense was supposed to be located, leaving the other parts completely free.

The latter method appearing the more positive and practicable, we seized several bees and compelling them to unfold their trunks, filled their mouths with flour paste; when this coating was dry enough to prevent them from divesting themselves of it, they were freed; this process did not seem to incommodate them, they breathed and moved as easily as their companions.

Honey was offered to them, but they did not appear to be attracted by its pretense, nor did they appear affected by odors most offensive to them. Pencils were dipped in oil of turpentine, and of cloves, in ether, in fixed and volatile alkalis, and in nitrous acid, and their points insinuated very near the mouth; but these odors, which would have caused a sudden aversion to them in their ordinary condition, had no sensible effect upon any of them. On the contrary, several of them mounted upon the poisoned pencils, and traveled upon them as if unimpregnated with any of these substances.

These bees had therefore temporarily lost the sense of smell, and it appeared to us sufficiently demonstrated that it had its seat in the cavity of the mouth.

We also wished to investigate in what manner bees would be affected by different odors.

Mineral acids and volatile alkali, presented on a pencil at the opening of the mouth, made upon these insects the same impression as the spirit of turpentine, but with greater energy; other substances did not have so pronounced an effect. On presenting musk to bees feeding at the entrance of the hive, they ceased and dispersed a little, but without precipitation or beating of wings; we scattered pulverized musk on a drop of honey; they thrust their tongues into it, but as if by stealth standing as far from the honey as possible; this drop of honey, which would have disappeared in a few minutes, had it not been covered with musk, suffered no sensible diminution in a quarter of an hour, although the bees had many times plunged their trunks into it.

Mr. Senebier having called my attention upon certain odors which might affect the bees, because they vitiate the air, and not because of any direct action upon their nerves, I thought of making similar experiments with substances which do not perceptibly vitiate it, such as camphor, asafetida, etc.

3rd Experiment: Bees not repelled by asafetida.

We mixed pulverized asafetida (A plant rosin used in cooking with a pungent unpleasant smell when still raw—Transcriber) with honey, and put it at the entrance of a hive; but this substance whose odor is insupportable to us, did not appear to annoy the bees; they took greedily all the honey which was in contact with the extraneous molecules; they did not seek to withdraw, did not vibrate their wings, and of the mixture they left only the particles of asafetida.

4th Experiment: Although camphor displeases bees, their attraction to honey destroys this repugnance

I placed some camphor at the entrance of a hive, and I noticed that the bees, both in coming home and going to the field, turned aside in the air to avoid passing directly over this material. I attracted some with honey upon a card; while their trunks were all dipped into the honey, I brought the camphor towards their mouths and all took flight. They flew about some time in my cabinet, and at last settled beside the honey; while they were sucking it with their trunks, I threw fragments of camphor into it; they receded a little, still keeping the end of the trunk in the honey, and we observed that they first took that which was not covered with camphor. One of them vibrated her wings while feeding; others agitated them seldom and others not at all. Wishing to see what a greater quantity of camphor would cause, I covered the honey entirely with it, and the bees took flight instantly. I carried the card to my hives, to ascertain whether other bees would be less attracted by the odor of the honey than repulsed by the odor of the camphor; and I also placed pure honey within their reach on another card; the latter was soon discovered and the honey consumed in a few minutes. An hour elapsed before a single worker approached the camphorated card; at length one or two bees alighted upon it and thrust their trunks into the edge of the drop of honey. Their number gradually augmented, and two hours after it was covered by them, all the honey was carried off and only the camphor remained on the card.

These experiments prove that although camphor displeases bees, their attraction to honey destroys the effect of this repugnance, and that there are odors which repel them without vitiating the air.

A great number of experiments convinced me also that the influence of odors on the nervous system of bees is incomparably more active in a closed vessel than in open air.

I knew already that the odor of spirits of wine was disagreeable to them, and that they vibrated their wings to get rid of it; but I had not yet made this test in a closed vessel.

5th Experiment: Alcohol was repugnant and deadly.

I put spirits of wine in a small glass under a receiver, I left it uncovered so that this liquid could evaporate; but arranged it so that the bees could not fall into it, in case they fell upon the glass; I then gave honey to a bee and when she had enough I placed her under the receiver; she traveled about in every direction, trying to escape; for an hour she did nothing but vibrate her wings and seek an exit; I then perceived a continuous tremor of her legs, trunk and wings; she soon lost the ability of standing on her legs, lay supine, and we saw her move in a singular manner; advancing on the table in this position, using the four wings like oars or feet, and all the honey swallowed, before exposure to the vapor of the spirit of wine, was disgorged by her at different times. As water, by combining with the spirit of wine might destroy its effect and bring about the recovery of this bee, I immersed her twice in cold water; the bath benefited her without giving her any strength; vinegar appeared to revive her, but its effect was not sustained and she soon perished.

House flies and wood bugs also lost their life when exposed to similar effluvia; but a large spider sustained the test without appearing affected.

6th Experiment: Odor of bee venom agitates bees.

As the poison of the bee exhales a penetrating odor, I was curious to ascertain its effects upon the bees themselves; this experiment yielded a lively result.

We took with pincers the sting of a bee with its appendages saturated with poison; we presented this object to worker bees which were resting in a tranquil state before their entrance; emotion instantly spread in the little throng; none fled away, but two or three darted against the sting and another wrathfully attacked us. It was not the threatening apparatus of this experiment however which irritated them; for when the poison had coagulated on the point of the sting, and on its appendages, we could offer it to them with impunity; they did not seem to notice it. The following experiment proves still better that the odor of the poison alone is sufficient to anger them.

We placed a few bees in a glass tube closed only at one end; we rendered them half torpid so that they might not escape at the open end. They were gradually revived by the heat of the sun. They were afterwards irritated by touching them with the barbs of an ear of wheat; all protruded their sting, upon which appeared drops of poison.

Their first signs of life were therefore demonstrations of anger, and I doubt not that they would have pierced each other or would have rushed upon the observer, had they been at liberty; but they could neither move nor escape against my wishes from the tube.

I took them out one by one with pincers, and confined them within a receiver, that my experiment might not be disturbed. They had left in the tube a disagreeable odor; that of the poison darted against its inner walls. I presented its open extremity to groups of bees in front of their hive. They became agitated as soon as they smelled the odor of the poison, but this emotion was not that of fear; they testified of their anger in the same manner as on the former trial.

Thus, certain odors not only act physically, but have a moral influence upon them.

Here doubtless commences a series of sensations of a particular class, eluding our researchers, and of which we can form but a confused idea; animals possess a sort of superiority over us in this regard. What varieties of impressions are produced by smell on the hunting dog! A sense developed to so high a degree awakening in its imagination ideas of fear, anger or love, instructs the animal upon anything which may affect its security, its inclinations or its industry,

In accounting for the conduct of insects in some circumstances, we must appreciate the influence of different sensations, which without drawing them out of their natural sphere, combine with their habits and momentarily modify them.

Certain odors, or too high a temperature, impel the bees to flight; but if some other cause, such as the attraction of honey, acts in a contrary sense and induces them to remain, they know how to preserve their present enjoyment, and shelter themselves from disagreeable sensations, by agitating the air about them. Retained in their hive by all the attractions which nature has there combined for them, and unable to withdraw from the mephitic gas without abandoning their young and their amassed stores, bees have recourse to the ingenious means of ventilation, for the renewal of air.

But why do not all the bees which are affected in the same manner, vibrate their wings at the same time? To what can we ascribe the general tranquility of the swarm, when a few individuals are occupied in procuring a salubrious atmosphere? Are there sensations of a sufficiently subtle nature to warn them that their turn has come to vibrate their wings?

We cannot suppose only a portion of them affected by a cause which has no operation on the greatest number; but perhaps this depends upon a temporary more or less favorable disposition.

We have seen all the bees of a hive vibrating their wings at once, when the air of their hive, too tightly enclosed, was not renewed at their will; but so urgent a case does not occur in the state of nature, and we usually see but a small number of bees occupied with ventilation.

Insects of the same species, although excited by the same causes, are not usually affected in so uniform a manner, that we may not perceive differences in the result of experiments to which they are submitted.

Some are influenced more promptly than others, as circumstances or occupations render them more or less sensitive, and it is only when the case is carried to an extreme degree that we see its action in full force.

Thus it may be that as soon as a certain number of ventilating bees have succeeded in bringing the air to sufficient purity; the others, not experiencing the sensation of its impurity to an equal extent, abstain from vibrating their wings and yield to more pressing occupations. Should the number of ventilating bees momentarily diminish, the first workers that would experience the alteration of the air would begin to ventilate, and their number would increase until their united exertions restored to this element the degree of purity essential to the breathing of so many thousands of individuals.

Such is the mode which we conceive of the establishment of this perpetual chain of ventilating bees; for no communication is observed between them. This hypothesis presumes a very delicate organization in the bees; it is evident that the continuation of their life, depending on the care with which they renew the air, they must be provided with senses sufficiently subtle to detect the smallest alteration in the fluid which they breathe.

The air may lose many degrees of its purity, before we are aware of it, though proving very noxious to our health; but nature has not placed us in circumstances similar to those of bees, and we should never need to provide for the inconveniences of confined air, if we did not depart from the conditions adapted to our physical constitution.

CHAPTER X: RESEARCHES ON THE USE OF ANTENNAE

...in some Complicated Operations of the bees

We have examined the general relation of the senses of the bees, to objects of immediate utility; but it is very probable that the sphere of their activity is not restricted to distinguishing odors and the substances they have to collect; the act of gathering and using those materials is only one branch of the history of bees; their conduct as a great society whose prosperity depends upon more or less variable elements, should offer civil connections so to speak, between all the members of the swarm.

Their senses must undoubtedly have a large share in the operations resulting from this state of things. It is essential to determine by experiments what degree of influence should be ascribed to them in the developments where instinct appears adapted to the most complicated circumstances.

One of the facts which appear the most deserving of meditation and research, is the formation of a queen in a hive that has lost its own by accident. If we take time to consider what an operation it is, for insects, to promote one of their brood to a different destiny from what which was intended, we are astonished at the hardihood of the undertaking; whether the worker be aware or not of the result to be secured in changing the food and the form of the cell destined for a royal worm, her conduct certainly displays a refinement of instinct, of which we could not believe an insect capable.

In given circumstances, though very rarely, the colony runs the danger of speedy destruction, by losing its queen; nature instructs the bees to avert so dire a disaster, by lavishing upon some worker larvae the attentions which are usually reserved for royal larvae. These attentions produce the desired effect; but how are the bees induced to do this; how can the absence of a queen guide them to so complex, so remarkable a proceeding, as choosing larvae of the proper age to fulfill the purpose to be secured?

The bees at first do not seem to miss the queen.

Did the absence of the queen alone produce these effects, we should observe them constructing new cells immediately after her disappearance; but on the contrary, when we remove a queen from her native hive, the bees at first do not seem to miss her; the work of every kind advances, order and tranquility are uninterrupted; it is only a hour after the departure of the queen that disquiet commences to be manifested among the workers; the care of the young no longer seems to occupy them; they go back and forth with activity; yet these first symptoms of agitation are not felt throughout the hive at once. They originate on a single portion of a comb; the disturbed bees soon quit their little circle, and when meeting their companions, the antennae are reciprocally crossed and they strike them lightly. The bees receiving the blow of the antennae become agitated in their turn and carry trouble and confusion to other places; the disorder augments in rapid progression, gains the opposite side of the comb, and at length the entire colony; we see the workers then run over the combs, rush against each other, hurry to the entrance and impetuously depart from the hive; they scatter about, go in and out repeatedly; the buzzing is very great within the hive, increasing with the agitation of the bees; it lasts two or three hours, seldom four or five, but never longer.

What impression may cause and stop this effervescence; why do the bees recover gradually their natural state and resume interest in all that seemed to have become indifferent to them? Why does a spontaneous action recall them to their young which they had abandoned for some hours? And whence comes the inducement afterwards to visit the larvae of different ages and select among them some to be reared to the dignity of queens?

In 24 hours the bees will start replacing a lost queen.

If we examine this hive twenty-four hours after the departure of the common mother, we see that the bees have been working to repair their loss; we will readily distinguish those of their brood which they intend to rear as queens, yet their form has not been altered, but those cells, which are always of the smaller diameter, are already distinguished by the quantity of pap in them, which infinitely exceeds the portion in the cells of worker larvae. It follows that, from this profusion of food, the selected larvae intended to replace their queen, instead of being lodged at the bottom of the cells in which they were born, are now brought very near to the orifice.

Larvae destined to become queens are floated to the mouth of the cell with pap.

It is probably for that purpose that the bees accumulate the pap behind them; and place them on this high bed; this is evidenced by the fact that this large bed of pap is not necessary for their food, for we still find it in the cell after the worm has descended into the pyramidal prolongation by which the workers terminate its abode.

We may therefore know what larvae are destined, by the aspect of the cells occupied by them, even previous to their enlargement and their change into a pyramidal shape. From this observation it was easy to ascertain, at the end of twenty-four hours whether the bees had resolved to replace their queen. Among the great number of mysteries which surround this great trait of their instinct, there is one which I hoped to discover and which would appear to lead to the clearing of other points equally obscure.

How do bees ascertain the absence of their queen?

It had always seemed difficult to explain how the bees ascertain the absence of their queen, when she has been removed, for those that are placed in the far corners or even only on the other side of the comb upon which she was should not take note of her disappearance; yet it was evident from previous observations, that within an hour they were all informed of it; that this condition caused sadness among them, that they manifested a great agitation and appeared to seek for the object of their solicitude.

How, then, did they make sure of the loss of their queen? Was it by means of smell or by feeling; should we attribute to some unknown sense the discovery of the critical condition of the colony, or must we suppose that these insects can communicate to one another, through some signs, such important information? I did not wish to conjecture upon a question which experience and observation might decide.

When I was called upon to remove a queen, I perceived that this could not be done without causing agitation among the bees; in such an operation one is always compelled to open the hive and consequently throw upon the combs the light of day and outside air which differs much in temperature from that of their hive. There is no resistance from the bees when we put out the hand to seize the queen, but the bees surrounding her might be affected by this removal: in order to dispel all doubts and all exciting circumstances I employed a process which would leave no uncertainty.

Experiment on bees recognizing the absence of the queen.

I divided the hive into two equal parts by means of a grated partition; this was done with so much celerity and care that no disturbance was noticed at the time of this operation, and that not a single bee was wounded. The bars of this grating were too close for passage of the bees from one to the other side but admitted the free circulation of air in all parts of the hive. I did not know which half contained the queen, but the tumult and the buzzing in № 1 soon apprized me that she was in № 2, where tranquility prevailed. I then closed the entrances of both, so that the bees seeking their queen should not find her, but I made sure that outside air should continue to circulate in the hives.

At the end of two hours the bees calmed and order was restored.

On the 14th we visited hive № 1 and found 3 royal cells begun. On the 15th we opened the entrances of both hives; the bees went to the field and we noticed they did not mix upon their return and that those of each half kept to their respective hives. On the 24th we found to dead queens at the entrance of hive № 1, and in examining the combs we found the young queen that had killed them. On the 30th, she emerged from the hive and was fecundated and thenceforth the success of the swarm was assured.

The apertures which I had preserved in the partition allowed the bees of hive № 1 to communicate with their old queen by means of smell, hearing or any unknown sense; they were separated from her only by a space not exceeding a third or fourth of an inch (6 to 8mm), which they could not pass, yet they had become agitated had constructed royal cells and reared young queens, therefore they had conducted themselves just as if their queen had been truly taken away and lost to them forever. This observation proves that it is not by means of sight, hearing or smell, that the bees notice the presence of their queen; another sense is necessary; but since the grating used in this occasion had only removed the contact with her, is it not probably that they must touch her with their antennae in order to make sure of her presence among them, and that it is through the use of this organ that the feeling of their combs, of their companions, of their brood and of their queen is communicated to them?

However in order to obtain complete satisfaction on this point, it was necessary to know whether the bees would become agitated in case the meshes of the grating were of such condition as to allow them to pass their antennae into the part in which the queen was confined.

As we did not wish to excite the bees, instead of opening the hive to remove the queen, we waited until she placed herself on a comb in view; we then opened the glass partition and took her from among her escort without alarming them. She was immediately confined in the glass box destined to receive her; but in order that she might not suffer from a condition so different from what she had been accustomed to, some bees of the same hive were enclosed with her, from which she received the ordinary care.

We remarked from the first that the distress commonly following the departure or loss of the queen was not manifested in this occasion; everything remained in order; the bees did not forsake their brood a single instant; their labors were not interrupted; and when we opened the hive 48 hours later, we did not find any royal cells begun; the bees had made no arrangements to procure another queen. Thus all the bees knew that they had no need to replace her, that she was not lost, and when we returned her to them they did not treat her as a stranger, but seemed to recognize her at once and we saw her lay eggs in the midst of a surrounding circle of workers.

The means of communication with the queen that these bees employed were very remarkable; an infinite number of antennae thrust through the screen and turning in all directions plainly indicated that the workers were concerned about their mother; she acknowledged their eagerness in the most decided manner; she was nearly always fixed on the grating, crossing her antennae with those so evidently seeking her; the bees attempted to pull her through; their legs passed through the meshes seized those of the queen and firmly held them; we even saw their trunks introduced through the meshes so that she was fed by her subjects from within the hive.

How can we doubt after this, that the queen and the workers preserved a communication by the mutual touch of the antennae, and that, knowing she was so near, the latter felt that there was no necessity of providing another queen.

It seems impossible now to assert that her odor had indicated her presence to the bees; however in order to acquire additional evidence I repeated the same experiment by enclosing the queen so that her odor only could reach them.

I took the queen of one of my leaf hives and had her introduced into a box composed of a double screen the meshes of which were too distant for the operation of the antennae; the result was such as we had foreseen; after an hour of quiet the bees became agitated, abandoned their labors and their young, emerged from the hive and afterwards returned, and tranquility was restored after two or three hours. On the day following, we examined the combs and recognized the rudiments of eight or ten royal cells, which had been commenced the preceding evening; demonstrating that the bees had believed their queen lost, though she was among them. Her emanations therefore, had not been sufficient to undeceive them; they required actual contact with her to be assured of her presence.

But since every bee cannot be in all parts of the hive, we must admit likewise that they communicate their disquiet to each other and labor in common to repair their loss.

Experiments on the privation of antennae of queens, workers and drones.

If we could still be in doubt about the part that touch fills in the labors of the hive and the intercommunications of these insects, it would only be necessary to read the following experiments. Those which we had attempted upon the antennae of the queen will be recollected. The amputation of a single one of these organs brought no change in their behavior, but when both antennae were cut off at their base, these beings so privileged, those mothers so much the object of consideration in their homes lost all their influence, even the instinct of maternity disappeared; instead of laying their eggs in the cells they dropped them here and there, they forgot their mutual hate, queens deprived of their antennae passed by one another without recognizing each other, and the workers themselves seemed to participate in their indifference, as if nothing but agitation of the queen had warned them of the danger to the colony.

It was no less interesting to learn the moral effect of the amputation of the antennae upon drones and workers: for this purpose we mutilated two hundred workers and three hundred drones; the former being released at once re-entered the hive, but we noticed that they did not climb upon the combs and that they no longer shared in the common household duties; they pertinaciously remained in the lower part of the hive which received light from the entrance; light alone seemed to attract them; they soon emerged from the hive and returned no more.

The same effects were produced upon the males by the amputation of the antennae; they likewise returned to the hive, but could not find the internal passages; they rushed towards the open shutter where the light was admitted and sought an exit there. We saw some of them begging for food from the workers, but in vain, they could no longer direct their proboscis, carrying it awkwardly upon their head or their thorax, thus obtaining no relief; when we closed the shutter, they rushed out of the hive although it was 6 o'clock, when no males issued from other hives. Thus their departure was to be ascribed to the loss of that sense which guides them in darkness.

We have stated that the deprivation of a single antenna produced no perceptible effect upon the instinct of a queen; neither had it any influence upon the males or the workers. The amputation of a small part of this organ did not impair their faculty of recognizing objects, for we saw them remain in the hive and pursue their usual labors. Therefore the conduct of the bees deprived of their antennae cannot be ascribed to pain, it must be due to the impossibility for them to guide themselves in the obscurity and communicate with the other members of the colony.

Weight is added to these conjectures by the fact that bees use their antennae particularly in the night; to ascertain this it is only necessary to watch their actions by the light of the moon, when they watch at the entrance of their hive to prevent the entrance of moths then flying about; it is curious to observe how artfully the moth profits of the disadvantage of the bees which require much light for seeing objects, and the tactics used by the latter to recognize and drive away so dangerous an enemy; vigilant sentinels, the bees roam around their entrance, their antennae always stretched forward, directed alternately to the right and to the left. Woe to the moth if it does not manage to escape their contact: it tries to glide along between them carefully avoiding the touch of this flexible organ, as if aware that its safety depended upon this caution. We do not wish to assert that these insects posses the sense of hearing, yet we acknowledge that we have often been tempted to believe it.

On hearing.

Bees watching during night at the entrance of their hive often produce a short, light rustling sound; but if a strange insect, or any enemy happens to touch their antennae, the guard is aroused, the sound assumes a different character from that produced by the bees while buzzing or in flight, and the enemy is assailed by several workers coming from the inside.

Should we strike the alighting board of a hive, the bees at once put their wings in motion; but if we breathe through a cleft of the hive they inhabit, we hear some produce with their wings sharp and interrupted sounds, and we then observe other workers in agitation directing themselves towards the side where the air has entered.

These observations seem to correspond with the effect of the queen's song, in leading us to admit a sense in bees analogous to hearing. Yet it must be observed that sounds which are not relative to their instinct produce no noticeable effect upon them.

Thunder, the discharge of firearms, do not seem to affect them. Thus the sense of hearing, if it exists n these small beings, is differently modified from the same sense among beings of a higher order.

We shall then restrict ourselves to the observing that certain sounds produced by bees apparently serve as a signal to their companions, and are followed by fairly regular effects: these additional means of communication may be added to those afforded by the antennae.

This memoir appears to give sufficient proofs of the existence of a language among these insects; there is nothing repugnant to the idea of a language among beings whose instinct is as developed as that of bees, whose life is very active, whose conduct is compounded of a thousand circumstances, and which, living together in great numbers, cannot share their respective labors, or aid each other properly without the means of mutual communication.

This observation applies to all insects that live in association, as well as those large animals whose existence is subjected to similar conditions.

Confirmation of Shcirach's Discovery.

Perhaps it may seem extraordinary to recur to facts with which we already entertained our readers in the first volume, and apparently corroborated by our own observations. But those mentioned in the fourth letter are of such great importance in the history of bees and animal physiology, that the reader will not be unwilling to have us speak of them here with more thoroughness than at first; and, besides the interest of truth, we must take the defense of a faithful observer, to whom the science of bees is indebted for its greatest progress, and whose reputation has recently been so outrageously assailed by an Italian writer.

On the sex of workers.

For a long time it was affirmed, as a fact beyond doubt, that worker bees had no sex. The observations of Swammerdam reduced them to the condition of neuters. Réaumur and Maraldi concurred in this opinion; most of the writers had ranked them in a distinct order; but Schirach's discoveries began to sap the foundations of this opinion.

By repeated experiments he proved that bees at all times can procure a queen, when their own is removed, if they have comb of common cells containing larvae three days old. Hence he concluded that worker bees were of the female sex, and that nothing but certain physical conditions, such as a special food and more spacious lodging, was needed for them to become real queens.

Views so adverse to those generally entertained were received with enthusiasm on the one hand and distrust on the other; it was not denied that bees could procure a queen when they had brood of all ages, since Schirach had secured this result in numerous experiments, made with care, in the presence of worthy and intelligent persons; but the conversion of a worker worm into a royal larva was denied. They asserted that there must be some royal eggs in worker cells and that it was such eggs that the bees confined by Mr. Schirach had promoted to the royal rank; vainly did he repeat his experiments, vainly did he oppose the improbability of such a supposition, the objection remained in full force: although aided by the best microscopes he could perceive no difference between the larvae from which he could produce at will either a queen or a worker.

Mr. Schirach, anxiously desirous of the support of a great philosopher, wrote several letters to Mr. Bonnet, in which he

described his discovery with such details as should have secured his assistance; but he found in him a zealous supporter
of the views of Réaumur, and it was only after sending him
numerous evidences of the correctness of his assertions that he
finally succeeded in weakening his opinion; but he nevertheless
did not succeed in convincing him fully.

Being requested by Mr. Bonnet to repeat the experiments
of the Lusatian observer, I recognized the correctness of his
assertions; I added new developments and gave very strong
proofs of the disputed conversion, but I felt with him that the
establishment of such important facts rested upon the material
demonstration of the sex of workers; I was still in hopes of
some day solving this great question.

The discovery of fertile workers, by Mr. Riem, confirmed
by my own observations, led me to anticipate that the whole
class of workers belongs to the female sex. Nature does nothing by leaps: fertile workers lay none but male eggs, in this
resembling queens whose fecundation has been retarded;
advancing another step, they may remain absolutely sterile,
while none the less females originally. I could not admit the
worker bees to be monsters or imperfect beings; too many
marvels are the result of their instinct and of their organization
to consider them as the outcasts of the species, or as imperfect
bees when compared with queens; it seemed to me that an
enlightened philosophy might conciliate all these difficulties.

Nothing is more repugnant to reason than the hypothesis
of an actual transformation; all those that were formerly admitted by credulity have been reduced by the observations of
great anatomists of the 16th and 17th centuries, to simple
developments still more admirable. At first view the following
question seems to indicate the idea of transformation. Will the
worm that is to hatch from this egg become a prodigiously
prolific queen unfit for any of the work observed among the
bees, or will it become a sterile worker, capable of the greatest
industry? These two modes of existence exclude one another.
The worker has organs appropriate to her destination which the
queen who gave her birth does not possess; strong jaws, a
palet and pincers of peculiar shape, which we have described,

wax organs, a longer tongue, wings proportionately longer, etc. Although the queen posses the same organs, they are modified in such a way as to be unable to fulfill the functions of workers. As long as we see fit to suppose that in order to convert a worker larva into a queen larva we must admit an exchange of these organs, we shall consider such a conversion impossible, and we will be correct. If, as I presume, these two beings are identical originally and have similar individuality, we may readily believe that they are as likely to produce a queen as a worker bee. Some will say that the queen was in the egg and that a peculiar circumstance has made a worker of her; others may equally assert that the worker was the original insect from which the queen has been produced through some modifications, for we cannot avoid thinking that the faculties and organs peculiar to the common bee pre-exist their development. We are then bound to conclude that this being which as yet is neither worker nor queen; that the worm before three days elapse, contains alike the germs of the insect which shall prove industrious and of the insect susceptible of fecundity; the germs of the organs of the two beings, the instinct of the common bee and that of the queen not developed, but capable of being so, according to the direction give by the circumstances of its rearing. In the one case the productive faculties will be repressed or will remain undeveloped; in the other the same thing will happen with the industrial faculties.

Perhaps between these two extremes, will nature present some mixed beings, participating of the essence of queens and of the qualities of workers; and hence the fertile common bees observed by Needham. It is easier to conceive how certain faculties and their corresponding organs may be annihilated, than how they may be spontaneously created; it is on this that my explanation is founded.

However, I wish to anticipate an objection that might be raised against this theory: how can we explain the opposite instincts of the workers and the queen in the same hive, in relation to other queens; for the workers entertain a kind of love for their mother, and render her the most assiduous attention, whereas queens are animated towards each other by the most implacable hate?

But do we know in what degree any sensation may be developed in insects by circumstances? I shall cite but one example, published in the transactions of the Linnean Society of London (6th volume). It is known that there are three sorts of individuals among the humblebees as among the domestic bees. In one of these republics which we observed, some very remarkable facts happened; several of the workers which, until a certain epoch, had lived in the best intelligence with the mother of the colony, having become fertile, they exhibited symptoms of the most violent jealousy; some fell victims to the rage of others, and we saw the principal female perish by the stings of the workers which she had produced; therefore, if such rivalry may arise among workers after they become fertile; if their affection for their companions and for their mother may in an instant change into hatred, the objection that we might draw from the different instinct of queens and of workers, the strongest what may be urged against their primitive identity, is reduced to its proper value; such a trait shows us that the germ of passions is only waiting for its development until circumstances harmonize with them; after this who will deny the mobility of instinct?

My conjectures regarding the sex of workers at length received the most unexpected confirmation; a singular fact, which was a striking example of the possible modification in bees, led us into researches the results of which appear of the utmost importance.

History of Some Black Bees.

In 1809, we remarked something peculiar in the treatment of certain bees by their companions at the entrance of their hive. On the 20th of June, a cluster of workers attracted our attention; the bees composing it were so irritated that we durst not separate them; night approaching prevented us from ascertaining the cause of this assemblage; but on the subsequent days, we frequently observed bees occupied in defending the entrance of the same hive against some individuals whose external appearance was absolutely similar to that of ordinary workers, a few of them were seized: their difference consisted only in color, they were less downy on the thorax and abdomen, which gave them a blacker aspect; but as to the limbs, antennae, jaws, body and size, the whole external form presented perfect resemblance to common bees.

Each day we saw some of these black bees at the entrance of the hive; it was evident that the workers expelled them; they had combats in which the ordinary worker always had the better; she soon killed her adversary or reduced it to such a state of weakness that it could not resist: she them would carry it off between her teeth to a great distance from the hive. We caught a number of the black bees and introduced them into a vase; but they speedily darted upon each other and were reciprocally killed; others were confined in a glass sand-box with workers from the same hive; but no sooner had the latter observed them than they were attacked and destroyed.

Each day we noticed a greater number of these proscribed bees; once driven from their native hive they never returned; so that when the sting spared them they perished of hunger.

This singular scene continued during the whole remaining part of the good season; sometimes the black bees did not appear to be so cruelly treated by the workers; and they seemed modified a little from the former; their hate had lessened and they did not repeat their mutual encounters; but the rigor of the common bees soon resumed against them, and they were again expelled.

We were not able to ascertain whether all the brood of this hive was attacked by this malady, or by the peculiar condition which rendered them odious to their companions, and we saw their number augment successively for several weeks, we had cause to fear that the entire offspring of the queen was affected. But at the end of September, black bees were no longer noticed; the colony had apparently suffered from the exile of so many individuals; it was weaker than previously; yet we were encouraged as to the condition of the colony when we satisfied ourselves that the queen had not lost the faculty of laying eggs which produced workers perfect in every particular.

From the month of April of the following year, we watched this colony and did not see a single black bee appear; the increase of workers was so great as to make us hope that it would swarm; but it did not happen that year (1810); we were then fully convinced that this anomaly, whatever it be, had affected only a part of the eggs of this queen.

Several other questions presented themselves here; was the queen entirely cured of this disposition to produce monstrous individuals? Was this vice hereditary? What would be the consequences upon the queens produced from her?

Observation taught us that she was not cured without relapse; for in 1811; that is two years after the birth of the black bees observed, others appeared in great numbers, in the same circumstances, and under the same character; lastly in the past year of 1812, this hive cast a fine swarm: as the old queen always follows the first swarm, we were not long in noticing defective bees at the entrance of her habitation.

But it was more singular still to witness the same phenomenon in both hives at once; the old one had swarmed on the 3rd of June, and on the 2nd of July we noticed defective bees at the entrance, which evidently could not belong to the brood of the queen that had passed into the new hive and this fact convinced us that the trouble was hereditary in her race. Note: Such bees could easily be from that queen. This year (1813) we have again seen some black bees maltreated at the entrances of both of these hives, but in small number.

This subject is only sketched here, our aim being to arouse the attention of observers, in order to obtain a combination of facts necessary to complete the history of the defective bees.

The desire of discovering the cause of the extermination of the black bees, led me to examine whether there was anything internal or external that would indicate a development of sexual organs in them; for I conceived that if they were real females, they might disquiet the common bees in respect to their queen, and that perhaps it was to protect her against such rivals that they expelled them from the hive.

Miss Jurine

There was but one way to discover whether there was any ground for my suspicions, it was to dissect these bees with particular care. I had no one near me nor in my family with enough experience in the difficult art of dissection to fulfill my views; such researches required extensive knowledge and great dexterity: but I remembered with gratitude what I already owed to the friendship and complaisance of a young lady who was alike distinguished by the combination of rare qualities, of striking virtue, of superior talent, who directing her ability in a manner corresponding with the tastes of a beloved father (Louis Jurine) to whom several sciences are indebted, had devoted to natural history her leisure and all the gifts which she had received from nature; she was an expert in painting the picture of insects and of their most delicate parts, as to discover the secrets of their organs; being at the same time a rival of Lyonnet and of Mérian: such was the one whom we were to lose so soon, such was she whose loss natural history was to regret for so many reasons, and who, shortly before that fatal time displayed her talent through discoveries that had escaped Swammerdam and Réaumur. It was to Miss Jurine (Christine Jurine) that I entrusted the important research in which so many anatomists had failed, the finding of organs that were to furnish evidence of a still unknown truth.

The first point was to discover whether the defective bees exhibited in their structure any differences from the common workers; Miss Jurine proceeded upon this research with her peculiar sagacity.

The exterior appearance of those bees indicated nothing to her that we had not already noticed; excepting, as had occurred to ourselves, a less quantity of down upon the corselet, she found no difference between them and the common bees; similar shape of thorax, head and abdomen; the legs, the jaws, formed in the same shape, same length in all the parts; complete external identity.

Fig. 1.

Fig. 2.

Volume 2 Plate XI—Ovaries of Workers and Geometry of a cell.

But when this expert naturalist extended her researches farther and removed the outer teguments of the black bees, after spreading apart the muscles and properly preparing the internal parts of the body of these bees, she discovered two very distinct ovaries, in which no eggs were perceptible indeed, but analogous in substance and form to the ovaries of queens, though more difficult to distinguish; we show the figure of them, on plate XI Fig 1 (aa) made by the same hand that dissected those bees; it also shows the sting (c), the poison sack (d), and part of the spinal marrow (b).At first we concluded that a solution of the question had been obtained; we did not anticipate that this would lead us to a more important discovery which was to overturn our conjectures as to the cause of the persecution of the black bees; but which would unveil a mystery long sought by the naturalists.

All workers are female

As Miss Jurine was desirous of carrying further the comparison between the defective workers and common bees, she dissected some of the latter with the same care and in the same manner, and she ascertained that all the workers had ovaries which had escaped the scalpel and microscope of Swammerdam: this discovery was principally due to the precaution which the Dutch naturalist had probably not taken, but which was very important, of keeping the open abdomen of the bee for two days in brandy; the advantage of this process is to give greater opacity to these transparent membranes which would otherwise be blended with the fluids. Miss Jurine dissected a great number of bees taken at random at the entrance of a hive and found in all of them ovaries formed like those of the black bees: she exhibited them to her father who assured us that they could even be distinguished with the naked eye.

Thus the existence of those black bees led us to a discovery the importance of which will be appreciated by all those who have followed the progress and the vicissitudes of the history of bees, and by all those who have read the objections which Schirach's antagonists opposed to his theory; which objections were based upon the supposed absence of ovaries in the workers.

Volume 2 Plate XI Fig 1—Ovaries of Workers.

Thus the theory of neuters among bees vanishes and the organization of those insects that have so excited our admiration exhibits one of the most remarkable physiological phenomena. Note: Mr. Curier says that the oviduct of queens has a vesicle and a long canal; and numerous chaplets on each side; "I observed," said he, "very small ones in the neuter bees, which would confirm the idea that they are undeveloped females."—Lessons on Comparative Anatomy, Vol. V. page 198.

The system which we have thus established on a solid foundation must extend to all insects, among which neuters have been observed; that is bumblebees, wasps and ants, for according to the observation of a great naturalist, the more important an organ in the animal economy, the more general must be its existence.

We will now examine whether this rule permits exceptions in the present case, or whether we again find here the uniformity observed in other works of creation.

We could not decide on the sex of the whole species from the fertility of a few, until we discovered the ovaries of worker bees; but since these two peculiarities are co-existent in the bees, wherever one shall manifest itself under the same circumstances, the existence of the other may be presumed from analogy.

According to Riem's observations, there are sometimes fertile workers in the hives but those individuals never lay except the eggs of males.

I believe I have given evidence of this fact in the former part of this work, and have shown also the cause to which we should ascribe their existence: a nutriment resembling that which is given to queens produces this remarkable change in their constitution. It would be of the greatest interest to observe in details the actions of those half-fertile bees, of those females whose external characters are the same as those of the workers; but the smallness of their number renders this almost impossible; perhaps if we should rear some in a box similar to that which Schirach used for producing queens, and if we removed the royal cells in time, we might observe their habits amidst a very few workers; we have not yet attempted this but it is one of the things which we propose to execute as soon as the season becomes favorable; at the same time we may examine whether the fecundation of workers is attended by the same circumstances as that of queens; all these researches are important in the history of bees and that of the generation and the development of the faculties and of the organs of the insects. It is necessary to show that this phenomenon recurs in the entire class of insects that live in association. In the memoir already mentioned, we explained the existence of fertile workers in the bumblebees; we described the jealousy awakened in these individuals by the sentiment of maternity, their rivalry, their anger and all the details of their laying. In comparing these small mothers with the true females, we found no difference except in their size; but having been unable to discover whether the fertile workers had a progeny of both sexes we later engaged in researches which gain in importance by their connection with the actions of the fertile workers among domestic bees.

We established a nest of red and black bumblebees (hemoroidalis Lin.) in an ordinary box, in a window; we soon perceived that the mother of the colony was not the only fertile bee; the motion and agitation of these bees every afternoon, their rivalry, their laying, demonstrated it; it would have seemed easy to ascertain the result of their fecundity, but it was necessary to avoid a certain possibility, which would lead us into error.

The mother bee often laid eggs in the same cells as the workers: so it was not possible to ascertain which individuals were produced by the one or the others, without completely separating them: we used the following process, which succeeded fully.

Bumble bees have laying workers

A fragment containing no brood was detached from the nest and placed in an open box at the spot where the bumble bees were accustomed to return into their nest: and the mother, with a number of the bees were transported with the other portion to a distant window. I calculated upon the bees now foraging in the country to people the portion wanting inhabitants. In fact they did so and lodged themselves upon the isolated fragment which had been substituted for combs and brood, although they appeared to notice the change. I was in hopes that some of these workers might prove fertile, nor was my expectation disappointed, for in the afternoon of the same day in which we made this artificial swarm, the workers prepared a cell for receiving their eggs and I saw several of them lay. The number of eggs multiplied daily; larvae were soon hatched, transformed into nymphs, which at the end of a month became bumblebees. I observed these individuals with the greatest care and all were males.

These males were in every respect similar to those originating from the laying of a female; they were equally large and colored in the same manner. I had selected the red and black bumble bees for this experiment because their males are more readily distinguished than those of other species, having bands of green hairs upon the thorax and a spot of similar color on the front; so I could not be mistaken regarding this fact, and I can affirm that neither workers nor female was produced in this nest while the other had as many females as males. Here, therefore, is seen a great analogy with the domestic bees; I must add to this that most of the workers of that nest were fertile, except a few very small ones, at least I did not catch them in the act, but most of the others laid eggs in my sight.

Here is another striking example of the generality of the law which proves that nature does not produce true neuters. Mr. Perrot, who has already furnished to us some interesting facts, permits us to use an observation which supports ours.

Studying a hanging wasp's nest with that scrupulous attention which denotes the genuine naturalist, he saw one of the workers laying eggs several times; he was impatiently awaiting the transformation of those eggs when an accident to the wasp next prevented him from following their full development, however he became convinced that they were all of the male sex; we will not take the liberty of publishing the interesting facts which enabled him to discover the sex of the workers and of their masculine progeny; but they confirm the relations which exist between bees, bumblebees and wasps.

Worker ants mate

Ants likewise afford a striking analogy; we have never seen the workers lay, but we have witnessed their mating. This fact could be attested by several members of the Geneva Society of Natural History, to whom we exhibited it; the death of the worker always follows the approaches of the male; therefore their conformation does not permit of their becoming mothers, but the instinct of the male proves them to be females.

All these facts concur in demonstrating that there are no neuters in this class of insects, which would interrupt the continuity of nature, for I do not know that they exist in any other kind: in other beings we sometimes see both sexes conjoined in one individual, but neuters seem monstrous and adverse to nature.

Who will be able to explain the singular peculiarity that the workers of insects in a republic lay none but the eggs of males, when they are fertile? Who can account for such a fact? They have ovaries similar to those of the queens or the mothers that gave them birth, yet they posses only semi-fertility; it is no easier to conceive why the queens that have been impregnated later than three weeks after their birth produce only male eggs. Doubtless there is a connection between these two facts. Note: Huber almost pointed to parthenogenesis in the above words. The student knows that parthenogenesis was discovered by Dzierzon a few years after Huber's death—Translator.

If we accept the opinion of a great physiologist, the seminal liquid is but a special stimulant acting upon the germs as a very substantial food suitable for their development; Mr. Bonnet, in trying to explain Shcirach's theory, used the following hypothesis, he writes:

> "I have established on apparently solid evidence, that the seminal liquid is a nourishing fluid and a stimulant, I have shown how it is able to produce the greatest changes in the interior part of the embryos; therefore it does not appear impossible that a certain and more abundant food should cause the development in the larvae of bees, of organs that could never have developed without

it; it is unimportant that this particular food should reach the organs through the intestines or by another route, it is sufficient that it has the property of extending them: it is for those organs an appropriate fecundation just as efficacious as that which gives birth to the animal itself."

Is it impossible that this kind of food, so substantial and so different from what is received by the common larvae, being administered too late or too sparingly to the larvae originating near the royal cells, may have consequences similar to the retarded fecundation of queens? Have not the fibers of the ovaries attained too great rigidity, to permit the development of some of the eggs, when the semen of the male, or the royal pap does not produce enough energy to act in the opposite way and destroy the equilibrium? While giving these conjectures, I do not pretend to explain everything I feel that they may be overthrown as well as defended, but I have thought it best to suggest them, as they may open a new path to the meditations and experiments of physiologists.

Address reproaches on Mr. Schirach by Mr. Monticelli

The sex of worker bees having been demonstrated as clearly as it is possible to do, we will investigate the reproaches addressed to Mr. Schirach by Mr. Monticelli, a professor of Naples, author of a work entitled: "Of the Treatment of Bees at Favignana." This writer accuses the Dutch philosopher with claiming the discovery of the formation of artificial swarms and with having borrowed the idea of it from the customs of a small nation inhabiting a cliff in the Mediterranean, near the coast of Sicily. Schirach was far from giving himself out as the author of a method practiced long anterior to his own time in the country in which he lived. At all times practice had preceded theory; it is success which leads to the discovery of the truths upon which it is founded, and the knowledge of those truths in its turn insures the wavering advance of the cultivators: assuredly no one will claim the discovery of the theory which the Lusatian observer had so much trouble in propagating, which appeared contrary to all accepted notions, and concerning which Mr. Bonnet, so wise in his opinions, had warned members of the Lusatian association not to support the conversion of worker larvae in queens for fear of discrediting themselves completely in the eyes of true naturalists.

Schirach's method of artificial swarming

It was only the passionate love of truth which led Mr. Schirach and his supporters to espouse a cause so inauspicious; he describes his discovery in the following words:

"I was compelled to use a large amount of smoke, for driving bees to the top of their hive, in order to cut out some brood, on the 12th of May. They were annoyed by it beyond my wishes; a number escaped from the hive with the queen without my perceiving it; but my younger daughter who assisted me in this operation warned me of it and her suspicion proved correct.

"To hear the plaintive sounds of the bees that had remained in the hive, one might have concluded that the subjects of this republic were unanimously mourning the loss of a cherished queen; I sought the neighborhood, the garden, the vegetable enclosure, even the meadows of the vicinity, without having the good luck to discover the fugitives; thinking that this swarm was lost without hope, I resolved to rear a new one by introducing into the hive a comb containing all three kinds of cells, similar to the one of which I had just deprived them.

"On the morning of the 13th, I prepared to clean the hives which I had pruned on the preceding day, and which never failed to carry out the rubbish during the night. I observed a cluster of bees the size of an apple on the support of the hive whose queen had fled. Being astonished at the sight, I undertook to separate them to look for the lost queen; I did find her, placed her at the entrance of the hive and she was immediately surrounded with bees: their extraordinary concourse, their activity, the pleasant humming which succeeded their lugubrious sounds indicated that she was indeed their queen; to make myself still better sure of it, I introduced her into the hive, which was raised for that purpose. What was my astonishment when wishing to introduce her among the combs, I saw that the bees remaining had already outlined and almost finished three royal cells. Struck with the activity and sagacity of these insects to save themselves from impending destruction, I was filled with admiration and adored the infinite goodness of God in the care that he deigns to take to perpetuate his works. Wishing also to see whether the bees would continue their operations, I removed two of the cells and left them but the third. The next morning I beheld with utmost surprise that they had removed all the food from the third worm so as to prevent it from forming into a queen; a strange fact; is there anything more surprising, more remote from the simple mechanism? etc."

The discovery of this kind of transformation soon rendered the practice of artificial swarms easier and less expensive. Formerly they thought it necessary to give the bees large combs containing three kinds of brood; Mr. Schirach showed that its success depended upon a single cell occupied by a worm three days old, and proposed several improvements in the process of swarm formation; but he never thought of claiming the invention of this method. In order to convince ourselves of this, it is only necessary to read a passage of a letter from his brother-in-law, Mr. Willelmi, who was not likely to yield to him on any point. He writes to Bonnet:

"Since a long time in these districts they make artificial swarms, in May, as soon as they discover brood in the hive; this method has been much improved by the researches of Mr. Schirach, as shown by the records of our society for the years 1766 and 1767"

The letters from which I have taken these quotations are found in the book of Mr. Schirach entitled "Natural History of the Queen Bee," translated by Blassiére. Is it likely that he should have left, in a book translated under his name, authentic evidences of the ancientness of the process of artificial swarms, if he had desired to appropriate that discovery?

The Italian author wishing to gain credit to his country for the discovery of the artificial swarm method, and forgetting that the great community of science is less interested in disputes about inventions than in their utility and the perfecting of them, openly charges Mr. Schirach with borrowing the plan of artificial swarms from Favignana, a distant island where travelers land rarely. A connection between the name given by Columella to the brood of bees (pullus) and that used by the inhabitants of this island (pullo) induces him to believe that the Romans and perhaps the Greeks knew the Favignana method;

another connection between the distance to which both Schirach and the inhabitants of this island carry the old hives in the
operation of artificial swarming, appears to him as sufficient
demonstration of the plagiarism of the secretary of the Lusatian
Society: but we must read what he says concerning this matter:

> "Urged by the desire of being useful to my fellow-men
> and especially to the Italians, I have concluded to describe in these
> memoirs the method by which the natives of Favignana manage
> the industry of bees; a method very different in several ways from
> that which is practiced in the Kingdom of Naples, and in the rest
> of Italy, and which, for this reason, deserved to be made known,
> especially as it unites the utility of transmigration of bees with the
> art of producing artificial swarms, known in Europe as the pro-
> duction and invention of Mr. Schirach, although the Favignanese
> practice it ordinarily in so ancient a manner that they have pre-
> served the Latin names in their process; we will thereby have an
> additional occasion to vindicate the honor of Italy, disparaged up-
> on that point as upon many others, by clever strangers who, while
> traveling in our country, visiting our libraries, reading our authors,
> take from our books the finest inventions to adorn their own
> selves.

> "Certainly, whoever shall read these memoirs and shall
> compare the artificial swarm method of Favignana, with that of
> Mr. Schirach, will not fail to recognize the origin of the latter in
> the former, as we shall prove in due time; I must however
> acknowledge that the Greeks and the Turks of the islands of the
> Ionian Sea make artificial swarms; which Mr. Schirach may have
> learned; but as the Favignana method is perfect, and of assured
> success it is but fair to grant to its inhabitants the honor of having
> preserved so useful a practice, which required as much perspicacity
> and thought in our ancestors as is showed correctness of bee ob-
> servation in what was transmitted to us.

> "Mr. Schirach passes among the people beyond the Alps as
> the inventor of the method of artificial swarms, which is still so
> noised about in Germany and in the North; the Favignanese knew
> this before Mr. Schirach and before the invasion of the barbarians;
> they have still preserved two methods, one of which, greater, more

generally used and more perfect is not known to Mr. Schirach who imitates the second method of the Favignanese, etc."

We shall not repeat all the assertions of this sort with which this work is filled and which indicate that the author did not read Schirach; we shall not even take notice of the darts personally addressed to us by Mr. Monticelli; it is evident that, blinded by national feelings he could not forgive us for rendering justice to the savant whom he tried to condemn as a plagiarist.

Had the love of truth induced this writer to verify for himself the facts which he denies, had he found errors in Burnens through his own observations, we could blame him only for the levity with which he expresses himself. But his incredulity relies upon the authority of a certain Father Tannoya, who may be a very respectable man, but with whom we cannot agree as does the Naples professor when he states that there are in each hive three kinds of bees, independent of each other, to wit: drones male and female, queens and workers of both sexes, each kind building its own particular cells, the queen building hers, the drones theirs, etc.; regardless of Réaumur, de Gers, Geoffroi, Linné, Buffon, Swammerdam, Latreille, etc. If they were not aware of the hypotheses of Father Tannoya, Mr. Monticelli challenges their reliability: we shall not complain of having to share the fate of these observers; we must, on the contrary, thank the Neapolitan professor for being kind enough to admit us into so honorable a proscription.

We cannot help regretting that these faults be found in the work of Mr. Monticelli, for it contains a fairly good practice in the art of caring for bees and of producing artificial swarms; it is written with interest and purity and contains a happy confirmation of the principles of Mr. Schirach and we are astonished that an author whose ideas of natural history appear to be taken from the best sources would have admitted in its notes the absurd system.

The industrious Favignanese constructed their hives of wood: they are oblong square boxes, the ends of which are movable; the box itself is open at the bottom and rests upon its stand; it is with these hives that they practice artificial swarming in the manner following: As the spring is much earlier with them than with us they begin as early as the month of March in the multiplication of hives; as soon as the bees bring back pellets of pollen they consider the time favorable for this operation; the hive is transported at some distance from the apiary; they open it from the farther end and the bees are driven with smoke to the forward part, when some of the combs commonly containing honey are cut out; next driving the bees to the posterior part, they take a certain number of combs from the anterior part, some of which are empty, some full of brood of all ages (worker brood which they call latin combs); these are then put into the new hive which they hold in an inverted position, and which is thus open from above; they establish them in it in the same order as found in the mother hive and fasten them with pegs driven in from the outside; this done, they carry the new hive to the spot occupied by the old one, and remove the latter fifty steps from the apiary; the bees that were in the field, coming home, find a hive similar to the one from which they had issued, lodge themselves there, rear the brood and prosper.

The success of this operation, which very much resembles Schirach's simply confirms his theory.

This gives us occasion to mention a slightly different and very ingenious method, invented by Mr. Lombard, a great cultivator of bees and the author of an excellent treatise on their practical economy.

The Lombard process is the reverse of that of Favignana: instead of making an artificial swarm, he forms, so to speak, only an early natural swarm.

He carries the hive destined for this purpose to a dark place where he has already brought the one intended to receive the swarm; the cylindrical shape of his straw hive facilitates the work which consists in driving a part of the bees with the queen from the old hive to the new; the old hive is then returned to its stand so that it may be repeopled by all those returning from the fields, and the new one is established at a suitable distance from it in the apiary; this swarm has a queen and can prosper without help, and enjoys the advantage of the blooming of fruit trees, which is not usually enjoyed by natural swarms. For the details I refer to Lombard's work itself, which is of essential utility to every cultivator of bees.

This method being founded, as is shown, on the production of a queen in a hive containing only brood, further confirms Schirach's doctrine, since its long practice has always been attended with success.

Thus experiment concurs with theory in demonstrating that the larva of a bee may become a queen or a worker, because in either of these modes, it is a female possessing either the physical qualities of maternity in the fecundity of queens, or the conservative properties, such as love, care and solicitude for the young displayed by the workers. This dividing of industry, and courage on one side, with prodigious fecundity on the other, this division originating from the mystery of the education of the larvae, is one of the finest subjects for mediation which natural history affords; we owe to Mr. Schirach's perseverance and perspicacity one of the most curious discoveries that have brought honor upon science; this fact, of which we have given material proofs, throws a great light upon the phenomenon of the development of organs in living beings, and belongs with the greatest researches of physiologists.

These are from the American Bee Journal serialized from 1922 through 1924.

Translator's Note

I had for many years the desire to engage in the translation into English of the "Unedited Letters of Huber." Mr. Ed. Bertrand, who published them in the original French, in Switzerland, in 1891, often urged me to undertake this. But the task was great and I did not have the time to spare. I have at last accomplished it, leaving out only such letters as contained repetitions or were uninteresting to beekeepers.

Is it necessary to mention the great value of Huber's observations? Very few beekeepers have failed to hear or read of the great naturalist, whose "First Observations on the Natural History of Bees" were published in the English language in different editions, from 1806 to, 1841. He enriched the public mind with a number of observations, very few of which have proven incorrect. He is quoted favorably by most of our leading apiarian teachers, and, to mention only those leaders who wrote in English, we find him praised by Bevan, Cook, Alley, Cheshire, Cowan, A. I. Root and, above all, by Langstroth, who called him "the prince of apiarians." Even his antagonists have added to his fame. Huish, whose work on bees was published in London, in 1815, and who was therefore a contemporary of Huber, ridiculed Huber's experiments and observations and called them "absurdities." Huish denied things that Huber had proven, he denied that the queen was fecundated in the air, on the wing; that wax was produced by the digestion of honey; that pollen was used to feed the brood, and many other facts which are now well proved. So Huber has remained as one of the leading lights of modern beekeeping, while Huish is well-nigh forgotten.

Since the "Unedited Letters" were gathered together by our late friend and published by him originally, we believe it is well to begin by publishing his "Introduction," as given in presenting the Letters to the public. This was done in 1897, and the Swiss edition was exhausted long before the death of Mr. Bertrand. We will publish these letters from time to time, as occasion offers, in the Journal.

Our readers must not expect anything positively new, in natural history, through the publication of these letters. But they will see the habits of bees under a new light and will perhaps recognize discoveries which they know now but faintly. Huber's style was delightful and I hope I may have retained some of this delight in the translation.—C. P. Dadant.

Introduction By Edouard Bertrand

The "New Observations upon bees" of Francis Huber make very interesting reading. When I resolved to read them, however, I did not anticipate the intense pleasure which they gave me.

Indeed, if there are still literary productions of the late eighteenth century that are read, we know in how small a proportion. Hardly one book in ten thousand has withstood the test of time. What a lesson in philosophy and what a menace towards the future of our contemporary works! Concerning works of science this proportion is still more disastrous. Everything has changed, everything has been perfected in so speedy a manner that the recital of information dating back a century generally offers no interest for us. From the enormous accumulation of scientific works of that time, there are few capable of instructing us yet; and they are nearly all on Natural History. Among this elite, the "New Observations" of Huber shine with a particular eclat, with an ensemble of qualities so harmonious and original that we would seek them vainly elsewhere. The charm of a style which is always pure is allied with a very simple and yet very clever expose; the ingenuity of the observations is so extraordinary that one soon gives way to the sentiments of an aroused admiration for this blind man, whose genius was at all times equal to well nigh insurmountable difficulties.

Francis Huber, born in Geneva in 1750, died in 1831. When he became blind he was engaged to a Miss Aimee Lullin, and this young lady was faithful to him, in spite of contrary advice which was given her. She was to be rewarded for it by the happiness of her entire life.

Huber narrates himself (New Observations, page 1) how he became interested in bees. He was fond of sciences and did not lose this fondness when he lost his eyesight. He had his servant, Francis Burnens, read to him the best works on physics and natural history. This man took great interest in these readings and Huber quickly noticed his wonderful aptitude as an observer. He resolved to cultivate this talent, and caused him first to repeat some of the most simple experiments of physics. These he executed with a great deal of skill, improving upon the few instruments that were entrusted to him, applying them to new uses and even making, himself, the implements which he needed.

"The continuation of our readings," says Huber, "having led me to the beautiful works of Mr. Reaumur upon bees, I found in his book such a fine plan of experiments, observations made with so much art, and logic so wise, that I resolved to study particularly this celebrated author, to shape my helper and myself at his school, in the difficult art of studying nature. We began by watching bees in glass hives; we repeated all of Reaumur's experiments, and we secured exactly the same results when we used the same processes. This agreement of our observations with his gave me great pleasure, because it proved to me that I could rely entirely upon the eyes of my helper. Emboldened by these first trials, we attempted to make upon the bees some entirely new experiments; we contrived the building of several hives, of which I had never thought, and which presented great advantages, so we had the good Luck of discovering remarkable facts which had escaped the notice of Swammerdam, Reaumur and Bonnet. It is these facts which I now publish in this work; there is not one of them that we did not try several times over, during the eight years in which we made researches upon the bees."

This modest expose retains surprises for the reader, for it does not give a presentiment of the importance and of the difficulties of the researches which followed.

Francis Burnens was not only an intelligent man, he was gifted with great tenacity. He often would follow, for 24 hours, without food or rest, the actions of a few worker-bees which he suspected of being fertile, in order to detect them while in the act of laying. Once, even, he spent 11 days examining the bees of several colonies, one after another.

Huber directed the experiments and devised them so as to retain the control. Nothing is more interesting than their association, which lasted too short a time, for in 1795 Burnens left him to live at Oulens, where his fellow citizens, aware of his capacity, made him a magistrate.

On the other hand, he did not cease his bee work, and from time to time he replied to the requests of Huber by additional experiments. I have had the good luck, through my friend Mr. Edw. Pictet, to publish one of those letters of Burnens, in answer to a question upon the sphinx atropos (Revue Internationale, 1885, page 85). A footnote of Huber, in communicating this letter to Mr. M. A. Pictet, of the Academy of Geneva, shows what sentiments Huber had towards Burnens.

"You will see that the writer of this letter has what is needed to become an excellent observer—good eyes and good logic. You will acknowledge that it is a pity that an instrument which I had sharpened be no longer in my hands. Burnens is justice of the peace at present (New Observations, Preface); he does not waste his time; his entire life is being spent in preventing his fellow countrymen from eating out one another's white of the eyes' and ruining themselves in law suits. I had not thought that my lessons would put him there. His observation is very important. It proves that bees, which contract the entrances of their hives when they are threatened with invasion, do not do it when it is unnecessary. It is therefore the circumstances which prompt them; they never make any mistake."

The first edition of the "Observations" on bees was published in Geneva in 1792. It contained a series of articles in the shape of letters to Mr. Bonnet, who had induced Huber to publish his notes. There was a reimpression published in Paris in 1796, in one volume in-12, to which was added a short practical treatise on bees, anonymous.

(Note. Pierre Huber, the son, was himself a naturalist of merit, already known through his "Researches on the Habits of Ants," published in Geneva and in Paris in 1810, and republished in 1861. Here is the list of a few of the bulletins which he published in periodical works: "Memorandum on Divers Instruments of Physics and meteorology" (Society of Physics and Natural History of Geneva, Vol. 2). "Notice Upon a Migration of Butterflies" (Ditto, Vol. 3). "Memorandum to Serve Upon the History of the Caterpillar of Hammock) (Ditto, Vol. 7, part 1). "Relations of Ants with Lice and Gall Insects" (Brit. Biblith. of Science & Arts, Vol. 28). "Observations Upon Several Species of Bees" (Vol. 6 of the Linnean Society of London). An extract from this was published in volumes 25 and 26 of The British Library under the title: "Observations Upon Several Species of Bees Known Under the Name of Humble-Bees." "Letters Upon a New System of Meteorography" (Biblio. Universelle, 1828). "Letters Upon Aeronautic Spiders," (Posthumous article in Biblio. Universelle, 1866.)

A second edition was made in 1814, in two volumes. For the second, Huber, for want of Burnens, employed his wife, and later his son, as assistant.

Born in Geneva in 1777, Pierre Huber died at Yverdon in 1840.

This curious and beautiful work made the reputation of Huber and secured for him a membership in most of the academies of Europe, especially the Academy of Sciences of Paris. It also caused his being called at present the founder of modern beekeeping.

Here is a resume of the discoveries of Huber, by the noted A. P. De Candolle:

"The origin of beeswax wax then a much discussed point of the history of bees, by naturalists: some of them had said, but without sufficient proof, that they made it of honey; Huber, who had successfully unraveled the origin of propolis, confirmed that opinion concerning beeswax through numerous tests and showed especially, with the help of Burnens, how it oozed from the rings of the abdomen, in the shape of scales. He made extensive experiments to ascertain how the bees prepare it for their combs. He followed, step by step, all the constructions of those marvelous hives in which the bees seem to solve the most subtle problems of geometry; he assigned the role which each class of bees plays in this work, and followed their labor from the rudiment of the first cells to the complete perfecting of the combs. He made known the ravages caused by the sphinx atropos (death's head moth) in the hives which it enters; he even tried to unravel the history of the senses of bees, and particularly to seek the seat of the sense of smell, the existence of which is demonstrated upon the entire natural history of insects, while their structure has not yet permitted to locate it with certainty. Lastly, he made interesting experiments on the breathing of bees; he proved by several experiments that those insects need oxygen just as do other animals. But how can air be renewed and retain its purity in a hive closed everywhere, except at a small entrance, with a sort of putty? This problem required all the sagacity of our observer, and he came to recognize that the bees, by a peculiar motion of their wings, set the air in motion so as to secure its renewal; after having taken note of this, he even proved his statement by imitating this ventilation through artificial means.

These experiments on the breathing of bees required some analysis of the air of the beehives, and this requirement caused Huber to come in contact with Senebier, who was making analogous researches upon plants. Among the means that Huber had thought out to ascertain the quality of the air in the hives was that of germinating some seeds within the hive, basing himself upon the idea that seeds will not germinate in an atmosphere too much deprived of oxygen. This experiment, though imperfect for the purpose intended, brought to the two friends the idea of making researches on germination; and the most curious part of this association of a blind man with a clearsighted man, was that it was usually Senebier who suggested the experiments, and Huber, the blind man, who executed them.

This is what was known, up to that time, of the works of Huber. He died September 22, 1831, and his life, after 1814, was unknown. It was, however, not admissible that he should have stopped making observations, after taking so much interest in the subject for 25 years. Moreover, the end of the preface of the second volume of his 1814 edition indicated exactly the opposite.

"I might," said he (New Observations, Vol. 2, page 6) "add several observations to those which I now give to the public; but they do not present a sufficiently connected aggregate, and I prefer to wait till they may be accompanied with facts upon which they have a bearing."

A lucky concourse of circumstances permits me today to partly make good this shortage.

In 1890, during a visit of apiaries which I made in Savoy, in company with Messrs. De Layens and Cowan, I learned from M. E. Mermey, of Aix-Les-Bains, a young beekeeper who had followed my course of lessons at Nyon, that the father of a neighbor beekeeper, M. Ch. De Loche, possessed among his family papers a number of unedited letters from Francis Huber, addressed to his grandfather, Count Mouxy De Loche. We hastened to visit the Castle of Loche to solicit the permission of reading those letters. The Count was momentarily absent, but we were given the best welcome by his sons, who promised to transmit our request to their father. The latter had the kindness to visit us that same evening at Aix and did me the great favor of entrusting those letters to me with the permission to publish them. His grandfather, Francis de Mouchy, Count De Loche, born at Gresy-Sur-Aix, in 1756 and deceased in 1837, was an observer and a savant of merit. After having served in the army of the House of Savoy and reached the position of Major General, he had withdrawn to Turin, later to Loche, to devote himself more completely to his taste for natural history and archeological researches. He published a great number of works on natural history, archeology, history, agriculture, etc.

But my good fortune did not end there. When I published, in 1894, a new edition of the remarkable memorandum of A. P. De Candolle upon the author of the "New Observations," I sent a complimentary copy of it to Mr. Georges de Molin, engineer at Lausanne, grandson of Francis Huber. This kind old man hastened to inform me that he was just then busy sorting papers which had been forwarded to his mother by the heirs of his uncle, Pierre Huber, after the death of the latter, and that there were among them quite a number of letters from his grandfather, nearly all relative to bees. Although he believed that his uncle had taken from these letters and perhaps inserted in the "Annals of the Society of Physics" of Geneva anything which might interest scientists, he offered them to me in case I should desire to inspect them. Looking through the above mentioned "Annals," we found no trace of these letters whatever.

In the file of letters which were kindly loaned to me by Mr. De Molin, I found a certain number of first drafts of letters addressed to Miss Eliza De Portes, at Bois d'Ely, near Crassier. Having obtained information from a friend of the family, I learned that the young lady correspondent of Huber had become Mrs. De Watteville, and that she was residing at Berne.

This venerable lady, now more than octogenarian, was kind enough to loan me the entire collection of those letters, found in a volume of manuscript, and sent with the parcel the following words, which I take the liberty of publishing:

"My niece, who is returning to Bois d'Ely, is kind enough to bring to you the letters of my friend and venerated master, Mr. Huber, of which I have copied a great number in order to make them more easy to read. You may keep them as long as you desire, and may use them freely for your magazine. I will be happy if they can inspire a taste for natural history, together with a simple and fervent piety."

In all those letters, the striking fact is the religious sentiment of Huber, his conscientious spirit, his constant desire of giving credit to his predecessors and his skill in directing and understanding the experiments of his helpers. "I am more certain than you are of what I am telling you," said he to De Candolle, "for you publish that which your own eyes alone have seen, while I take the average of several testimonials."

It would be difficult to show greater philosophy and greater resignation to one's infirmity.

We may admire, also, the correction and clearness of his style, especially in the "New Observations," for we must not forget that he was an octogenarian when he wrote to Miss De Portes, and that his dictation was through two inferior clerks at least: the one to whom he dictated the letters and the one who copied them for the bound manuscript.

One was astonished at all that Huber had discovered; one will be much more so after reading these letters, in which new views and the very best practical suggestions abound. After him, little has been discovered outside of parthenogenesis; his observations were so precise and so positive that all the modern works, however considerable, have only proven a following of his and a confirmation of his, without amending them. For this reason, I believe that the publication of his unedited correspondence will be welcomed with lively interest by beekeepers in all countries, and I here republish The expression of my hearty thanks to Mrs. De Watteville, the Count De Loche, Mr. De Molin, and Mr. Edmond Pictet for their kindness in entrusting to my care, for publication, the unedited writings of the great observer of the bees. Edouard Bertrand (1897).

UNEDITED LETTERS OF HUBER

Gentleness of Bees. To Miss Elisa De Portes, Lausanne, May 15, 1828

Your mother, my dear Elisa, does not disapprove that I should interest you with the subject of my favorite studies, those good bees which have diverted me from the inseparable sorrows of humanity and have done me so much essential good that they will surely do for you what they did for me, if you are in need of it, and surely will do you no harm. Be it so!

I should like to see bees about you and to think that they will sometimes remind you of the friend who has had so much to do with them. The first and only word that I wish to say to you about them today is not to consider them as formidable as is generally believed; it is a truth proven by me through a half century of observations and which the most simple reasoning might have taught us.

If the bees, the wasps, the bumblebees and all the beings that are provided with stings had received from nature an offensive instinct or hostile dispositions, in view of their prodigious number, the wings with which they have been provided and the speed of their flight, the earth would be uninhabitable for us and for all animals.

If chance had presided at this part of creation, such a condition might have obtained, but it is to a Father, to a true Father, that we owe our existence. He has also thought of the happiness of his children, otherwise the bees, instead of being a blessing would be but a curse to us and the treasure that they could bestow upon us would have been a dead loss: their wax and their honey would have cost us too high a price.

If truly fearful weapons have been given to the bees and other insects of their kind, it is uniquely for their defense, to preserve that which is dearest to them—their queen, their young, their companions or their sisters, and their treasures, against the attacks of numerous enemies. When you have given this some thought, kind Elisa, and will believe a friend who has not the least desire to see you struggling against the poisoned dart of the bees, I will advise you, and your mother will permit you to observe my favorites in a glass hive. One finds beautiful lessons in the study of natural history and especially in that of the beings which I have most studied.

Constant obedience to the laws which have been imposed upon them, and the happiness which results from it are a spectacle of the highest interest for us. If wisdom is without merit when it is compulsory, it is a great merit for the bees that we be compelled to seek the Law-maker and see Him in His works.

A thousand caresses for you and yours, my beloved Elisa.

The Sting of the Bees Has Been Given Them for Their Defense—Lizard Killed in a Hive—The Odor of the Sting Irritates the Bees. To Miss Elisa De Portes, Lausanne, May 17, 1828.

You do not believe, dear Elisa, that those bees which I desire you to love have invented the laws which rule them. I ended my last letter in telling you what you must believe as I do; that it is to the supreme Lawmaker that our admiration is due, as well as our love and our gratitude, for He has evidently thought of the existence and the well-being of creatures which, like ourselves, have no means of defending themselves against the attacks of those who are constantly provided with a sting accompanied with mortal poison. What would be our fate, if we could not walk about our gardens without being in risk of attack and pursuit from thousands of winged and wicked beings?

Let us see what has been done for those bees, which are, also, his children, by this best of Fathers. If attack has been forbidden them, they have been ordered to defend themselves; do they then have enemies? A very large number of insects and reptiles plot against their treasures and try, through robbery, to enter their homes. Others try to enter there, to deposit upon the combs eggs which will find there the only food that they need. Since it is every day and at every hour of the good season that the bees are in danger of the invasion of so many enemies, preserving Providence demands of them a sustained watching, very wonderful for the brains of a fly, a supervision in every moment which is worthy of admiration.

I tell you this because I have seen it, not with my own eyes, but through the help of those who have put theirs to my service, and upon whom it has been necessary for me to rely; this observation has been the first one of all those that I have made. I already knew, through others and especially through the eminent Réaumur, the fine order which reigns in the bee hives, but I ignored entirely when and how this order could be disturbed; chance taught it to me.

One day we were expecting a swarm to issue; I had stationed myself near the hive which was to swarm.

It was a great glass bell, sheltered from light which would disturb the bees, with a veil that could be removed—just as you remove your own—so that we might see what took place within the hive without causing any noise or jars that might alarm them. It was warm that day, drowsiness overtook me and I went to sleep, with my head resting against the hive which I had undertaken to watch. Suddenly I was awakened by a noise coming from the hive and which appeared to me much greater than the humming that one always hears in the habitations of the bees and which is usually very soft. I rang for Burnens, to seek its cause. Great was our surprise when, after having lifted the veil, we saw, on the bottom board of the hive, a fine and big green lizard, lying on its back and slain with violence, as you will soon see. Near its dead body some thirty dead bees were also lying. Had they been killed by him in defending himself? This was our first impression; but we soon altered it when we saw, driven into the belly of the lizard, all the stings of the bees which had put him to death by sacrificing their own lives for the safety of the household.

Paley says, in his "Physical Theology ," that one finds in the insects the models of useful instruments. One finds there also, dear Elisa, beautiful examples to imitate. Is not death in defense of one's country the first and most honorable of our duties? The ancients who did not disregard this, wrote in their beautiful Roman language:

"Dolce et decorum est pro patria mori." (It is sweet and beautiful to die for one's country.)

My sleepiness had not permitted me to see the first act of this tragedy; but other examples of a similar occurrence, noticed in similar circumstances, enable me to tell you without hesitancy what had evidently happened.

The beauty of the weather and of the expected harvest had evidently attracted a third, or perhaps a half, of the workers to the blossoms; those which other cares retained in the hive were probably thinking about the proposed foundling of a new home, and perhaps did not, as usual, watch the entrance of the hive for enemies and keep a sufficient guard there.

The lizard was thus able to enter without finding great opposition. He was perhaps lucky enough to eat a few of the sentinels in passing, but it was not with impunity. In case of an attack, general or individual, the rustle of the workers, caused by the rapid buzzing of their wings, produces a sound which may be termed a danger call.

This call, with which I am acquainted, and which I can readily distinguish from other, is, you may believe, still better perceived by the bees. This buzzing finds an echo in all parts of the hive; when they are made of glass it is as easy to see as to hear it. It is therefore thus that they transmit advice of any danger which threatens them and the request to be on their guard in any part of the home. If the signal which announces danger to them has but the duration of lightning, its effects are truly equal truly equal to those of a thunder-bolt.

Worker-bees in sufficient number, and doubtless in pro- portion to the strength of the enemy, rush upon them and at once put them "hors de combat." We know by our own experi- ence that their death must be as painful as it is prompt.

The bite of the viper, so dangerous, is not at all to be feared when its venom has been drained by repeated biting. That which renders the venom of the bee so painful for us and so deadly for their natural enemies is also the presence, at the end of the two spears which compose the sting-, of a bright crop of poison which shows itself on its forward point.

At the will of the irritated bee, the venom is carried, or rather forced, into the body of the enemy and causes its almost instantaneous death, for from the poison sack, located at the root of the sting, the poison has but a short space to travel towards its extremity in order to reach the full depth of the wound which the two spears have produced.

You now know What happened to the lizard of which I wrote a minute ago and how the bees get rid of usurpers. Will you now, my dear girl, take a few steps more with your friend? Please follow the thread which he has put in your hands, in order to help you out of the labyrinth in which you are now engaged, with him.

The hives which are governed by a young and fertile queen and are filled with a numerous population are but little in danger of invasions; I have seen some that did not have to repulse a single attack or need to avenge a single insult during the entire year of existence; I say insults to avenge, because I must acknowledge that my cherished bees a decidedly vindictive; it is their failing and I must not conceal it from you.

One day I ran the risk of testing this myself; having caused a hive to be raised from its bottom to cleanse the latter, the person who was doing this for me probably touched and wounded a few workers. I heard the danger call; some hundreds of workers answered it, rushed out of the hive and upon me; my clothing and the promptness of my flight permitted me to reach the house without being stung. Remember my blindness and think of how little I could have done in my own defense at so critical a moment. Certainly I had to be thankful, and I feel so yet.

The greater number of the bees that had rushed at me returned home, but three or four remained which did all in their power to enter the parlor in which I had taken refuge, by flying against the windows and keeping it up for half an hour with a very remarkable fierceness. When I thought they had withdrawn and imagined I could go safely out of my retreat, one of the most furious workers threw herself upon the person who had taken my arm, stung him miserably under the eye and died herself, leaving in the wound her stinger and her entrails. I have often seen their resentment prolonged a much longer time.

Whenever my gardener was raking too near the hives, the workers that rested upon the ground, killed or wounded by the rake, were soon avenged. The danger call was heard within the hives; the gardener was often punished for his clumsiness.

During the two or three days following such excitement, no one could approach the apiary without suffering the effects of the offended bees' rancor. Those that had followed me with the fierceness of which I wrote, would stop sometimes long enough on the panes of the window to enable one to distinctly see the end of their abdomen; and the bright drops of poison on the end of their stings indicated that they had been drawn and poisoned for my benefit.

If the primary cause of their anger was not always noted by us, it was perhaps not so difficult to understand their prolonged anger. The cause was probably entirely natural.

My first thought was that the presence of the escaped poison, its odor probably perceived by the bees, might have an irritating action upon some of their organs. An experiment was to prove it to us; here is what I devised:

We introduced a few bees in a tube of small diameter, the length of which did not exceed 6 inches, its lower opening was hermetically closed, the other could be closed with the finger or in some other manner.

In order that the bees might give this tube the odor of poison, they were slightly disturbed with a straw or the stem of a flower. Then the opening of the tube was presented at the entrance of a hive, after having uncovered it. The effect was immediate; a few bees came out of the hive at once and threw themselves upon us. We would have been stung, undoubtedly, if a veil, some gloves and a good hood had not protected us from their anger.

Causes of Swarming-Royal Cells—Jealousy of the Queen—Travel Supplies of The Swarms. To Miss Elisa De Portes, Lausanne, June 30, 1828.

You are a musician, my dear girl; if I had known that you had bees at Bois d'Ely and swarms to expect, I would have called upon your sensitiveness and upon your ear for music for an observation which I have often made and which might have interested you as it did me; let us hope that it is not too late.

Let us suppose that you have just heard the charivari which indicates everywhere the issue of a swarm; you come running to witness it; there it is above your head. I see you in the midst of many bees, enjoying this fine sight, without being frightened by the tumultuous bustle of so many beings which, we are told, are armed with stings that are so dangerous—but do not believe it.

It has been recognized—and those who know how to care for them will tell you—that bees are never milder than on the days when they swarm. Yet to secure their swarms people treat them in a manner that might irritate them. Those bees, so irascible and vindictive, are never thus in such an occasion and when the proposition is swarming, the redoubtable sting is neither felt nor seen.

Take note, I pray you, of a truly balsamic odor which spreads about you; the odor of honey, which this recalls, often allays their anger. I have caused many fights to end by throwing a few drops of honey upon bees which appeared to be furious. Is honey, for them, when it is scattered in their atmosphere, a talisman which brings them back to their natural gentleness and keeps them from becoming angry?

Do you hear any discord in this numerous concert? This soft humming is, to my sense of hearing, composed only of accurate tones. This aerial music goes straight to my heart; I acknowledge that I never heard it indifferently; is it possible that what I find in it expressive, touching, melancholy and even solemn, comes only from myself or my imagination? I will not deny the natural exaltation which rises within me through this interesting event and this apparent agreement in will and sentiment in beings which are placed (by us it is true) almost at the foot of the scale.

Although I have not said a word to you about it, I am sure that you will divine at least one of the reasons which cause the periodical departure of swarms; that which is true, wise, useful, may be often foreseen. To help you a little, however, permit me to use a comparison which is within reach of the master and of the pupil and convenient for both.

If you had been but a simple shepherdess, would your kindness and your natural reasoning allow you to retain your sheep or your goats within a space of pasture that could feed but half of them? No, doubtless you would not doom them to the horrors of famine. It is to preserve the bees from this danger that nature has instructed them to seek, like nomad tribes, a salvation in periodical migrations.

The queen, which you know only by reputation, is the motive which directs the multitude, whose mother she is. They say that she can produce, in a year, from sixty to eighty thousand brood. This is enough to make up the swarm which is, the following year and perhaps sooner, to seek far away the sustenance necessary to the keeping of the new population.

As the substances which are suitable for the food of bees cannot be increased indefinitely in a limited space, they have been taught to seek far away the food which is required for a constantly growing population; it is for this that wings have been given them, with the knowledge for using them. Let us study now what has been prepared to determine their migration.

Accept my word, dear girl, until you see it with your own eyes. I assure you that I have not accepted anything till I have secured positive proof. The care with which Burnens has informed his master and friend has been a great help in this occasion.

But I must ask of you here again much faith and docility; for will you readily believe that an insect, a simple bee be susceptible to jealousy? You must accept this statement, for nothing is truer; all you require is the evidence. For this purpose a few details are necessary.

You know that a wax-comb is composed of a greater or less number of contiguous cavities which have been named cells; it is in those little lodges that the bees deposit their crops of honey or of pollen and that the queen lays her eggs when they are fit to receive them.

Have you noticed some openings much larger than the cells and with no regularity about them? They are not the result of accident; the bees have left those spaces in the thickness of the combs. Through this arrangement, whenever they are in a hurry to travel over both sides, they can do it much more promptly than if they had to go around the edge of the comb. It is, if you please, like public squares or alleys; in our cities similar spaces have the same utility. Among the bees they have still another; it is there that they build the royal cells of which you have probably heard. In their original shape, those cells resemble an acorn cup, later they will become, as the work progresses, inverted pyramids, at first more or less truncated. It is when the royal cell is only in the shape of a cup and is not deeper than two or three lines (one-fourth to one-sixth inch), that it may receive the eggs that the queen lays in it, perhaps in passing, while she goes from one side of the comb to the other. I am inclined to believe that it is a trick devised by the architect bees. That which confirms this conjecture is that the bees, being unable to build the royal cells horizontally in the comb and give the same direction to the pyramidal part without extending it too far between the parallel combs, in the space reserved for passage, could do nothing better than fasten the royal cell cups vertically, under the edge of the spaces intended for passage; then the pyramidal part could be fastened to the cup and extended vertically in the open space below.

There is another reason which explains fairly well why the royal cells must not be built in the thickness of the comb. The queens, larger and longer than the workers for whom the ordinary cells are intended, would not find in them a space sufficient for their ulterior development.

The queens, in a hurry for laying and finding all the small cells occupied, pass to the other side of the comb through one of these passages, but perceiving the orifice of the outlined cells, insert their abdomen into them after having ascertained that they are not already occupied; they fall thus in the snare which has been prepared for them.

As fast as the small cells are emptied, through the hatching of the worker bees, the queen lays in them, as well as in the different cell cups which she finds open and empty. Her eggs will produce successively royal larvae and nymphs more or less advanced. It is not only by supplying a broader and differently located lodging that the bees bring to the queenly condition those which were intended only for simple workers. A more exquisite food, perhaps more stimulating and more abundant, brings about the extension of the queen organs in the cradle and especially the development of the sexual organs. Mr. Bonnet, during the visit which he paid me at Pregny, saw in one of my hives, from which I had removed the queen, more than 20 royal cells begun.

A very singular and very important thing which has not been sufficiently noticed and of which I understand but now the usefulness, is the perfect coincidence of the laying of drone eggs, always observed in the season of swarming, with the building of royal cells. A secret link assuredly exists between these two great preparations.

Here we are again reduced to admiration, is it not enough? Without this arrangement the young queens would run the risk of never becoming mothers, or of securing but imperfect mating in case their fecundation should be too long delayed, but, as has been said, everything is in harmony in the natural history of bees.

Follow me another moment and you will see a new point.

For me to have told you that queens were susceptible to jealousy, I must have very evident proofs to give you of so singular a thing.

By what means can they be brought to that and how can a feeling of jealousy and irritation be inspired in them, through the accomplishment of the views that Nature intended?

Let us return to the royal cells; it is there that the thread starts which will lead us out of this labyrinth. Their construction cannot be instantaneous; several days are needed during which many workers are employed successively to build a pyramid out of that which at first was shaped only like an acorn cup.

The queen, after having deposited her egg at the bottom of the cup, continued to lay elsewhere very peaceably without giving the least sign of alarm; it was only when the pyramid was finished that we noticed in her bearing a beginning of restlessness. The royal larva was then filling the cell to its extremity, she was about to pass to the state of nymph, during which she has no longer need of any food. The closing of the cell at that time proves it incontestably.

The agitation of the queen increased as fast as the young larva grew towards its goal; from a very noticeable displeasure the queen passed very quickly to anger, and it is not to be doubted that her rival was the object of it.

When we see her bending her energy upon her destruction and killing her in her cradle when the bees do not put any obstacles in the way of this fury, do you not recognize that the most cruel jealousy has been the only incentive of it? The intention of nature would not be fulfilled if that of the queen was accomplished; if she could kill her rivals in infancy there would be no hopes for swarms, and the colony would perish; the workers taught by kind Nature to oppose this, do it effectively, by surrounding the royal cells with guards numerous enough to prevent the effect of the queen's rage; they always succeed in doing so by opposing her approach without ever using their sting against this mother so cherished; they succeed in drawing or driving her away, by climbing on her back and striking her with their antennae, which is now known to be a very expressive language.

The bees, the ants, like all the beings which live in association and whose operations require a sort of concert, must understand each other and have some means of communicating to one another their thoughts, their needs, their desires, their fears and above all their dangers. Among insects which we have observed, the repeated and varied touching of the antennae warn them and instruct them of what they need to know.

Another means of information instructs the bees of that which interests the queen; I have made sure of that in case of her death or her disappearance. To convince oneself of this, it is only necessary to remove the queen from the bees; one will see nothing in the first moments to prove that her loss has been detected, but at the end of a half hour one cannot doubt it. The confusion which reigns in the hive, the abandoning of the brood, the running about of the workers, their precipitate flight at undue hours, their researches around the hive, later the re-establishment of good order and especially the preparations which they make to rear another queen prove that they have perceived the loss, but do not explain how.

It is always the old queen that leads the first swarm; she goes with it after showing by her growing agitation that she gives up to the terror caused by the existence of young rivals in the cradles, but as she does not wait until they have reached the end of their growth and can leave the royal cell, she goes with her swarm without having done any harm to her young rivals; murder takes place only after the departure of the old queen. The one who succeeds immediately finds rivals, at her birth, they are very dangerous for her; their age about equal to hers does not permit her to wait until they also hatch, but she pounces upon the still sealed cells, pierces them and kills with her sting the royal nymphs of which she perceives the existence through some unknown sense.

The appearing of royal cells and the jealousy which they inspire in the reigning queens are therefore truly that which procures the accomplishment of the views of Nature and the means employed by the latter to induce the bees to fly away from their native home and seek their conservation by periodical migrations.

I thought that I had seen and faithfully described everything that has reference to the natural history of swarms; that which has just happened to me proves that one can never be too careful or too modest. I find in a forgotten memorandum of mine the detail of an observation which had taken my attention in the old days and of which I had not retained the recollection; it is dated of the year 1816.

That year which has properly been called the year of famine, did not open in Geneva as likely to be as fatal to bees as it was to all our crops.

The fine blooming of the early spring, the warm and moist temperature which reigned at that epoch caused the honey and pollen to abound in the blossoms. The drones, which appeared early in all our hives, announced early swarms; that expectation was realized; I never saw so many; 10 or 12 hives which I had at the end of winter multiplied by the end of June to the number of 60.

I was then using leaf hives, glassed only at their posterior end. That is where our attention was directed, when we recognized the well-known signs of swarming; that moment is when all the bees, excited by the irritation of their queen, think only of following her, leaving their native home and going elsewhere for a new country. That is what every one knew, or should have known, according to the excellent memoirs of Reaumur.

Let us see what will happen to those fugitives, leaving foolishly their apparently well furnished homes, supplied with everything that they needed, to prefer to it such homes as they would accidentally find and which would undoubtedly be lacking in what would be to their convenience.

What will happen to them if the weather changes at the moment of their entrance into a tree trunk or in the cavity of a rock, especially if the bad weather is prolonged 5 or 6 days? That is not difficult to divine; they will starve infallibly. Their greatest torment will be the discouragement into which they will fall when they will see that their queen, finding no cells in which to lay her eggs, will be compelled to drop them in the air, and consequently that all hope of posterity will vanish. (This discouragement in similar cases has been observed by others).

No, no. it is not at a time when these beings which prove of so great an interest to us have the greatest need of a superior direction that it is refused to them.

When the bees are about to leave their home forever, when everything seems to be in confusion among them, one can see them pounce upon the combs in which the honey has been stored, which are always the farthest away from the entrance. We have seen them entirely strip 3 large combs of honey in a few minutes. Time pressed, it was necessary to follow the queen, and they knew it.

We made this observation on so large a number of swarms in 1816 and since that date, that I have no doubts whatever upon this matter.

What Happens in a Colony of Which the Queen has Been Removed, and How The Bees Manage to Rear New Ones

Having had no trouble in the method which I followed, I will need to speak to you a moment, my dear girl, about myself and what I found it necessary to do. Since I wanted to study bees, it was necessary, previously, to study their natural history in the writings of the best nature students, both ancient and modern; then seek a faithful helper who would lend me the aid of his eyes.

After having read a great deal, I gave all my confidence to Mr. Reaumur. My Secretary, Francois Burnens, a young Vaudois husbandman, gave me so many proofs of his faithfulness and zeal that, after having ascertained the quality of his eyesight, I selected him to repeat the observations and delicate experiments that I might wish to make; it was he who constructed my glass hives and suggested to me the shapes and the dispositions which would best fill my plans and render my endeavors more successful and less dangerous.

(I have told in the preface of my book how much I owed to the care of this excellent young man).

He caused me to forget and almost set at naught the obstacles which my blindness placed in the way of success in these difficult researches.

1. I wanted to know of that queen of whose existence Reaumur had about convinced me; those drones, which according to him were the males of the breed; but especially the workers themselves to which we were indebted for honey and wax.

2. After having made sure, through the eyes of Burnens, I ascertained, as per Reaumur, that there is usually but one queen in a hive, but hundreds of drones and thousands of bees or common workers.

3. It was not difficult to recognize the functions of the three kinds of bees. That of the queen would have deserved for her the most beautiful of all names, that of mother of her people, as the drone is entitled to be called its father. The common workers, in charge of all the cares required for the young and for the construction of the structure, could be entitled to the names of architects or of nurses.

4. My own researches upon the duration of the life of the mothers were ineffectual; it is to the pastor, Mr. De Gelieu, that I am indebted for the knowledge that they live 4 or 5 years.

Mr. Reaumur says that the drones do not live longer than a few weeks; I have ascertained that they may live one or two months and that there are circumstances when their life may be prolonged; that of the workers is never a year.

Colony Activities

To render to the worker bees the entire justice due to them, I must add that, by constant care, they preserve the greatest neatness about them, they make sure that the purity of the breathing air, which is constantly altered by their emanations, is thoroughly brought back instantly to the proper degree of salubrity, they constantly keep at the entrance of their hive a guard entrusted with the important duty of keeping away enemies. The courage with which they repulse their attacks, even at the peril of their lives, and especially their apparent attachment for their queen are laws upon which they are never found to falter. The cares that they give the drones were also noticed by Reaumur; I will perhaps mention it later.

Some people have complained that I did not say a word about all this in my letters on bees to Mr. Bonnet; It was, I believe, because they were addressed to him that I did not think it necessary to remind him of things which he already knew so well; I made the mistake to overlook the fact that the public might be ignorant of them and uninformed of the acquired knowledge. It is in order that I may not incur a similar complaint that I have consigned you, my dear girl, to the annoyance of reading these details before you hear of their importance.

5. If you are curious to know the duration of the life of the swarm or of the colony, you will need to remember that the life of the queen, according to De Gelieu, is of 4 or 5 years.

Mr. De Reaumur speaks of a colony which, to his knowledge, existed for over 80 years. At Tepic, in Mexico, (1) some are known which have been in existence for a century.

In the cases of queens living 4 years, it required but 25 succeeding queens in the same hive to reach this term. Twenty will be sufficient in the other case. The two examples cited prove that it must be thus, with us, as in America, and this would probably be the case if the queen bees were an exception to the common law, if they could not be removed from their people by disease or by some accident and perish before the term which nature grants to them.

This danger, foreseen as are those to which all beings are subject, is avoided in so strange a manner that it appeared incredible to Mr. Bonnet; that which refers to it will be the subject of my next letter.

Loss of Queen

The queen may thus die of violent or accidental death, or through some disease unknown to us, or of old age when the end of her life is reached.

If she dies, leaving in the small or worker cells eggs or larvae from which worker bees were to hatch, the loss of the queen will soon be remedied, that is what the Pastor Schirach discovered and which Mr. Bonnet could not believe.

As soon as I heard of the natural history of the queen by Blassiere and the assertion of the German pastor, I went to Genthod to talk with Mr. Bonnet about his doubts and about the reasons which he gave for them; I took the liberty of asking my wise friend whether he had renewed the test made by Schirach and which had caused such marvelous consequences. His negative answer emboldened me to propose to make the test which he had been unwilling to attempt. His great kindness showed that my temerity was not displeasing to him and that he would put confidence in the results that I might secure; he did more, he told me what I should do and indicated the caution that I must use in order to deceive neither myself nor others; the sequel proved to me that this excellent man was much more anxious to secure the truth than to retain his acquired opinions.

In order to verify the assertion of the German pastor, it was necessary to remove the queen of a hive, and see what would happen. Would her people, deprived of their mother, become discouraged? Would they leave their home, their treasures so laboriously gathered, and especially their young which had been so carefully nursed, thus far? That is what one might have thought; could the best naturalists, even Reaumur, imagine that the loss of the queen was not irremediable? Schirach, not having told all the details which led him to this great discovery, I resolved to seek them and for this purpose to open the book of nature.

Experiment

Burnens selected for this experiment one of my finest colonies in glass hives, the one whose numerous population showed the greatest activity and in which the industry of the workers had maintained the finest order. It was in a fine evening of spring, and when all the fielders had returned home, that he hunted for the queen, and soon found her. He removed her from the comb and did it with such mildness that not a single bee appeared to perceive it; they continued for a half hour all the labors entrusted to them. I perceived then that the humming was becoming stronger every moment. Burnens saw a few bees running about the combs, without stopping over the brood, and passing over one another. The number of running bees increased as well as the hum. A few moments later all was confusion in that hive; the workers left the combs and the brood, ran towards the entrance and rushed out with the greatest haste. We thought at first, having at last noted the disappearance of their mother and her possible loss, they had decided to leave. We saw very soon that such was not the case, that the temporary leaving of the hive was due only to their ardent desire of finding the lost queen, for none of them took flight. It was only to hunt for her that they had gone out of their home to run in every direction, outside of the hive, from which they did not stray far. Their wanderings lasted over half an hour; when they re-entered the home, their humming, much less loud than at first, gave me only the impression of their eagerness to return to the brood that we thought they were forsaking. Calm was re-established gradually, and the finest order soon reigned in every part of the hive.

This taught us only that the bees ascertained the loss of their queen, but did not enlighten us on how they had learned it. Was it really to make up for this loss that they were return-ing home; was it not rather because night was approaching? The sequel was to give us the answer.

First Observation

If my supposition was correct, if the swarm deprived of its queen had no hopes of finding her or means of replacing her, I should expect to see them desert the following day. We resigned ourselves to the task of keeping in sight of them. We saw, at the dawn of the following day that order reigned in the hive, that the bees covered the combs of brood, or rather that they were actually setting upon the young, lodged in their cells, as was unquestionably indicated by a higher temperature in that part of the hive. In that part of the comb, the greater number of the cells were about to be closed or were already sealed; the little larvae in other cells were very close to the change into nymphs, a dozen cells at most were still open; when the nurses would move away for a little while we could see the young larvae in the bottom of the cells which served as their cradles. At noon of the same day, three of the open cells showed a remarkable peculiarity. Their larvae, apparently of the same age, were no longer coiled at the bottom of the cells; they had reached the center of the tube; we did not then understand how they had been brought there; since they were apod (without feet) it seemed very singular. By throwing a better light into the comb we saw that the rear part of the cell was filled with a semitransparent substance resembling the jelly which is used to feed their young. Was this jelly the result of digestion in these same larvae? Or, was the pap which is fed to them packed behind them by their nurses, as one places a cushion behind the loins of a sick person, or of a child, so that it may better sit up in bed? However minute in appearance this question be, I must not omit any new feature that may be useful in the bee industry (it will be better established later).

As the extreme softness of the young larvae, and especially of those which are now in question, does not allow the nurses to draw them forcibly to the front of the cell, they can bring them forward with the help of this so-called cushion which they spread behind them.

Second Observation

The three cells observed were not in close proximity to each other; those which surrounded them were closed and contained either nymphs or larvae ready to become nymphs.

As early as the previous evening, we had seen those cells covered with bees, doubtless actively occupied with some important work, but of which we could not discern the purpose; a few hours later this purpose became manifest. These bees appeared to be bent upon destroying the cells upon which they were working, together with the larvae or the nymphs which inhabited them, thus enlarging the three cells in their diameter, taking away, for that purpose, the cell walls of the hexagonal cells and changing them to a cylindrical form.

It appeared to us that the bees were opening, almost at right angles, another cell on the horizontal tube.

At this stage of their work one could hardly see the larvae any longer, but they were so near the opening of the old tube and its right angle junction with the new, that we hardly doubted but that they had been brought or pushed that far to lower them into the part which had been added to the horizontal tube. The new cell, prolonged downwards and almost vertically, took the shape of an inverted pyramid, the open summit still permitted a worker to enter into the pyramid to care for the young larva; whenever she emerged she was at once replaced by another, and this lasted until the cell, closed in a point, became a real pyramid; in every particular similar to the royal cells so well described by Reaumur. Thus the discovery of Schirach was apparently almost demonstrated.

Third and Last Observation
It was entirely convincing to us, when we saw, emerging from these three cells, real queens, similar in every respect to the one which we had removed two weeks previously. Schirach has therefore said truly that bees can repair the loss of their queen.

The Queens Whose Mating Has Been Prevented Up to The 21st or 23rd Day, Lay Only Drone Eggs. To Miss Elisa De Portes, Lausanne, September 13, 1828
In one of the letters that I was permitted to write to Mr. Bonnet (New Observations, 3rd letter), I wrote that the pastor Schirach, who became celebrated in Germany, for his love of the bees and his great discovery of the possible transformation of a common larva into a queen, had found, in one of his hives, a swarm almost entirely composed of drones, a very astonishing fact, never mentioned by any one. The author of this discovery understood that one should attribute to some imperfection of the queen her inability to give birth to ordinary workers and with good reason concluded that it was necessary to give another queen immediately to this unfortunate colony, if it was desirable to save it. He therefore removed the sick or imperfect queen; taking advantage of his great discovery, he substituted another queen; in this hive and added to the drones that were there a sufficient number of workers to care for them; since these drones, deprived by nature of the necessary instruments and weapons, could neither feed, nurse nor defend the colony. Under other requirements, they are entrusted with the perpetuation of the species.

This expedient of Mr. Schirach was entirely successful; his new queen, of proper structure in every regard, filled her hive with a numerous population, composed, as usual, of workers and drones; happy in this deserved success, its author did not seek for the cause of the mishap which he had experienced, he was satisfied with having discovered the remedy.

Finding The Reason
Being curious of investigating a matter which appeared to me to be as new as it was important, I did everything that I

could think of to reach an explanation. I will spare you the recital of my researches, but will say to you that the queens upon which I experimented produced only drones when I allowed them to mate too late, that is to say, when their nuptials could not take place before the 22nd or 23rd day from the date of their egress, as full grown insects, from the cell which had been their cradle; on the contrary, they laid eggs of two sexes whenever they were mated a few days earlier. But why does this delay of fecundation disable the queens from laying worker eggs? It is a problem upon which analogy does not furnish any light. I can say now, as I wrote it to Mr. Bonnet, that in the entire physiological history of animals I know of no observation which has any analogy with this. Be therefore satisfied, my dear Elisa, with an acknowledgment of ignorance from your so-called teacher, who prefers to remain silent rather than give you fanciful advice.

(Note: It is well known that, some 15 years later, Dzierzon gave the solution of the problem. It was in 1845 that, for the first time, he gave his views on the reproduction of bees and expressed the conviction that the drone eggs did not need fecundation, while the co-operation of the drone was indispensable for the production of workers. Four years later, in 1849, in his work "Theorie and Praxis" he made a complete expose of his theory on parthenogenesis, to which the works of Siebold and other savants have given scientific confirmation.)

My own researches, therefore, proved the possibility of the accident signalized by the German professor. The silence preserved upon this subject by all the naturalists, and especially by those who had most observed the honeybees, proved to me that an accident so fatal for them, and which was, for them, a real catastrophe, must be infinitely rare. Was there a doubt that it had been foreseen and provided for? I could not guess it. I had to see it, and see it many times, to believe it. The previous accidents should have led me on the way; it was to the want of drones at the proper time that the real sterility of queens should be attributed; in order to avoid it, it was necessary that the birth of the queens and of the drones coincided. Their too early or too tardy appearance would be equally injurious to the hive; the parallel hatching of the two sexes was, therefore, indispensable; the queens needed to emerge at the same date as their mates, and that is what actually takes place.

Foretelling The Sex

Reaumur was the first man to see that the females of the bees have been given a privilege of which all other mothers have been deprived, that of foreseeing the sex of the child which they are to bring forth, which is proven by the choice of the different-sized cells in which they deposit the eggs of both sexes; it is in the little ones that the workers are raised, since their size is better proportioned to them.

Has some similar faculty been given to the workers, so that they may know intuitively what is happening about them? When the queen enters her new home, she needs worker cells, and it is always with worker eggs that her laying begins, those of drones come later; it is when the latter descend from her ovaries that the workers prepare to build queen cells.

The rearing of the young drones is a little slower than the rearing of workers or queens; 17 to 18 days are sufficient for the latter, 20 for the worker, but it takes at least 24 days for the drones, from the time when the eggs are laid until they become adult and are able to emerge from the cell which has served them as cradle or prison.

Providing for Emergencies

The young queens are therefore assured, by this arrangement, that their wedding may take place, that is to say that they may mate with a drone, in the air, on the wing, during the first days of their life; there is another mishap to foresee, it is in case the young bride should die on the way or should be the prey of a swallow, of a lizard, of of some other enemy. It is therefore not only to furnish queens for the swarms that the bees have been taught to rear more queens than they will need, and it is undoubtedly for that reason that they build, during the entire drone-breeding time, a number of queen-cells which is far in excess of what would be needed; five or six would be more than sufficient; it is not rare to find at that season eight or ten royal cells which could give birth successively to as many queens. I do not doubt that beneficent Nature has in view, in this occurrence, the making up of the possible losses of queens by accident during their aerial and adventurous flights.

Mr. Bonnet counted 25 royal cells in the hive which I opened for his inspection at Pregny. It was, I believe, when I reminded him of this observation that I told him in one of my first letters that the simultaneous appearance of drone eggs and queen cells, always observed in the same circumstances and only at the time or the great drone breeding, indicates some secret connection between such operations performed simultaneously, in beings of the same family, but so different in essential respects.

The Beemoth an Enemy of Bees—Renewing The Combs. To Miss Elisa De Portes, Lausanne, November, 1828

My Dear Elisa : When I began occupying myself with bees, the first thing that impressed me was the scant interest which was taken among our people in the cultivation of this insect, whose utility was, however, fully acknowledged. The best informed of our farmers agreed that this was due to our climate—the nature of our crops, the proximity of the lake and especially the ravages made in the hives by a little moth, which Réaumur calls, I do not know why, the most dangerous enemy of bees, designating thereby the worm from which it hatches under the name of beemoth. He gives in his memoirs the history of this moth and knows how to make it interesting; it is in that book that you must read it and that I learned the most curious facts concerning it. The peasants and the naturalists whom I consulted appeared equally positive of the impossibility of checking the ravages of this dangerous enemy of bees, its diminutive size, according to them, permitting it to enter wherever bees themselves can go. They were right, but I very soon saw that the bees had been taught to hunt them; they often succeeded in frightening them away from their homes, and it was only by ruse that the fatal moth sometimes penetrated within the hive. What did the bees do then? Not wishing to rely upon mere conjecture, I placed my swarms in glass hives and entrusted this important matter to the care of Burnens. He advised me one day that he noticed important crowds of bees on parts of the combs where nothing should have drawn them. I noticed that they caused there the production of more heat than they usually produce on combs that contain no brood; the gathering of bees in such spots necessarily had a cause which it was advisable to ascertain. The presence there of workers and their apparent fierceness rendered observation difficult. It was necessary to turn them aside, and Burnens succeeded in so doing, without being stung. After having removed them we noticed:

1st. That a great gap had been opened in that part of the comb from which we had driven the bees.

2nd. That this gap was due to the entire destruction of the cells of which this comb had been built.

3rd. That the disappearance of the cells had taken place on both sides of the comb and that it was pierced through at that spot.

4th. By an examination of the condition of the cells which were near the empty space just perceived and which should make a new edge to the comb, we saw that the neighboring cells were no longer of the same length, that the last rows had undergone a great alteration. (Bees always work at several jobs at one time.) While those which I have just mentioned were busy destroying their own work, others did that which we had never seen them do: they busied themselves in shortening the cells of the outer four or five rows, all previously equal and similar. This gradual shortening operated at the same time on both sides of the comb, gave to the new edge the shape of a declivity.

5th. The bees worked upon this with such activity that this trait would have escaped our attention had we delayed till the next day our watching of their actions; at that time, all would have been repaired, the cells then, equally lengthened, left no space between them, and it was difficult to distinguish the points of junction of the new edge.

Bees Drive Out Moths

6th. It was only then that we saw what had made this great work necessary; the moth miller had penetrated within the hive, unseen by the guards, and had laid eggs upon these combs. The mildness of the temperature had been sufficient for those eggs to hatch. The young larvae, placed within reach of their natural aliment, had fed upon the wax, had penetrated within the thickness of the comb, but had not done so without taking steps to hide themselves from the bees. The soft webs which they know how to spin at their birth, secured this purpose, and as they were trained to give them proper dimensions, they could crawl on and grow in these galleries without being perceived by the workers; it is to these galleries that Réaumur gave the name of "covered way."

7th. If the preceding observations had exhibited to our eyes the invasions of the beemoths and the danger which they presented to bees, they also proved to me a presentiment which I could not abandon and in which my past knowledge of natural history increased my confidence.

This family, so evidently favored, could not, to my mind, remain powerless at a time when a little succor, independently from our own help, would be absolutely necessary.

8th. This idea, or rather this wish, was secured when they tore down the cells and made in the middle of their beautiful combs the great gap which I have just mentioned; with a remarkable determination, my bees failed not in telling me that they had perceived the presence of their enemies among themselves; that their ruse was discovered and that all their forces were now employed in overcoming it; a few shreds of their covered ways, which I saw them drag and throw out of the hive, brought this fact to the light of day.

The larvae of the moths, eight or ten lines long, (3/4 to 7/8 inch long), which were hidden in their subterranean galleries, showed us that the damage was not recent, and we were surprised that the guards of the hive had not sooner tried to oppose their ravages. Would it be that the odor exhaled by those moths became intolerable to them only after 15 or 20 days of their sojourn in the hive?

9th. The bees, by keeping up their instinct and all their strength, can always protect themselves from the ravages of their most dangerous enemies and oppose to their ruses the most ethcac1ous and natural methods.

Weak Colonies Perish

It is, however, true that many colonies perish when the bees, reduced to too small a number or discouraged by some imperfection of their queen, seem to lose their instinct entirely, or at least partially; then they neglect to keep up the temperature of the brood nest at the degree which is suitable for their young and for themselves.

The cleanliness of their home does not seem to interest them any longer, the abandonment of their entrance watch allows their enemies to enter the hive. The sequel proves evidently that they no longer seek to defend it. On this subject, therefore, I entertain the same fears as my advisers and the no less respectable plain farmers conceive. I believe that I can advise them that they will find, as I did, in the pastor De Gelieu's "Conservator of Bees," a sure way to preserve their colonies against the invasions of the moths and their fearful consequences.

This means, which other writers have also advised, is nothing but the uniting of colonies in twos or threes, or in other words the marriage of swarms.

Repair of Combs

Subsequent observations, of which I had best suppress the details, taught me that the ravages of the moths in the combs are not the only alterations which the bees have been taught to repair. The dampness which concentrated within the hives, in the autumn, on the combs that are remote from the part in which the temperature is maintained by the bees, covers these combs with mold, the odor of which is probably unpleasant to the bees, for, in the powerful colonies, this mold soon disappears through the same method employed by them to get rid of the moths; that is to say, the destruction of the cells which are infected with it, and very soon replaced.

A greater evil, if possible, than that with which the colonies are threatened by the moths, troubled me concerning their welfare as soon as I discerned it. The bees, taught to preserve the salubrity of their home, carefully remove from it everything of a noxious nature; even the air which they must breathe is the object of tireless vigilance which requires from these simple insects the most sustained efforts, of which we have known the absolute necessity for only a short time. The accumulation of the remains, which so many larvae leave in the cells that have served as cradles for all the brood, would soon taint the atmosphere of the hive, if the workers did not do their duty in this occurrence; but they acquit themselves of this in a manner to leave nothing to fear in this regard.

Great was my surprise, then, when I read in Swammerdam's "Bible of Nature," that the workers did not remove the cast skins of the nymphs as they did the remains from the larvae; did this last swaddling-skin of the adult insect, so thin and dried, escape the effects of fermentation, could it not deteriorate the air within the hives? I do not know it, but Swammerdam recognizes in it another danger.

Accumulation in The Cells

He counted 17 cast skins of nymphs in a single cell in which that many larvae had hatched within a few years, and concluded, from this observation, that the diameter of the cells or their capacity would undergo, in time, such a shrinkage that it would soon render them unfit for the use to which they were intended; a major inconvenience, which would endanger the hives in the most important point, by bringing forward such an obstacle to the propagation of the race. I have not witnessed so dire a catastrophe, but the accumulation of the nymphs' cast skins in the cells which serve to rear them is a positive fact.

A similar observation which I find in the memoirs of Réaumur, does not allow me to doubt that the bees have been instructed on how to bring their cells back to their original capacity and to the dimensions which facilitate the development of their young, for this author, who deserved our confidence in all regards, speaks of colonies which have lived for 30 years under his control. It is therefore certain that the cast skins of the larvae must have been removed in proper time and the cells cleaned up.

(Transcriber's Note 1. Dr. Roy Grout did the modern research and came to the same conclusion.)

In case the cells should need to be repaired, by treating them in a way similar to the method employed in repairing the damages of the moths, the bees would soon bring them back to their original condition. New wax being used in place of that which is damaged or altered by weather, mold, hive vapors, etc., the oldest hives may thus be apparently renovated. This faculty of restoration, which we employ ourselves, has perhaps been granted to other beings in the inferior orders, as possibly to the beavers. I do not know it, and such information can be ascertained only through visits and observations to so interesting a family with a more philosophical purpose than is common at present.

My correspondents in Mexico write me also of hives which exist at present at Tampico, and which are not less than 100 years old. The "flies" which inhabit them belong to the family of bees; they gather much honey, better, they say, and more perfumed, than that of our own bees. Wax is also abundant in the hives of Mexico. These American "flies" make with it "honey jars," as do our bumblebees, and cells for their brood; although the aim of their work is similar to that of our bees, their method is assuredly different.

It is in the recital of the trip of Captain Basis that you may find all that concerns the bees of Tampico. I have seen nothing, in the hive which I received from that country, which did not confirm the accounts of the English observer; his conjecture upon the absence of a sting has been verified by our own observers and confirmed by those of Mr. De La Treille, who found no sting on any of the bees of Mexico which we have submitted to the examination of this excellent observer.

More About the Waxmoth. To Mrs. Sophie De Portes,
Lausanne, Dec. 1, 1828

Did you not tell me, Sophie (Sophie was the mother of Eli-sa), that you have in Bois D'Ealy, probably in the attic, an old hive in which nothing is left but the combs? If I did not dream it, examine it at once, to ascertain its interior condition; the important thing is to ascertain whether it is or not tainted with moths. If it is, you will see it readily by bringing it to daylight (the webs woven by this dangerous enemy of bees will leave you no doubt) ; in that case, the hive should be destroyed for this reason: the wax, which is at the same time the home and the food of the larvae of the moths, conceals their nymphs whenever they have attained this degree of development, and from these nymphs will come a legion of small moths whose first care will be to scatter in early spring among your hives and those of your neighbors; it is there that the females of the species are to deposit their eggs.

You will ask me how it is that those so vigilant bees, ac-cording to my statements, allow such dangerous enemies to enter their homes, and why, knowing it, neither your friend nor anyone else has yet been able to protect them against these. Let us first exonerate the bees, we will then try to exonerate ourselves.

Fruitfulness of Nature

You have surely noted, while caring for the plants that you like, that surround you and that grow in our gardens, our fields, our woods, the enormous quantity of seeds which serve to their annual reproduction and at the same time to sustain the life of the numerous animals which feed upon them. To perpetuate the existence of a plant, of an oak, for instance, one or two acorns would suffice; it is by thousands that we number them. You know that a queen can give birth to thousands of beings of her kind. The great multiplication of pigeons, of canary birds, etc., is known to you. You probably do not believe that our planet could feed all the beings which are daily born in its different climates; are they therefore lost? No; nothing is lost under heaven. We lack neither hawks to catch our pigeons, nor wolves to destroy our sheep and reduce their number to that which our pastures can sustain; the equilibrium resulting from this wise disposition is one of the laws which conserve the universe. To have enough it was then necessary to sow too much. Before knowing all this, I remember a time when I cordially hated the enemies of the pigeons, of the sheep, of the bees, etc. I see now that those which I then called their natural enemies did not deserve that name; their existence, in my eyes now, is a boon of the Creator.

In spite of the wolves, the hawks, etc., created in the beginning of things, do we not still have now as many inoffensive doves, lambs, goats, bees, as we need? The number of the animals of prey is very small, while that of the animals which serve as their food is truly innumerable. Has Nature abandoned them without defense to the voracity of their pretended enemies? This is another thing which you cannot believe and you will be right; force alone is not sufficient for the bird of prey to master the game which nature has destined to it; ruse is also needed. Their doomed victims have also means of resistance; hunters know the means of defense that were granted to the game which they ordinarily pursue.

Since a Genevan observer (Jean Huber, father of Francois and a talented painter) studied the natural history of the birds of prey and has followed them with his eyes in the sky, we know their various modes of attack and those that are employed by the innocent and unarmed beings which are destined to serve them as food.

I have just told you that the waxmoth was one of the most dreaded enemies of bees; all our hives are exposed to their attacks, however not all perish under their efforts; the strongest escape their ravages, the weak alone are sacrificed.

If you are as anxious as I am to learn what has been prescribed to the bees to protect themselves, their young and their treasures, from the dreaded invasions of their natural enemies, your own observations can divulge it to you better than I could, and may amuse you, while teaching you a part of their natural history which is not without interest.

During all the good season the hives are exposed to the ravages of the moths; although safe during the day, it is in the evening that the phalaena tries to enter them (you will remember that this is the name which the naturalists give to the nocturnal butterflies, to distinguish them from the day butterflies).

Habits of The Moth

To fully see their maneuvers, moonlight will be necessary. Select summer evenings and place yourself in front of one of your best colonies and close to it. See what happens at the entrance, on the board upon which they rest. The more or less numerous guards will first draw your attention; notice especially those which walk about in front of their door; all will have their antennae extended and directed in front of their head, which fact will lead you to believe that it is feeling upon which they rely to know what happens, or might happen, to them, during the night time. You will not wait long before seeing some moths appear and recognizing their very marked desire to enter the hive, in spite of the guards and their fear of them. The phalaen evidently knows that there is some danger in approaching too near the guards; the timidity, the hesitancy of its bearing and all its motions indicate it; it is especially afraid of being met by the antennae; if those of the phalaen meet those of the worker, one sees the phalaen fly away at once; the bee, warned by this touch, of the presence of the enemy, dashes upon it, seizes it with her mandibles and destroys it quickly if it does not find means of escape.

If the phalaen of beeswax conducts itself in this occasion as if aware of the danger which it runs, in obeying the instinct which draws it to the entrance of the hive and which is nothing but the urgent necessity of laying its eggs in the only place assigned by Nature, its young also seem to be informed of the peril which their stealthy introduction by their mother within the pale of the hive incur. That which can help us to make progress in the knowledge of the customs and habits of animals, from the elephant down to the mite or to the least worm, is, to my feeling and to my taste, the most enjoyable part of the researches with which I am occupied. Allow me then to enter into a few details.

The egg of the wax-moth is very minute, the insect which hatches from it is no less so, perhaps more so; it would be difficult and unsafe to assert that it is not seized with some fears; from the time of its birth, its behavior permits little doubt of it.

Réaumur informs us that the first care of the hatching larvae is to hide within the thickness of the combs upon which the eggs from which they emerged were laid. To escape the vigilance of the bees and the results which this vigilance would unfailingly cause, it is not sufficient for these little larvae to bore through the wax, by eating that which is in their reach, and building for themselves a little cell in which they may be contained; it is also necessary that the bees should not perceive them; their organ of smell would soon cause them to discover them and exterminate them. The ability to weave a very strong silk has been granted to them; this silk serves them in building galleries or covered ways within which they can creep without being noticed and of which they increase the dimensions as fast as they grow and enlarge themselves. Another very singular thing is that their galleries are not made in the hexagonal cavities of the cells, where they would be too much exposed to the visits of the workers. It is always in the pyramidal bases of the cells that they direct and build the galleries, in which they may be better sheltered and crawl in safety. This skill would be very fatal to the bees, if they had no way to guard against it, but, as they are warned of the multiplying of this mortal enemy by touch, odor, or by some unknown sense, we see them rush upon the infected spot, break the cells and cut up the walls of those tubes, clear to the midrib of the comb; then, reaching the rhomboidal part, they pull to pieces the moths' soft galleries and the worms that they contain. This expedient succeeds very well when it is in strong colonies that the moths have dared enter; on the contrary, in those whose population has been too greatly depleted, it is the moths that prosper, the hives perish. If you visit them in those unhappy circumstances, you will find in them only the wax reduced to a black and noisome dust, and the bodies of such of the moths as have starved or have been chilled in their cocoons before having undergone their last transformation, that is to say, before they have reached the degree of development in which, as perfect insects, those little beings have nothing more to acquire. The wings with which they are then supplied permit them to leave their prison, to live a different life and to give life to others.

Let us see now whether it would have been possible for us to oppose their ravages; it would then have been necessary to find the means of preventing them from entering the hives. If anyone has tried it, he has soon found it impossible; since those dangerous phalaens, being smaller than the bees, could not be kept out through the reducing of the entrances. You will notice that Nature employs a much more energetic method to prevent the wax-worm from penetrating within the hive, it is by leaving that care to its natural guards.

The potato caterpillar or death'shead moth larva is the largest of those which inhabit our climate; in its moth condition it bears the name of "sphinx," and that of "atropos," which distinguishes it from others and foretells clearly the ravages which it may do within the hives. I have described them in a memoir to the British Library; if I can secure it, I will take from it that which would interest you. You will see there that everywhere the resources of Nature and the methods of conservation are infinite, as is the kindness of its divine Author.

Your friend, my dear girl, commends himself to your interest and to your indulgence which is as dear as it is necessary to him.

Influence of Harmony in The History of Bees. To Miss Elisa De Portes, Lausanne, February, 1829

Are the people with imagination more or less happy than others? If the pictures which they paint for themselves always come to life, they are surely to be envied, for, being masters of their palette, being always able to select their colors and assort them properly, their horizon is made up mainly of pleasant perspectives. They are, however, accused sometimes of painting too flattering images and to welcome with too much partiality air castles upon which wise and cool minds would never have stopped.

You see, dear Elisa, that it is of your teacher in natural history and one of the faults which he acknowledges, that it is now question. But do not believe him ungrateful in that which would surely be a great imperfection in his nature. This so-called teacher sees (every day in his life) a thousand reasons for thanking restoring Providence, which knows how to supply consoling chimeras, to those whom just but inexplicable decrees have deprived of realities which have been lavished upon others who would think it impossible to do without them. This morning, while thinking of you and rereading one of my letters in which I mention music in reference to that made by the swarms which I love so well, the thought came to me that the effect which it always produces upon me is not caused directly by the voice of the bees or of their drones, which, in certain occasions are heard in the air above our heads at such a distance that they can be heard only by good ears and seen by good eyes.

But whence does this music come, as well as the impression which it works upon me? My imagination is going to try to tell it to you. Do not too hurriedly reject this idea, a law of physics sustains this weak perception and seems to give it authority.

A resonant body, that is to say a bell, a bass string or a violin string, a flute, a harpsichord, a simple board, a cliff, being struck, produce sounds very different from the principal sound, which is only the product of the vibration of the air which surrounds the resonant body and which is brought to us by the undulations of the circumambient air.

These sounds which reach us are what is called the harmonics of the principal sound or of the resonant body whatever.

These harmonics are very distinct from the body that produces them, for they are always the major twelfth and seventeenth; these two notes, joined with the one from which they derive, constitute the perfect chord, chord supplied by nature, which supplies only that which is beautiful and consequently in tune.

If your harpsichord is in tune, strike the "do" (C) or any other note of the bass; if you select "do," strike at the same time, with the right hand, the "sol" (G), which is the twelfth, and the "mi" (E), higher up, which is the seventeenth. These notes, so far apart, will form a perfect chord, to me the most ravishing of all when it is performed by 15,000 to 20,000 bees, workers or drones . . .

To Miss Elisa De Portes, Lausanne, Feb. 8, 1829

For myself, rather than for you, my dear girl, I think best to add a few words to the end of my previous letter; having been hurried by the departure of the mail, or by some other circumstance, I did not end the subject which I had undertaken with you, as I should have done it, and you might very well ask me whether I have really heard the harmonics to which I attribute the charm that I always experience in the moment of the departure of a swarm. No, doubtless, those harmonics, much fainter than the sound from which they proceed, are never distinct enough for our ear to perceive them and separate them from the principal sound, that is to say that of the resonant body itself. But since every resonant body has its harmonics, their sound certainly reaches our ears, though we may not perceive it.

The three notes which compose it and which, by their reunion, form the most beautiful of all chords, may and must produce upon our nerves, upon our heart and upon our entire being, physically or morally, an effect which every person must have felt and appreciated in his or her way, effect which is not produced and cannot be produced by the isolated sound of the isolated body. To produce the sound which has always charmed me, the principal sound must be united, as it is in nature, with that of its two harmonics.

After having struck one of the low notes of your harpsichord, keep the finger on that key listen to the sound until you can no longer hear it, then your good ear will undoubtedly distinguish these harmonics. You will recognize easily, not the fifth of your "do," but its octave and higher the double-octave of the major third of the principal tone, or the "do" which is still under your finger. Of all the movements of the perfect chord, that which nature offers to us is undoubtedly the most beautiful.

Who knows, and who can tell, the feelings of the swarm, in the harmonious atmosphere with which it is surrounded? Would you not believe and say that this mass of sensitive beings surely experience some modification similar to that which this soft harmony causes in those who feel the impression of it as I do myself? If I had to say what I think in this regard, you surely do not doubt what my answer would be; it would not be in the negative.

After you have breathed, as I have, in the atmosphere of the swarms, the idea of the happiness of all those beings will surely take possession of you; you will be glad that it was granted to them. Penetrated as you are with recognition for all the gifts that are lavished upon us, you will thank the great Dispensator for having overlooked nothing which may make the least of its children happier.

The bees, very irritable by nature, do not seem so at all when it comes to swarming and do not allow themselves the least mutiny or reprisals for the ill treatments which they often withstand. Their mildness at that time allows us to enslave them and to make them our property. There is no doubt that the benefit is in our favor; let us become worthy of it. Let us treat those good bees, not as slaves, but as members of our family, as good laborers whose recognized services should be rewarded.

To Miss Elisa De Portes, Lausanne, Feb. 13, 1829
Do not blame your ear, my dear Elisa, if you have not perceived the harmonics which I have announced to you; it is on the viol, on the violoncello and on large violins that this

experiment succeeds best; it often fails on the harpsichord. I transcribe here what Rousseau says of it; it is the exact truth:

"If we vibrate with some force one of the large strings of a viol or of a violoncello, by striking it with the bow a little closer to the bridge than usual, we will hear distinctly, if we possess a trained and attentive ear, besides the sound of the string, at least also that of its octave, that of its octave fifth and that of the double octave of its third; we will even see all the strings vibrate and will hear the sound of all of them in consonance with those sounds. These accessory sounds always accompany a principal tone whatever it be, but when this principal tone is acute, the others are less sensitive to it."

The following is taken from the dictionary of music, at the word "Consonance:" "If I strike the chord "do"; the chords at its octave, at the third "mi" of the double octave, even at the octaves beyond, will all vibrate and resound together; and even if the first chord was alone, one would still distinguish all these sounds in its resonance; this takes for granted a good harpsichord, well in tune.

"The consonances are all produced by the perfect chord, itself produced by a single sound, and reciprocally the perfect chord is produced from the consonances. It is therefore natural that the harmony of this chord be communicated to all its parts, that each of the parts fill its place in it and that no other interval, which does not belong to this chord, should participate in it.

"Thus nature, which has given to all objects of each sense qualities proper to it, has decreed that any sound should be accompanied with other agreeing sounds, just as it decreed that a ray of light should be composed of the finest colors. If we press the question and ask whence comes the pleasure that the perfect chord gives to our ear, while the latter is shocked by the concourse of any other sound, how can we answer except with the question, in return, of why green rather than gray pleases the eye and why the perfume of the rose charms us while the odor of the poppy displeases us?"

My idea that the bees may enjoy their own music and that the pleasure which they find in it, by softening their irascibility momentarily, may render them happier, milder and more tractable, is perhaps, only a dream of my imagination, better fitted for the age when one sees everything of rose color, or sky-blue if you will. I love to think that you may listen with indulgence to that which may be judged by some others more severely.

My life observations have penetrated me with the sentiment that all that comes to us from the divine Author is lavished upon us, as well as upon the smaller creatures, with an endless kindness which can exist only through the omnipotence, which is infinite. I am therefore unable to refuse to estimable beings the enjoyment of pleasure which is in their reach and the result of which is happy for us; no intercourse would be possible between us and the bee species if their swarms preserved, at the time of their departure, the desire to resist our will as they might. See, in this, one additional favor; I have thought that it was worth while to point it out for your gratitude and that of my other cherished children.

Precautions to Be Used in Observing Bees. To Miss Elisa De Portes, Lausanne, May 17, 1829

Dear Eliza:

In a letter which has been misplaced, the question was, I believe, concerning the precautions to be used in beginning to observe bees; the first is to examine them from the side, in front one would run the risk that, upon their return from the field, one of them should get caught in your hair and sting you, in its irritation from being unable to escape from this net at its will. 2nd. You must not, in observing them, have the sun before your eyes, The direct light blinds, while if it is reflected one may observe better and more quietly. 3rd. One must not make quick motions near the hives nor permit others to make any. 4th. The hive which you observe must have shutters which may be opened and closed without jars or noise and which must be opened only during the observation; a continuous light would displease the bees and might determine them to establish curtains of wax inside, upon the panes which, blotting out their transparency, would render observations impossible.

Double flowers have no stamens and, therefore, no pollen; if you wish to please your bees, establish for them a bed of simple flowers which have all that is needed, sow buckwheat, rape, Reseda luteola, crimson clover, etc; that will be good for the days when you would not wish them to wander far from home. In the fine days they will not stop much upon the flowers within easy reach, as they will be more powerfully attracted by the great masses of flowers; it is upon our meadows and wherever there are flowers that you will see them rush and scatter in order to bring back to you their best crop.

Your glass hive must have a roof that will keep the moisture from it.

Hood for The Visit to the Hives. Swarm in a Flue. Uselessness of Noise to Stop Swarm. To Mrs. De Portes
Dear Madam:

I am at this moment in receipt of a letter from your spinster sister, which relieves me of a great anxiety; imagine that I wrote 6 letters in succession addressed to Bois-d'Ely without getting any reply and that I had concluded that you were all sick and that perhaps my young correspondent, a victim of her curiosity or of some imprudence, had been too ill-treated by the bees to write about it to her unhappy friend; there was nothing of the kind, thanks to the Lord.

I have upbraided myself for having failed to tell her of all the accidents which might follow too intimate an acquaintance with these interesting, but we must say also formidable beings; the word "hood," for instance, has not been mentioned in any of my letters, it should have been written in all of them. It is a large veil with which one covers oneself when visiting a pesthouse or when one causes a little vexation to the bees. It must be sewed around a broad round hat which keeps the bees sufficiently far from the face and from the neck. It is made of a very transparent muslin with broad sleeves that fasten to the wrists and are terminated with thick woolen gloves, that should be at least three lines thick so that the sting, which is only 2½ lines long, cannot reach the skin; the very loose tissue of these gloves permits the bees to withdraw their sting and thus save their lives. The lower part of the hood should reach down to the waist and be fastened there firmly, so the bees may not reach the upper part of the body. To protect ·the lower limbs, high shoes are useful. I beg pardon for all these details.

For want of having followed this advice rigidly, Burnens, my very faithful Burnens, was once stung on the face, on the neck and on the breast, by so great a number of bees that a high fever followed, changed to a quartan fever (ague) with which he suffered for nearly a year, but which, however, did not prevent this good man from continuing his occupations with the bees; he gave them his attention and his cares, in the intervals of the attacks. Tell all this to your kind Elisa.

Please also tell her that I several times wished to take possession of a swarm which has unfortunately established its home in a chimney flue; but that, considering the great danger of this operation for a gardener or a chimney-sweep, even the most skilful and boldest, I have not attempted to secure them out of this singular abode and I still believe the deed impossible or too dangerous. Let us leave those bees then, to their unhappy fate; if fire is built in the chimney, the smoke will soon smother them; if no fire is made and they are left alone, they may swarm next year, or perhaps even this year; we will only need to watch them.

The custom of beating kettles and caldrons has been practiced at all times and I believe everywhere, and I do not understand any better than you do what influence it could have.

(Translators Note: Aristotle, who lived over 2200 years ago, tells, in his "Story of Animals," Lib. IX: "Bees seem to have a liking for noise and from this observation it is claimed that, by making a noise and striking upon earthen jars, one can gather the swarm in the hive. However, whether they hear or not, we do not know whether it is pleasure or fear which induces them to gather together when there is a noise.")

The bees which are hived in glass hives do not seem to take any notice of thunder. I have caused the beating of drums about my apiary and, although I used, to make a noise, all the cauldrons, The watering-pots and the bells, that has never succeeded in stopping a flying swarm for me; one succeeds a great deal better in this by throwing at them water or dirt. This prejudice has perhaps been established for the benefit of bee owners, who, knowing through this noise that a swarm is out, soon ascertain whether it has escaped from their apiary and may claim it; I have seen that reason in Oliver De Serres' or in some other agricultural book.

Metamorphosis of the Bees up to Their Perfect Condition— The Laying of Eggs. To Miss Elisa De Portes, Lausanne, June, 1829

My Dear Eliza:

Let us come to your questions. This form of conversation suits me as it suits you; I will not even change the order in which they have presented themselves to your mind.

You wish to see some eggs and our dear Madeline shares your desire. That which you saw in your first observation was not eggs, but young larvae which had just hatched from them, and the queen of the hive had begun her laying 3 days before their appearance under the shape of grubs, for the grub or the larva of the bee passes 3 days in the shape of an egg. To make sure of it, I removed eggs from my young queens at the moment when they had been laid in the proper cells; those cells cut out of the combs, were put inside of small screened boxes in the center of their own hive, in order to learn : 1, whether the larvae of bees needed the care of the workers in their first state; 2, whether it was sufficient, for their hatching, that they be exposed to the heat which they incite about them and which raises the temperature of the hive to the 27th, 28th and almost 29th degree of the Reaumur thermometer (93 to 97 degrees F.) A glance upon this box, daily, displayed them to us 1irst as small, white, oblong bodies, larger at one end than at the other and about one line in length, the apparently milky fluid which filled them seemed homogeneous and had no organism.

On the second day, the appearance was different. By exposing the box to a strong light, we saw, through the transparent membrane which served as the shield of the egg, some very thin and very indistinct filaments which reminded us first of the tracheae—which are the respiratory organs of worms—or of muscles, which are the organs of motion; the enveloping membrane was still unaltered at that time. The following day, or third day, the twelve rings which form the body of the larval were visible, but still through the environing membrane. Continuing our observations, we noticed very marked motions within those eggs: they curved and straightened alternately, slowly at first, more quickly later. At the end of a few minutes, the membrane of the egg was torn at its large end; the head of the worm appeared then. The continuation of the same motions soon split the membrane to pieces from the back to the tail; its fall permitted us to see the naked worm, which, probably tired by its own efforts, sunk down and appeared to us in the slightly curved shape which you noticed.

We conclude from all this that: 1, the queen bee is oviparous like our hens, that is to say her young are not alive when she brings them forth; 2, neither the queen nor the bees give them any care as long as they are in the shape of eggs. The membrane which envelops them would not permit the workers to reach them for feeding them or to care for them, any more than the shield of the egg permits the hen to do it; so the necessary cares are reduced to incubation of the young during the first part of their existence.

Laying of the Queen

I have just stated to you that the laying queen must place her eggs properly in the cells prepared by the workers; you will soon see that they build cells of different kinds, large and small. The large ones serve as cradles for the drones, the small ones for the workers. They have two principal parts, the tube and the bottom; the tubes are composed of six sides and the bottoms of three only. The walls are trapezia, that is to say geometrical figures, of which two sides are parallel and the other two are not. The ensemble of these pieces constitutes hexagons. The bottoms are made of three pieces in lozenges or rhombs, which when assembled give them the form of a depressed pyramid.

I will mention the royal cells at the proper time; let us return to the queen making haste to lay. We see her walking about the combs, whether they are entirely composed of drone cells or of common worker cells. She looks into their apertures, that is to say she dips her antennae into their tubes and even sinks in her head, which she withdraws only after having examined the cell, or, if you please, after having "felt" it in the inside, as if to make sure that it is clean and fit to receive the egg which she proposes to deposit in it. She then turns about and inserts her abdomen into the cell that she has just examined. Believe my statement, or better still, that of the great Reaumur, however incredible what I am about to relate. Whatever be the diameter of the cell in which she has laid under your eyes, you will always see a drone hatch from a large cell and a worker from a small one. Is the queen then endowed with a faculty which has not been granted to other females, that of knowing the sex of the being which she is about to produce, and never to make a mistake, for it is not by mistake that she behaves differently in certain circumstances?

Care of the Larvae

If at that time the young larvae have received no care, either from the mother or from that legion of nurses with which they are surrounded, everything changes at the time of their actual hatching; the larvae, from then on, are the object of constant solicitude on the part of the workers. It was necessary to make sure of this. Burnens would tell you that he never found a minute when the larvae were neglected. The body of the workers, or rather their corslet, fills the cell so well that it is impossible to see what the workers are doing in it, who keep their head and and a large part of their body sunk within it and who, if other cares are required of them, are at once replaced by their companions. To see what they have done, disturb them by pushing them aside lightly with the end of a feather or by blowing on them. You will then see the little larva coiled on the bottom of the cell; its body, slightly curved, will have its concavity turned the same way.

If the cell in question is in a good light, you will see something shine at its bottom which resembles jelly, or rather pap; I will retain this word which it deserves as the first food of infancy among bees as well as among ourselves. You might wish to taste it; a hair pencil will help you to take a bit of it. If you rob very young larvae of their breakfast, you will find their pap rather unpleasant and without any distinct flavor. By repeating this experience the following days, as Reaumur did before we did, you will find that it becomes better every day and that on the fifth day it has acquired all the perfection of which it is susceptible. It is precisely then that the workers close the cells with a cover of wax and that the larvae begin to weave the silk web which is to line them. By looking still closer, it will appear to you that this pap has been placed exactly before the mouth of the young larva; you will surmise that it is for the purpose of attracting it. As it has neither feet nor legs, it may come only by stretching its rings; the first one, near the head, attracted by its odor, comes first, the second follows this motion, etc.

The larva of the worker has thus spent the first three days of its life in the egg state, avoiding our eyes; I have told you what we could ascertain with the help of the magnifying glass.

The five days following, the cell being open, we might have seen it distinctly were it not for the interposition of the nurse's body which watched its actions and supplied its wants, which we could ascertain only by pushing her aside.

Spinning the Cocoon

You now know about the first eight days of its life. Everything will change on the ninth, it does not need to be fed any longer, it is time to wean it; the nurse may leave it and shut it up in its cell. Will it remain inactive? You do not think it; another idea has seized it, pardon this expression for want of another; it is the desire of sheltering its body against any friction which might be noxious, against even the air which might too quickly hasten the evaporation which must be imperceptible. How will it succeed in this? Does it possess a spinneret as does the larva of the silk worm? Does it know how to spin? I often found silk in shells that had been inhabited by some flies; in order to ascertain that the larvae of bees use the same expedient as so many other insects, I procured glass tubes with the imperfect shape of the bee's cell, but of about exact dimensions. Burnens removed from their cells larvae nine or ten days old and enclosed them within these glass cells. This experience succeeded; the larvae spinned cocoons; we were able to see their maneuvers until they were surrounded with a silky tapestry and disappeared from our sight. (It appears that this work occupies them for 36 hours, at least. Three hours afterwards they were metamorphosed into nymphs and spent seven and one-half days in this shape.

The larvae of workers reach their last condition, that of winged insects, only on the twentieth day of their life, from the instant when the egg from which they come was laid.

Ventilation. To Miss Elisa De Portes, Lausanne, June 14, 1829

Dear Eliza:

When the prophet-king urged us to look at the ant and the bee, he gave us advice of high wisdom.

The mother cannot always be there. Among the bees, as you perceived, her presence, so necessary at this first epoch, is marvelously filled by the worker, who watches the young larva until the time when it may go about and take care of itself. When the good nurse is compelled to go elsewhere, her place is always filled and one may say that the cradle of the young bee is never abandoned. The cleanliness of the hive is another point which is strongly recommended to the bees. I suspect that the purpose of Nature in this occasion is to preserve the purity and therefore the salubrity of the air in the hives.

Now that you have a hive that you can watch and can see for yourself, instead of telling you what I have seen, I will point out to you what you have to see which may interest you and instruct you.

Are you acquainted with the useful invention of ventilators? One can readily force air through all parts of any space. A door or an open window would not be sufficient to operate its renewal; for that purpose two opposite openings are needed. The ventilator, when applied in a window or in a hole of the wall, by allowing the air to enter or exit alternately produces, through this double play, the effect of two opposite openings. The air set in motion at the entrance of a hive penetrates within it necessarily; a stroke from the fan in your hand does not bring the air to your cheek any better than the motion of a ventilator brings the outside air to the inside of the hive to replace an equal volume of the inner air, and that operates the renewal.

You will surely ask me where that ventilator is found, when the ventilation of the hive and of the bees is at stake. Seek for it yourself and you will find it. It is not within the hive that it must be placed; neither is it within the door, the space of which, needed for the passage of the bees must not be obstructed; it will therefore be on the outside of the hive and opposite the entrance that it must be established and that you must look for it.

What do you see there, kind Eliza? Workers going about their affairs and going without stopping; you see nothing there reminding you of a ventilator; but let us look closer. Among these bees in action do you not notice some which appear stationary? It is upon the stand, in the part which juts out from the hive, that those bees are located. A very simple figure will give you a just idea of the manner in which they are ranged there, that is: c, supposed to be the center of the hive; a, b, its door; it is upon the imaginary lines which form the sides of this angle that the ventilating bees stand.

Try to perceive their wings. What are they doing with them, please? Tell me, if you can, their number and their shape, their direction, etc. You cannot do it. All this disappears and shows you only a shapeless little cloud around each bee; it is due to the extreme rapidity of their motion.

One can produce the same illusion by agitating rapidly a stick, one end of which is afire.

But how does it happen that so great a motion of their wings does not cause them to take fight? Look at their attitude, it will tell you better than any words could do it; their corslets draw very closely to the stand, the abdomen is away from it; their six legs, especially, appear to sink within the position; they are like so many anchors, with which they are fastened down.

The ventilating bees are far enough apart to be out of each other's way; I even believe that the going and coming bees avoid approaching them, so as not to be struck and confused by the beating wings.

Experience was to teach me whether the living ventilators had upon the hives as salutary an influence as those which we invent have upon the air of our apartments and the halls in which many people assemble daily. You divine the test which came to my mind and which proved conclusive.

The only question was to deprive a swarm, for a few moments, of its natural ventilators, by closing the hive. The result was asphyxy or apparent death of the entire population; by restoring the air with the ventilators, the swarm was soon brought back to life.

The advice of the prophet-king showed us, in the behavior of the bees and of the ants, the example which we have to follow. The first childhood, cared for by us as with their young, all their needs foreseen and provided for; who knows but that the least fancies and the most tender caresses have been bestowed? The gentleness which I saw them lavish and use in all their motions would indicate it and would tend to avoid the unpleasant effects that contrary ways might have upon, irritable beings; those inspired by kind Nature cannot cause any such inconveniences.

Harvest of Pollen and Honey. To Miss Elisa De Portes, Lausanne, June 15, 1829

Dear Eliza:

Treasures were bestowed upon our bees, my dear girl; the honey which they find ready-made in the nectaries of the flowers and the pollen in their anthers.

Your new hive must have taught you already, if you did not know it, that it is in the cells of the combs that these two precious substances are deposited. Honey is the food of the adult bees and pollen is the basis of the pap which they feed to their young. The cells, which are intended to receive the eggs laid by the mother, later are the cradles and later still the store rooms.

It is with their tongue or broom (balai) that the honey is gathered from the flowers. To transport it to the hive, the bee must swallow it; by contracting her stomach she can at will bring it back to her mouth and disgorge it wherever she pleases, through her proboscis. I advise you to try to see this with your own eyes, remembering that I see nothing with mine, and you will be kind enough to tell me what you have seen. Take note of your observations for this purpose, it will probably not be for you an unpleasant task and it may be useful to you.

Let us come now to the pollen. They called it formerly the dust of the stamens; since its most marvelous use has been known, it is designated the name of fecundating dust.

Conceive, my dear child, that these almost microscopic grains, with which the anthers, that is to say the top of the stamens, are filled, are the life-giving principle of the entire vegetable kingdom. Whether this little box, with which you are acquainted, opens spontaneously at its maturity and becomes the toy of the winds, or whether it is accidentally carried and deposited, by some insect, upon the pistils, it penetrates them and reaches the germs or the eggs, its touch is sufficient to fertilize them, that is to say to render them capable of reproduction. Without pollen, no fruits.

I do not ask you to excuse these long details, you realize their interest.

But you will want to know how the bees secure the fecundating dust to make with it the food for their young. This question also attracted the attention of the naturalists; I had the same curiosity, but neither Reaumur nor your friend have completely solved it, to my mind. The speed of the motions of the worker, when she is busy with this harvest, does not permit to distinguish them clearly, but you must judge of this for yourself; I do not give up the hope that your young eyes may be more successful than ours in seeing the little details which may have escaped us.

Gathering Pollen

Approach, then, a plant in full bloom that may have around it some bees whose attention has been also drawn by it. You will first see some that want the honey and that, more or less buried within the calyx of the blossom, seek for it in its nectaries. These are not the ones that you must watch; see rather, among those workers that fly above the flower without apparently touching it, whether there is one which makes extraordinary motions in the air. You will notice that it is the six legs which are moving below its body. You will understand, as your elders did, that this bee must have begun by opening the anther with its mandibles and removing that which interests her, and as the anther contains only pollen and as you see some of this pollen in the little triangular basket of the legs of the third pair, simple common sense will inform you that the mandibles of the bee have given what they took to the first pair of legs, that this pair, after having packed and brought it together, transmitted it to the second pair and that the little ball, evidently increased, finally reaches the basket; from there it is transported to the cell, where you have found it yourself. You will notice that there is something here to guess; it is not exactly as I stated it that the thing happens, but by holding to it, we are not very far from the truth.

That which we have best seen is the care which the bees take to arrange these pellets of pollen in the cells which are to serve as store rooms. For that purpose they must back into the cell, empty their pollen baskets, and press with their feet the pellets against one another, to cause a greater number to be packed in the least possible space; it does not appear that those cells are ever sealed.

When it is a question of existence or conservation, no precaution appears useless or too minute. Nothing in this respect has been neglected in what concerns the bees; to bring home in safety the honey and the pollen which they have just harvested is therefore an important matter, for their life depends upon it. You wish to know how they manage to run no risk: the too thin honey may not be held within the open canal of the proboscis, it would leak out and be lost on the way, and its odor, attracting the numerous insects that are fond of it, it would not fail to be robbed away after having caused dangerous flights; to transport it to the hive without losing any of it, the bees can do no better than hide it away within their stomach and empty it promptly within the cell which is intended as a store-room. You know that a simple contraction of the honeysack is sufficient to cause the honey to return to the mouth and secure its disgorgement.

You have surely learned before this that it is only after the bee has swallowed the honey and disgorged it that we can eat it ourselves, and I trust this will not disgust you with it. The young larvae are subject to the same law, pollen is used by them only after it has been eaten by the nurses and has undergone in their stomach (1) a modification or elaboration which converts it into a jelly and makes of it a pap appropriate to their requirements. It is by an analogous operation that the food of the females of larger animals is changed to milk within the mother's breast.

The differences which Mr. Reaumur has observed in the flavor of this pap, during the few days when the larvae have to feed upon it, indicate undoubtedly that some substances unknown to us have been mixed with it to proportionate the food with the age and the changing needs of the larva; this improvement is best perceived when one compares the flatness of the pap during the first days, with the much more pungent flavor which it acquires at the end of its distribution. Would not these changes in the flavor of the pap be rather the effect of a fermentation caused by the warmth of the hive, than the mixture of foreign substances with it? That which would cause me to believe it is that these changes take place in winter when the queen begins her laying, at a time when the bees can bring nothing home from the outside. The proofs of this in the next mail.

Upon Pollen and the Use Made of it by the Bees, Which Differs Essenentially From What Was Believed Before. To Miss Elisa De Portes, Lausanne, June 22, 1829

Dear Eliza:

You did me a real pleasure, my dear girl, in telling me that you had secured a glazed hive; you had guessed that you were doing much for your instruction and amusement; to see things by yourself or to know them only through simple recitals is assuredly very different. You have also thereby facilitated the little explanations that I might have to give you and I am not afraid of your not comprehending me when I speak to you of combs, workers, drones, royal cells, etc.

But where did we leave off? I believe I promised you, at the end of my last letter, to give you the proofs by which I was able to say that the fecundating dust of the flowers was the basis of the food which the bees give to their young; it was for the purpose of not making the letter too lengthy that I closed it without going farther.

When I published my first observations, I believed, as did Reaumur, Bonnet and all the naturalists whose writings I knew and prized, that it had, with the bees, another purpose, which was of producing their wax. (Note: It is known at present that the origin of the wax scales had already been discovered in Germany, and by the Swiss, Duchet.-Editor.) It was only in 1793, during a stay which I made at La Liniere, that I was compelled to abandon this opinion.

One day, while I was watching the bees of the farmer of this country place, Burnens made a very singular observation, which had escaped the attention of all our forebears; this apiary was composed of hives of more or less age, the greater number were filled with combs and had no more room for new cells: five or six hives had just been stocked with new colonies. We saw, to our great wonder, that the bees that returned from the fields brought back a great deal of pollen in the old hives and brought none at all in the hives which were inhabited by the new swarms; there was a problem of which we had to seek the explanation; it required but a moment of reflection, and I was almost ashamed of not having thought of it sooner. Here was my reasoning, which was not beyond the reach of a child:

The bees which compose the swarm find the hive which they have selected entirely deprived of everything; but what do they need? Cells to receive the eggs of their queen; but those cells must be made of wax; should it not be at that time that pollen would have been most necessary to them? Would you then not have concluded that it was useless? Remember, my dear friend, first, that the larva enclosed within the egg hatches only on the third day from the time when it was laid, and second, that during those three days the expected larva does not need to eat; it is then for that reason that the kind nurses dispense with the bringing in of pollen; if, on the contrary, they bring a great deal of it in the cells of the old hives which are all inhabited by larvae one to five days old, is it not very probable that it is in order that it may be used as feed?

Source of Wax

Pollen is not the only substance that the bees seek and harvest upon the blossoms of our meadows and of our gardens; is then the honey which they bring in their stomachs the primary constituent of beeswax? I will acknowledge to you that I did not suspect it, but I felt that these facts, so important in the history of bees, needed to be confirmed by experiment; I had a colony which had become useless through the sterility of its queen; we sacrificed it for this experiment. It was in one of my leaf hives, of which both ends were glazed. W e removed the queen and substituted, in place of the combs of the first and last leaves, some combs filled with brood, that is to say occupied with eggs and young larvae, but we left in them no cells containing pollen.

The behavior of the bees in these circumstances deserves some attention. During the first and second days nothing extraordinary happened, the bees covered their young and appeared to take great care of them. But on the third day, after sunset, we heard a great noise in that hive. Desirous of knowing what occasioned it, we opened one of the shutters and noticed that all was confusion in there: the brood was neglected, the bees were running about the combs in disorder; we saw them rush down by thousands to the bottom of the hive; those that were near the entrance were gnawing with fierceness the screen with which it had been closed; their intentions were unequivocal, they wanted to emerge from their prison. It must have been that an imperious necessity was compelling them to seek elsewhere that which they could not find in the hive. I feared to see them perish by preventing them any longer from yielding to their instinct; we gave them liberty. The entire swarm emerged, but the hour was not favorable for the harvest, the bees did not stray from the hive, they flew about; the growing obscurity and the coldness of the air soon compelled them to return there. The same causes probably calmed their agitation, for we saw them peaceably climb back upon the combs, order appeared re-established; we took advantage of this moment to again close the hive.

The next day, July 19, we saw two royal cells which the bees had begun on one of the brood combs. In the evening, at the same hour as on the preceding evening, we again heard a great roar in the closed hive; agitation and disorder were displayed in the highest degree; we were again compelled to allow the issue of the bees; they were not long outside of their home; the bees, pacified, returned as they did on the preceding day.

On the 20th, we noticed that the royal cells had not been proceeded with; they should have been, in the ordinary status of things. In the evening, again a tumult, the bees appeared in delirium; we gave them liberty and order was again established upon their return.

Feeding Pollen

The captivity of these bees lasted five days; we considered it useless to continue it. On the other hand, we wanted to know whether the brood was in good condition, whether it had made the customary progress, and try to divine what could be the cause of the periodical agitation of the bees. Burnens brought to the light of day the two combs of brood which he had given them.

He first took note of the royal cells, but he did not find them enlarged; in fact, why should they have been? They contained neither eggs nor larvae, nor even the jelly which is peculiarly provided for the individuals of this class; the other cells were also deserted, no brood, not an atom of pap; the worms had starved to death. By suppressing the pollen, had we taken from the bees all means of nourishing them? To decide this question, it was necessary to entrust to these bees some more brood to care for, while giving them abundance of pollen; they had not had any occasion to make a harvest while we examined their combs; this time they had been freed in a room the windows of which were closed. After having substituted young larvae in place of those which they had allowed to perish, we again confined them in their prison.

The following day, 22nd, we noticed that they had regained courage. They had strengthened the combs which we had given them and were staying upon the brood. We then gave them some fragments of combs in which other workers had stored some fecundating dust; but in order to see what they would do with it, we took some pollen out of a few cells and spread it upon the floor of the hive. The bees at once noticed this, as well as that which was contained in the combs; they took the pellets with their mandibles and into their mouths; those which had taken of it the most greedily were the first to again climb upon the combs; they stopped upon the cells containing young worms, went into them head first and remained in them more or less time. Burnens opened carefully one of the panes of the hive and dusted the workers which ate pollen so as to recognize them when they would climb upon the combs. He observed them for several hours and made sure, by this means, that they were taking pollen only to give it to their nurslings.

On the 23rd we saw some royal cells outlined.

On the 24th we pushed aside the bees which covered the brood, and we noticed that all the young larvae had pap just as in the ordinary hives; that they had grown and had lengthened themselves in their cells; that others had been newly sealed, because they were nearing their metamorphosis; lastly, we no longer doubted of the re-establishing of good order when we saw the royal cells lengthening. Out of curiosity, we removed the fragments of combs which we had placed upon the bottom-board and saw that the quantity of pollen in them was considerably reduced; we returned them to the bees, at the same time adding to their stock, so as to prolong the performance. Before long we saw the royal cells sealed as well as several of the common cells. We opened the hive, everywhere the worms had prospered; the ones had still before them their food, others had weaved and their cells were closed with wax. This result was already quite striking; but that which excited our astonishment was that, in spite of their long sustained captivity, the bees no longer seemed anxious to fly out; we did not any longer notice the agitation, the growing and periodical excitement, the general impatience which they had manifested in the first experiment; although some bees attempted to escape during the day, they soon saw the impossibility of it and peaceably returned to their young.

This trait, which we have seen several times, and always with the same interest, proves so clearly the affection of bees for the larvae whose rearing is entrusted to them, that we need not seek elsewhere an explanation of their behavior. John Hunter studied bees and conjectured, long before we did, that the pollen of flowers was the basis of the jelly or of the food that the bees give to their young in the larval state. See the Encyclopedic Journal for the year 1792.

Concerning your glass hive, I must advise you, my dear girl, to glass it also in its lower part; for that purpose, you will need to substitute, next spring, two ekes similar to those that you have given them, but which will have panes of glass and shutters in the parts corresponding to the observable sides of the hive body.

Origin of Beeswax. To Miss Elisa De Portes, Lausanne, June 23, 1829

The reasoning which had led me to doubt of the pollen being the raw material for beeswax and the experiments which changed this doubt into a certainty, as you have seen in my preceding letter, brought the thought forcibly upon me that honey, being the only harvest which bees made in addition to pollen, the uselessness of which had been fully demonstrated for this purpose, honey was the only product remaining to which we might look for the origin of beeswax but it was necessary to make sure of it; the reverse of the preceding tests was indicated as necessary and appeared to me to be likely to bring out the solution of this new problem.

It was only necessary then to retain the bees in their hives and thus prevent them from gathering, or feeding upon any of the fecundating dust. It was on the 24th of May that we made this experiment upon a swarm which had lately issued from the mother colony.

We hived this swarm into an empty straw hive, with what was needed of honey and water for the consumption of the bees and we closed the entrance with care in order to prevent any possibility of flight; we left, however, a free passage for air, the renewal of which would be needed for the captive bees. They were at first much excited; we succeeded in quieting them by placing their hive in a cool and dark spot. Their captivity lasted during five whole days; at the end of this time we allowed them to take wing in a room, the windows of which were carefully closed. We were then able to visit their hive more commodiously; they had consumed their store of honey, but the hive, which did not contain an atom of wax when we hived them in it, had acquired, in the five days, five combs of the finest wax. They were suspended at the ceiling of the skep, the structure of them was of a perfect white color and of great fragility. This result, from which we will not yet draw the consequences, was already very remarkable; we had not expected so prompt and complete a solution of the problem. However, before concluding that the honey with which they had been fed had alone caused them to be able to produce wax. it was necessary to make sure, through other evidences, that no other explanation was possible.

The workers which we held captive might have gathered the fecundating dust while they were at liberty; they might have taken supplies of it the day previous or even on the day of their confinement and have enough of it left in their stomachs or in their pollen-baskets to produce from it all the wax which we had found in their hive. But in case it was true that it was produced from the fecundating dust harvested previously, this source was not inexhaustible and the bees unable to secure more, would soon cease to construct combs; we would see them fall into complete inaction. So it was necessary to continue the test in order to make it decisive. Before attempting another experiment, we carefully removed all the combs which the bees had built during their captivity. Burnens, with his usual skill, caused all the bees to return to the hive; he closed them up in it, as he did the first time, with a new supply of honey. This test did not require a long time; we noticed. as early as the evening of the following day, that the bees were working with new wax ; the third day we came to visit the hive and found indeed five new combs as regular as those which they had made during their first experiment. We removed the combs thus five times in succession, being always careful not to allow any of the bees to escape outdoors; they were still the same bees. They were fed solely with honey during this long confinement which we might have prolonged with similar success had we judged it necessary.

Each time that we gave them honey, they built new combs; it was therefore doubtless that this food incited in them the secretion of wax without the help of fecundating dust, but it was not improbable that pollen might have the same virtue. We were not slow in clearing up this doubt, through a new experiment which was only the reverse of the previous one.

This time, instead of giving honey to the bees, we gave them only fruits and pollen; we closed them up under a bell glass under which we had placed a comb containing only accumulated fecundating dust. Their captivity lasted eight days, during which they did not make any comb; we did not see any wax scales under their abdominal rings. Was it then possible to raise any doubts about the origin of wax? We had none.

Could one say that beeswax is contained within the honey and that those bees set it aside from the liquid to use it when they need it? This last objection was not without likelihood, for honey most always contains parcels of wax, we see it rise to the surface when it is diluted with water; but the microscope, by informing us that those particles of wax had belonged to cells already built, that they had the shape and the thickness of the rhombs, sometimes of the broken sides of the cells. enlightened us upon the thought which had stopped us for an instant.

In order to answer in a positive manner this objection and to enlighten ourselves on an opinion which we held particularly, to-wit: that the sweet principle was the true cause of wax secretion, we took a pound of Canary sugar reduced to a syrup, which we gave to a swarm enclosed within a glass hive. We made this experience still more instructive by establishing for comparison two other hives in which we introduced swarms which were fed, the one with dark brown sugar, the other with honey.

The result of this triple test was as satisfactory as it was possible to hope.

The bees of all three hives produced wax. Those which had been fed with sugar of different qualities yielded it even more abundantly than those which had been fed only with honey.

A pound of Canary sugar, reduced to syrup and clarified with the white of an egg, produced 10 gros, 52 grains (1/4 ounce or 7.2 grams) of a wax less white than that which the bees produced with honey.

The brown sugar, in equal amount gave 22 gros (1/2 ounce or 15 grams) of very white wax; the sugar of maple produced the same thing.

To make sure of these results, we repeated this experiment seven times in succession with the same bees, and we always obtained wax in about the same proportions as indicated above.

It therefore appears demonstrated to us that sugar, or the sweet part of honey, places the bees that feed upon it in a position to produce wax, a property which the fecundating dust does not possess.

The facts which these experiments taught us soon received a more general confirmation; although no uncertainty remained any longer upon those questions, there remained to ascertain whether the bees in natural condition behaved as did those which we had held captive. A long series of observations, of which I will give here but an outline, prove to us that when the fields offer to the bees a large crop of honey, the bees of the old colonies store it eagerly, while those of the new swarms convert it into wax.

I did not then have a large number of colonies, but those of my neighbors, country people for the greater number, were used in comparison, although the hives were made of straw and did not offer the same conveniences as my own.

Some special remarks which we made upon the appearance of the combs and of the bees themselves when they work in wax allowed us to take advantage of those hives so inconvenient for observations.

Beeswax is white at its origin, soon afterwards the cells become yellow; with time this color becomes darker and when the hives are very old their combs have a blackish cast. It is therefore very easy to distinguish the new cells from those which have been built previously and consequently to know whether the bees are presently building combs or whether the work has been suspended. It is sufficient, in order to make sure of it, to raise up the hive and glance at the lower edge of the combs.

Observations on The Secretion of Wax

The following observations furnish us indications of the presence of honey in the flowers. They were made upon a rather remarkable fact, which was not known of our forebears;

it is that there are two kinds of workers in the same hives; the ones susceptible of acquiring a considerable size after they have taken all the honey that their stomachs could contain, and are intended generally for producing wax; the others, whose abdomen does not change perceptibly in its dimension, take or keep only the quantity of honey which is necessary for them to live and give out to their companions the surplus which they have gathered. They are not in charge of the provisioning of the hive, their particular functions are caring for the young; we will call them nurse-bees or small bees, in opposition to those whose abdomen may be dilated and who deserve the name of comb-builders.

Although the exterior signs by which the bees of both sorts may be recognized are not numerous, this distinction is not at all imaginary.

Anatomical observations have taught us that there is a real difference in the capacity of their stomachs; we have made sure through positive experiments that the bees of one kind could not alone fulfill the functions which are apportioned out between the workers of the same hive.

In one of these tests, we painted with different colors those of each class to observe their behavior, and we did not see them change their role.

In another hive, we gave to the bees, deprived of their queen, some brood and pollen. We immediately saw the small bees feeding the larvae, while those of the wax-making class took no care of them.

When the hives are full of combs, the wax-producers disgorge their honey into the ordinary storage cells and make no wax; but if they have no cells to deposit it and if their queen finds no empty cells to deposit her eggs, they keep within their stomach the honey which they have gathered and, at the end of 24 hours, the wax oozes out between their rings; then the work of comb-building commences. One might think that, when the fields do not furnish any honey, the wax-workers might pounce upon the provisions stored in the combs, but they are not permitted to touch them. A part of the honey is carefully put away, the cells in which it is deposited are sheltered with a capping of wax which is removed only in case of extreme need and when it is impossible to secure any elsewhere; they are never opened during the good season. Other cells, always open, supply the daily needs of the colony, but each bee takes only as much of it as she needs to satisfy a pressing want.

One does not see the wax-builders show themselves at the entrance of the hive, with big abdomens, when they return from the field and have made a great harvest there; they produce wax only when their hive is not filled with combs.

One conceives, from what I have just said, that the production of the waxy substance depends upon a concourse of circumstances which do not always present themselves. The small bees also produce wax, but always an amount very inferior to that which the true wax-workers elaborate.

Another characteristic through which an attentive observer will not fail to recognize the moment when the bees gather enough honey upon the flowers to produce wax, is the odor of honey and wax which is strongly emitted from the hives at that time, an odor which does not exist with this intensity at any other time. From these data it was easy for us to recognize whether the bees worked at comb building in our hives and in those of the farmers of the same canton.

In 1793, the inclemency of the season delayed the going forth of the swarms; there were none in the country before the 20th of May; the greater number of the hives swarmed in the middle of June. The country was at the time covered with bloom; the bees harvested much honey and the new swarms worked in wax-building with activity. On the 18th, Burnens examined 65 hives; he saw wax-workers at every entrance; those which entered the old hives immediately put away their crops and built no combs, but those of the swarms converted their honey into wax and hastened to prepare cells for the eggs of their queens.

On the 19th it rained in intervals; the bees flew, but one could not see any wax-workers, they brought only pollen; the weather was cold and rainy until the 27th. We desired to know what was the result of this condition of the atmosphere.

On the 28th, we raised all the baskets, Burnens saw then that the work had been interrupted; the combs which he had measured on the 9th had not received the least increase, they were of lemon color; there were no longer any white cells in any of those hives.

On the 1st day of July the temperature being higher, the chestnuts and the basswoods in bloom, we again saw the wax-builders. They brought back much honey, the swarms lengthened their combs, we saw everywhere the greatest activity; the honey crop and wax building continued until the middle of the month.

The year was, therefore, very favorable to the work of the bees; I attributed it in part to the condition of the atmosphere, which was loaded with electricity, a circumstance which has great influence upon secretion of honey in the nectaries of flowers. I have noticed that the crop is never more abundant and the wax-working more active than when a storm is preparing, when the wind is in the south the air moist and warm; but too lengthy hot weather, the drought that follows, cold rains and north wind suspend entirely the elaboration of honey in the plants and consequently also the operations of the bees.

Concerning Ventilation. To Miss Elisa De Portes, Lausanne, June, 1829

How happy I am, my dear friend, to see your mother, your aunt and yourself occupied with a subject which has much interested me and which offers observations so singular that, in spite of my confidence in the worthy Burnens, I am delighted that other good and dear eyes have seen what he saw. I have once before desired to procure this satisfaction; for that purpose I addressed Mr. De Vegobre, being well satisfied that if he saw what we did, his opinion would draw that of other learned naturalists and would give more weight to mine. He had a few hives of bees at his disposal and complied with my desires with his usual kindness. His first attempt was unlucky and I had the chagrin of learning that he had seen nothing of what we had seen. I understood what had prevented him from giving in to my first assertions; but without insisting, at a moment when his health perhaps did not allow him the leisure of taking part in my little interests, I resolved to wait, that he should come back to it himself in more favorable circumstances. That moment has arrived, I as I had foreseen.

I here transcribe for you a portion of his letter in which he tells me that we are now agreed upon the existence and necessity of ventilation, applied in the hives to the renewal of the air, the only process capable of keeping up the salubrity and therefore the life of their numerous inhabitants. The letter of which I speak is of May 29, 1829. Mr. De Vegobre inhabited then the protestant parsonage of Fernex; he had the use of a large and beautiful garden. Here is what he wrote, in exact words:

"But this garden, in which I am still able to drag myself, I find in it a fine company, neither more nor less than a hive of bees... Ah! here is Mr. Huber waking up, a hive! Well, speak. Alas! yes, a real country skep, a big round basket, that is all. What can I see there? I have at least verified the observing of ventilation at the entrance; the great speed of motion of those grayish wings, almost transparent, is the reason why, in a dark spot, it evades the sight of eyes which are not good."

It is exactly what I had guessed. In a better lighted spot, and in the middle of a fine day, we have often noticed that the extreme speed of the motion prevents one from seeing distinctly the shape of the ventilating wings and that they appear then only in the shape of a little cloud with which the body of the bees appears surrounded. By the watch, the same workers appeared to ventilate for 14 or 15 minutes, though sometimes less. What muscular strength do not the least oscillations indicate in the wings of bees? A strength equal, if not superior, may also be noticed in the muscles of their legs; you will have many occasions to ascertain this when you see a single bee, hanging to the ceiling of your hive, sustaining many others fastened to her legs by the hooks of their feet.

Will you kindly, dear Elisa, add this sheet to that of my letters where I speak of ventilation? It is well that an extraordinary fact should not want for confirmation.

In another occasion, Mr. De Vegobre has also corroborated one of my most important observations. I will mention it to you when we raise the question of the architecture of bees.

The Laying of the Queen. To Miss Elisa De Portes, Lausanne, July 7, 1829

No, my dear cousin, I did not think you capable of risking the danger which you would run if you were to observe the bees without the obstruction of the glass; you will be able to see a great deal without running any risk. The experience which you have just made of it and which placed under your eyes so many interesting facts, must enable you to go very far, by keeping on the defensive. One must open a hive when one wants to take honey, but you have not gone that far. I have written to Sophie that a hood is indispensable; you have a year ahead of you to secure one. Until then you must leave your glass hive at rest and give no trouble to your bees. Their storing of supplies takes a great deal of time; the question for them is not only to live from day to day, their future is also in their hands; they are not, as some people believe, dormant during the bad season. The honey and pollen gathered during the fine days must serve to feed the entire colony in the bad days, and through the order which has been given them for this, we can see that nothing essential to them has been forgotten.

You know well that some other beings are not subjected to this apparent foresight, the dormouse, the marmot, become torpid, sleep; and during their more or less deep hibernating, they have no need of food; the bad season is a time of vacation for them. The bees have no respite, and here is why:

1. Their queens, according to Reaumur, have at least 100,000 eggs to lay each year; therefore they have no time to lose, so they begin their laying in the middle of January, that is to say, in the height of winter. What would become of those

poor young ones if they did not find around them nurses and food to be given them?

2. Since your hive has been inhabited since June 3, it was in the first days of that month that its queen must have begun her laying; you know that 21 days are sufficient to hatch adult bees from the time the eggs were laid in the cells. Worker bees have therefore had more time than needed to go through their entire development. The first care of their companions is to fix those cradles so they may receive new eggs, for several generations are reared successively in the same cell; you have caught them in the act. It is not in this as it is with our hens, whose eggs need to be set upon; in order to hatch, the queen's eggs need no incubation, the temperature of the hive is sufficient; it is only when the egg is hatched and when the little larva comes to life and has thrown away its shell that the workers care for it more closely. The number which you have seen gathered together were there for that purpose.

Whenever you wish to know whether there is brood in the hive, that is to say in any part of a comb, touch the glass with your hand and compare its temperature with that of neighboring parts; your eyes will also tell you that something interesting is happening there; you will see the bees there moving about much more and fret, so to say, and even hum more strongly.

The Departure of the Swarms. To Sophie and Elisa De Portes (mother and daughter), Lausanne, July 10, 1829

To know that you are together, my dear girls, is to believe that you are happy; will you permit me to come and talk a little while with the four of you, as if we were face to face? It is to Elisa that I want to speak at this moment and probably about the bees. Why might I not interest, also, her sister and her mother? You have probably found that I had sufficiently proved, in one of my last letters, that wax is produced from honey and especially from the saccharine part of it. I have still another proof to offer you of this fact; it will be my fault if you don't discover it.

Permit me to transport you into your own garden, and that I select, for that, one of the finest days of spring, that the air be soft and just as it should be for the exit of swarms. At that time the country is covered with blossoms; you see what the bees do; you have seen them thousands of times working upon the flowers of your gardens and of your meadows. Their humming, which I find so true, I was about to say so harmonious, so solemn, you have heard it; it pleased you thousands of times like the softest music that the ear may hear, but the gentleness of the bees is still more remarkable. Out of these thousands of stings, did one ever turn against you? Let us consult the oracle, let us see what is taking place at your home, that is in your glass hive. What disorder, what trouble do we see there? What has become of their vaunted orderliness? I see there but the greatest confusion; every one of them passes before me with such haste that I hardly know whether they are drones or workers. Do I not see there their queen running also, passing, without looking, over the. body of the workers, striking them with her legs, her head, her antennae? Her march over the combs produces upon the bees which she meets, and which she appears to address in passing, the effect of the wake of a vessel; in spite of her speed one can always see where she is going or whence she came. Am I mistaken? See, are not her workers following her? Does not the disorder, which was evidently begun by the queen as she advanced, spread around her as she goes? Wherever she goes, is she not followed by those which her racing have excited'? Yes, for their number diminishes upon the comb on which she was a moment ago, and she is now on the other side of the same comb, after having given them the signal of departure.

Second act. What do I see? What has become of that comb full of the finest honey, a few minutes ago? At present, nearly all its cells are empty. That is also what the queen ordered and wanted. But let us see better, if possible. Let us go to another hive which is in the same condition and also has a swarm to cast, especially one the last comb of which is full and glassed. The work of emptying the comb is already well along, many cells are only half full but there is enough left to see what will happen when their turn comes to be emptied.

Preparation for Departure

I have regretted, often, not to have found in my hives many cells which permitted of observation as fully as those which you saw lately, one of the sides of which, being glassed, permitted to see the inside, in which a worker should have her head thrust. In the case in question, we saw many cells full or half full and as many workers with their heads into them. The speed of their motions was noticeable, but as to what they did we could only judge by the disappearance of the honey with which they had been filled.

Those bees, after having gorged themselves, had really changed in shape, their abdomen looked like a little barrel and we could have recognized them at the door of their new home.

I will repeat here that honey is the primary substance of beeswax. The bees, caught in the act, as I have caught them every time that I have attempted it, have led me to the same conclusion.

Far from being proud of this discovery, I am sometimes ashamed of not having made it sooner and even not to have guessed it. Such fine work could not be left to the hazard of rain and sunshine.

Behavior of The Queen

The behavior of the queen, when she reaches the moment when the fear of her young rivals becomes strong enough to induce her to leave her hive, shows that another idea possesses her, and this is not the least astonishing point which her history presents. She remembers that she is a mother and appears then to think of it for the first time. I tried to describe to you this unique being in the delirium of fear, occupied only with the danger which threatens her and with the means of escaping from it. Her actions and especially their outcome do not permit to doubt that another care absorbs her and possesses her almost entirely: that of giving life for the second time to the numerous children with which she is surrounded, who must follow her and be led with her to a new abode. But let us forget her for an instant, let us think rather about that maternal instinct which has been awakened so marvelously and opportunely. Look about you, in your own heart, dear Sophie (Note 1), the answer will not require waiting:

> Si Dio veder to vuoi
> Cercalo in ogni oggetto
> Miralo nel tuo petto
> Lo troverai con te.

> If you wish to see God
> Seek Him in every object,
> Admire Him within you,
> You will find him with you.

Let us examine what would have happened if the bad principle in which too many believed should have a part in the government of the universe, with the father of nature acting as by blind hazard; it might have canceled the law of the bees' code, of which we have just seen one of the finest applications. The bee's species, barely called to existence and happiness, would have had but a moment of life; all the beings which accompany the queen, finding the new hive absolutely destitute of all the necessities, would soon have undergone the horrors or famine, having not brought any honey with them nor constructed any cells of wax; the queen's young, finding no cradles to receive them, would have perished at birth or before birth; long ago the industrious family would have ceased to exist; it exists, however. Sorry hazard did not preside. Before being great philosophers, let us begin by seeing that which we can enjoy, and being thankful for it, it is, in my mind, the best philosophy.

Elisa may also conclude, from the picture which I placed before her eyes that a language appropriate to their needs and to their organization has been granted to the beings which are placed upon the different rounds of the animal scale, and especially to those that live in association. This language is not boisterous among the bees, any more than among the mutes of our own species. The antennae are the organs of it among our favorite insects. Their dictionary is more or less abundant, doubtless the flexibility of the organ allows of much variety in the degree of force, as well as in the direction and speed of its touch. This expression, through which a skilful musician imparts to us what she thinks or what she feels and which tells more than voice can do, could she not furnish it as well at the foot of the scale as in the highest regions? I have often heard you say to me, dear Sophie, upon your keyboard, that which was not written upon your music book.

Functions of the Queens and of the Workers. To Miss Elisa De Portes, Lausanne, July 31, 1829

1. The queen bee is, as you know, to the letter, the mother of her people.

2. You are aware that she has two sorts of eggs to lay.

3. That it is the part of the workers, whom she rules, to construct the cells in which they are to be reared.

4. The cradles of those young are of different shapes and sizes, and disposed as most convenient for the usage which they are to fulfill.

5. You have not forgotten that the queen knows, or seems to know, the sex of the young which she is about to lay, of which we have made sure by noticing that it never happens, except in rare exceptions, that she lays drone eggs in cells intended for workers, nor the egg intended for a worker in a cell made for drones. This observation of Reaumur excited against him the feelings of his country women neighbors, who were disinclined to believe that a simple "fly" could be gifted with faculty of which they were deprived themselves.

6. You have seen that the queen-mother limits herself to giving birth to the young, but gives them no care: it is to the workers that the duties belong which are in other beings exclusively entrusted to the mothers. Their task begins at the moment when the young larva tears the membrane which kept it imprisoned during the three first days of its existence. It is in the anthers of flowers that they find the first food suitable for their young; they know how to proportionate the dose of it to their age, to their digestive strength and to their other needs.

The milk of the first days is at first flat, it acquires a better flavor on the following days. The pollen, whatever be its origin, like the milk which serves as first food to animals and to us, must be eaten, digested and elaborated within the breast of the nurse. It is the pap intended for the royal larvae that our taste perceives more fully the differences which we note and which prove that this admirable arrangement is one of the positive laws wisely ordained by kind Nature.

7. You ask me what honey is. The Ancients had judged by its sweet flavor that it was a true nectar and they had given it the name of the glands which are found at the bottom of the calyx of flowers; vegetable physiology and chemistry do not give us any further information. If we cannot yet say anything more positive on its nature and its utility for the plants in which it is most ordinarily found, we see it in a light which is sufficiently interesting to satisfy us. If this liquid is not useful to the plant which secretes it and of which it seems to be but an excretion, see of what use it is for a host of insects which feed upon it eagerly; the large animals find in it, as we do, a delectable pleasure and a precious remedy. The ancients advised to eat it with the wax, so as to suffer no inconvenience from it. As it is on the upper surface of the leaves, or that which faces the sun, that honey is ordinarily found, their poets, if not their naturalists said that honey came from heaven itself, it was for them a sweet perspiration from the stars; in the language of Pliny, sudor siderum (sweet of the stars) was its name.

The Prolific Queen

I told you, my dear girl, that the laying of the queen is of about 100,000 eggs for the first year; it is according to Reaumur that I dare assert it, but even if this number should be exaggerated, do you think that one-half or three-fourths of this task would be great enough and that it would perhaps be too great if the care of giving life to so many had to be divided with other occupations? She has received the title of mother; did she also deserve that of queen? If the most constant observation can grant the right of an opinion and of expressing it, upon such a subject, I will take the liberty of telling you what I have always thought upon this, since I have been occupying myself with bees. I believe, then, after the great Reaumur, the best of guides in such a delicate subject, that the first rank among the bees belongs without doubt to their queen; among many proofs that I might give you, I will select only the fact which I narrated to you the other day, when you were at Lavigny; you may be sure that it is the queen that decides upon the departure of the swarms.

When everything is still quiet around them, when the workers are still busy with their employment as maids or nurses or occupying themselves with the care of the crop, if we follow the queen with our eyes in a glass hive and the weather is nice, we will see her all at once fretting, changing place, leave the circle which composes guard, pass over the bodies of her faithful wardens, change her slow and stately gait to a more speedy run than appears suitable in one of her size and maternal dignity. In spite of the terror which she shows concerning her young rivals and the apparent aberration which appears to possess her, another idea seizes her; to that of her royalty is joined that of the mother and it is several thousand children that she must look after. Divine kindness, you overlook nothing, nothing is too small in your eyes; our dear Master should have seen this last trait in the natural history of swarms. It has only been seen by myself, and not through my own eyes; I hope my dear girl will not be the last one to have that pleasure.

In another occasion still, the queen holds the reins of government; this, however, is but conjecture, I have not seen the queen touch or strike her subjects with her antennae, as if she meant to tell them to take from the cells of their hive all the honey which they will need in their new home.

Experiment: To change into truth this supposition, I enclosed, in a glass sand-box, a young queen with a vigorous drone and a few workers to give her the necessary care. The slaughter of the drones had begun in a few hives. The queen paid no attention to the workers, and at first took no notice of the drone either, but all at once, perceiving him but too well, she pounced upon him and stabbed him with her sting; the stroke was mortal.

Other tests had the same result; the workers remained absolutely neutral; they took no part in a murder which had not been ordered.

The intervention of the queen was then of prime necessity, for, as you know it already, it is the workers who are usually entrusted with the execution. If I accuse the queen of having given the order, it is because I saw her do the act under my own eyes, and, moreover, because I have witnessed the cares of every moment of which they are the object, from their birth till the end of their life, and I cannot believe such a change of conduct towards them without justification or motive, except the obligation of obeying a law whose rigor cannot prevent us from admiring its wisdom; at this epoch of their existence, the drones are only useless mouths, their number is such that famine would soon be the scourge that would desolate the hive, in which they would feed at the expense of their nurses and without supplying anything of their own.

I agree that there may be some doubt in this regard; here is a fact which I have better ascertained: the queen and her female subjects absolutely share the Empire. If the desire of destroying her young rivals in the cradle is most manifest in the queen-mother, the desire of opposing it is not less so among her workers; they are the ones who rule, in this occasion, and the queen, though queen she be, takes flight. This first and unique contradiction is what determines her departure; the equilibrium will soon be re-established between the opposing powers. When the running of the queen has excited the bees and her most expressive language has recalled them to obedience and especially to the injunction of looking after the future, they pounce upon the honey cells, gorge themselves and have only to follow the queen-mother to the spot where she sees fit to settle with them. What name will you give, dear girl, to the society of bees, for which one is needed? If, after my last observation, the name of Mixed Monarchy appears proper, I will not hesitate to adopt it with you, and with common sense.

To Miss Elisa De Portes, Lausanne, August, 14, 1829

A visitor from Geneva took the pen out of my hands yesterday; I was sorry of it. I do not like to delay my replies, especially when it is my cherished children who ask for them.

I also have put red color upon some of my bees, to follow with my eyes a young queen in the air, when she takes flight, when she rises on high; this paint has often given me the pleasure of having the means of discovering them. If we wish to know how long it takes a bee to return home, after having gone a certain distance, sprinkle her at her exit and upon her return: the two moments, noted from a watch, will tell you what you wish to know; but if you take one when she is about to join her companions and go home, the multiplied contact will soon have cleaned her of this strange ornament and rid her of her domino. Bees have a taste for cleanliness which has often confused me; what to do about it? It is a law of nature. Here is what I devised, which is the only method that ever succeeded: With pincers grab the worker which is to endure this coercion close to the base of the large wings, without injuring it, and with a single stroke of the scissors cut one of her antennae. This method of marking them is infallible, would you believe it? It appears to do them no harm, I do not know of any of their operations in which this proves an impediment: they lose none of their instinct. Perhaps you will not easily believe that depriving them of the antennae tips deprive them of it entirely. The bees, the drones, the queen even, after such an operation recognize neither their mother nor their young, not even their home; with antennae nothing is hidden from them. The help of the eyes even seems or is useless to them in the dark: they work in the deep darkness of their hive, as well in the night as in the day. I would like to respond as pertinently to your second question, but it would be now only to acknowledge my ignorance.

Robbing by Bees or Wasps. To Miss Elisa De Portes, Lausanne, September 16, 1829

I told you a few days ago that I had never seen robbing of which many speak, and that I was, upon that point, scandalously ignorant. I find, however, in my memory, a fact of which I can give you an account and about which I have not read anything anywhere.

The bees have many enemies but, informed on how to defend themselves against them, they usually do it with success. In other circumstances, rarely, however, they happen to succumb and perish under the attacks of their too numerous enemies. The bees, that share with us the privilege of living in societies, share also the inconveniences of this. They have their vandals as we do, and their invasions are to be feared. That of which I was a witness, in 1816 or 1817 (which was properly named the year of famine) was due to too great a multiplication of wasps on the one side, and on the other side the weakness which the scarcity of food had produced among the bees. At first glance, the number of the attacking forces was at least ten times as great as that of the legitimate inhabitants; thus, I lost all my colonies that summer. It was not only the honey which those mean robbers sought. I had also the sorrow to see them kill the bees, cut them to pieces, pull off the heads, separate the corslet from the abdomen, rejecting that section, although it was the only one that might have contained honey, and bring to their young only the heads and the corslets in which they could find only hard parts, difficult of digestion. This most singular fact was also noticed by an able observer, M. Perot-Dios. There can be no doubt in this regard (what you have said to me about it proves it); you have very correctly seen and I must advise you to instruct your own self, afterwards reading the best authors on the subject which interests you. If you read them first, you will run risk of becoming prejudiced; the opposite method will not have the inconvenience; it is to Reaumur's works that I refer you; they are entitled "Memoirs to Serve in the History of Insects."

Here are a few words on robbers which I find in some letters from my son. He writes me as follows:

"I believe that in most cases they are not bees of the same apiary. I made the experience of it once, by dusting them with white and I saw all of them going to another apiary. It is natural that in their travel the bees recognize the weak colonies; they are always attracted by the odor of honey when the fields do not yield much. A good bee flies from her hive straight, that is, she departs from it usually in a direct way through the air and comes back in the same way. She is not likely to perceive or visit the hives situated on the same battle front."

However there is an inconvenience in the proximity of hives to one another; to isolate them is much better. I am going to give you a proof of this that you will not find elsewhere.

When the queen has gone out of the hive and comes back, she rests herself indifferently on its stand, without concerning herself of whether her stopping is in proximity of another hive; in such case she may be stopped and seized as a suspect stranger by the guards of the hive which she has approached too closely; narrowly held, restrained in her motions, not receiving the food which she may need, she finally loses her strength and even her life without having been wounded. The strange bees have objected to her visit and through this quarrel her own hive becomes queenless, which means lost; isolation of the colony prevents this entirely. Those who know of the discovery of Schirach know how her loss may be remedied. But I will not repeat it here.

Your mothers, my dear Elisa, have accustomed me to a tireless interest. This interest has followed us during our entire existence and that which you will notice in me is simply the continuation of it. I thank you nevertheless for having noticed it; your mention of it moved me very perceptibly. I saw, if only in a flash, that our sentiments, our friendship especially, may continue and perpetuate from generation to generation; to feel is to live, is it not?

How Bees Repair and Consolidate Their Combs to Prevent Them From Breaking Down. To Miss Elisa De Portes, Lausanne, May, 1830

We were examining, one day, Burnens and I, some hives of different forms and dimensions, but which were all thoroughly glassed and transparent. The works of the bees, of the greatest regularity, and especially the cells of the first row, drew our attention. The perfect transparency of the ceiling of the hives, to which the combs were fastened allowed us to see that they contained no honey; a little pollen only filled the cells on both sides; the lower cells were occupied as cradles for eggs, larvae or nymphs. The greatest order reigned. . . .

At that date, the hives were not entirely filled with combs, but in view of their number the weight which had to be sustained by the cells of the first row (upper row) must have been considerable, 10 to 20 pounds is surely not an exaggeration . . .

If we follow with attention what happens to the cells of the first row, we will soon see that, fearing their want of strength, the bees do precisely what is necessary to give them as much as is required to sustain the weight that these fundamental cells support. This precautionary work renders them unrecognizable. These filmy wax cells change into heavy and shapeless pillars: Reaumur, who had seen them only in this last condition, called them the braces of the combs, a name which, owing to their changed condition, fits them perfectly. The Workers continue to add propolis to the wax in the lower combs, but in less proportion and without altering their forms and their dimensions. I have given elsewhere the details of this simple and useful operation.

First Observation

In December, 1795, I took advantage of a fine day to visit the colonies which had been brought with me by boat from Geneva to Lausanne and to make sure that the trip had not disarranged the bees nor their combs. Among those hives, some were glassed; those of which Reaumur has given description interested me most particularly; it was in them that I had been able to read the first pages of the natural history of bees and secure a just idea of it. Some had been stocked in the spring of this same year; others were the homes of older swarms. Thanks to Burnens' carefulness they had all arrived safely.

The finest or strongest one of my swarms had been for two years in a cylindrical bell-shaped hive. As bees cannot hang properly when they are gathered under a glass surface, I had wanted a better support for that May swarm; triangular strips of wood, narrow and properly spaced, had been glued under the glass which served as ceiling to this hive. The workers, finding in these strips a surface more suitable to penetrate than the glass, grasped them with their claws and fastened themselves to them so firmly that their weight could not pull them down when they choose to be hanging together.

This hive was almost entirely filled with wax and honey when we examined it at the end of autumn. The temperature of the season keeping the bees from coming out, they had gathered in the upper part of their home. The thermometer of Reaumur, the bulb of which was in the center of the cluster, indicated 22° R (82° F 27.5°. C), the one which was outside was under 3° R (39° F 4° C) at the same time. The humming of the bees appeared to me to be about as loud as it is in a better season; it was, in fact, produced by the same number of breathing bees.

As the cold had kept the bees in the hive, those that died daily when they had reached the term of their life, that is to say about a year covered the bottom-board; I feared that the healthfulness of their home be altered thereby. I did, in removing those corpses, what they would have done themselves in a different season when the cold weather could not have caused their chilling; but in order to prevent a danger, we reduced the entrance so as to keep out mice and other enemies which could injure them. But we took care to leave a free passage for outside air and its circulation in all parts of the hive by the aid of ventilating bees. Since then, I discovered the method which the bees use to keep in their home the purity of the air at the proper degree; my observations were confirmed by naturalists who wanted to see with their own eyes. I was especially charmed to see a young lady properly understand this maneuver of the bees, of which she did not suspect the existence nor the great utility. To become convinced of the absolute need of ventilation, we only need to close the bees up within their hives; asphyxia and death are the almost instantaneous effects of the interruption of the air circulation within the hives.

Second Inspection of The Hive

It was only in the beginning of January that we uncovered it to examine it and see whether the bees needed us.

This hive, stocked since two years, was, as I have said, filled with comb, honey and pollen; the combs suspended from the top, reached almost down to the stand which served as its floor and were separated from it only by a space of a few lines, at the time of our first visit.

This time, we found that the conditions of the hive were not the same in some essential respects. The middle comb, which was sixteen or eighteen inches high, had become loose from the ceiling and had slipped down apparently without touching the two parallel combs; it rested then on the bottom of the hive and could not go any further; it was even too far down to suit the workers. One of the rules which they follow in their architecture is to leave some space between the bottom of the combs and the floor of the hive; the space thus left being about equal to the passage needed for the body of the bee. We may be sure that, in doing this, they want a passage which permits them to pass and remove anything in their way.

It was upon this that they were working when we uncovered the hive. The wax which they were cutting with their mandibles and that we saw dropping in this spot left no doubt of this observation; there remained to determine the cause of the fall of this comb. We could not understand what had caused its breaking away from the top, when no jar had shaken it, to our knowledge; unless it was due to the softening of its upper fastenings, through the action of too hot sunshine to which they had been exposed at noon during our previous visit, and to the weight of the honey, which they could not support in this soft condition. This conjecture was confirmed in another occasion.

Third Observations

One would fear, as I did, that the fall of the comb would be the inevitable result of the maneuver which I have just described; by cutting it away from the hive base, the bees were removing its sole support. I was doubting their foresight, for the first time, but I was soon corrected in my error; a glance from Burnens upon this comb which had been detached taught us that its stability had been insured better than I had imagined and I admired the simplicity of the method which rendered such an accident impossible. If one remembers that the distance between the combs is only of 4 or 5 lines, one will not think it a very difficult work for the bee to do that which will unite them and prevent their separation.

The wax is the only substance at their command that they may use, but where will they find it, even if the cold did not prevent them from going out? The fields offering no crops in the winter, could they be induced, in extraordinary but foreseen cases, to take from their combs all the wax they might need? We had not divined it, but it was what we saw them do. A great number of bees, considerably scattered or grouped at different heights upon the fallen comb as well as opposite upon the two parallel ones, appeared to work in very distinct spots with a great deal of activity. The workers that were about this work kept it hidden from us entirely by the obstruction of their bodies; it was only when it was about finished that we saw: 1st, that braces, made of dark wax taken evidently from old combs, had been constructed in ogival shape and fastened on one side to the fallen comb and on the other side to the parallel comb; 2nd, that these braces were heavier at the contact point with the combs than in their center; they looked in no way like cells; 3rd, that their shape was that of a clepsydra, of a salt cellar, or of such pillars as the wasps build to separate and support the nests of their young. At a short distance from the center of this same hive some other combs had been loosened from the ceiling, probably for the same reason. (see illustration chapter IV pg 409)

In a cylindrical hive, one may see the edge of the combs just like the pages of a party open book, by looking from the edge, the space between their edges cannot be observed. We therefore could not see whether the bees built braces between those spaces as they had done upon the edge that we had

watched: this was in no way different from the accident mentioned and the way in which it was repaired. We understood
that those simple and so wise dispositions were not intended to
prevent only the fall of the combs in our domesticated colonies;
they were applied on a large scale in all the hives that were
exposed to the winds and to their more or less wild jolts.

Fourth Observations

As the least things in natural history may be of great
consequence when one seeks to know the instinct and the
habits of beings which are so remote from us, I desired to
analyze better all that was presented in the previous observation. I therefore asked the person who had the care of this to
give it increased attention; he did so conscientiously; his
report, which I have here under my eyes, leaves nothing to be
desired. The hive of which he took notice had, like the one just
mentioned, its ceiling and all its sides glassed. Wooden triangles, mentioned formerly, had been glued at their extremities
under the horizontal ceiling and had supplied the bees with all
the supports which appeared necessary to their combs. One
day, however, surprised by an examination from my young
friend, I asked him whether anything extraordinary was happening. "Sure," said he, "your bees appear confused: they are
covering the cells of the first row, those at the top of the
combs; some of the workers are destroying those fundamental
cells; the wax which they are cutting up is dropping on the
lower combs, its fragments have no shape left in which we can
recognize either rhombs, trapezes or hexagons." What had
happened? Claude Lechex, this man, at present filling the place
of Burnens, and whose varied talents are well known in Geneva, gave in this occasion a proof of his zeal and capacity. He
noticed a slight bending in the triangles which sustained the
combs, this inflection, almost imperceptible at the ends was
more marked as they neared the center; the straight line which
they formed at first had taken the shape of the outer side of an
oval. This could be attributed only to the weight of the honey
which had forced the triangle to part from the ceiling and to
curve so as to alter, in an essential manner the shape of the
base cells. The behavior of the bees proves that this change
had been perceived by them and it turned out, from the obser-

vation of Claude Lechex, that they had found instant need of repairing the disorder. They went to work, some to fill the space between the triangles and the glass, with propolis, others to rebuild the cells which they had torn down. When examined closely by a good observer, these cells appeared similar to those which had been the first outlines of fundamental cells.

If the works of bees are not proofs against accidents, one cannot see without admiration, I would even say without some gratitude, that bees have been taught to do, in every case, that which is best to remedy it.

When I mention the extreme pleasure which this unpublished observation has given me, is it necessary to give the reason of it? Without refusing to grant our bees a share of intelligence, how can we grant to them the foresight of precautions to take against casual dangers? That ideas so different, and yet the best possible under the circumstances should have come to them, at the same time, so that some of them would tear their work to pieces while others gave it more strength under a changed form! What better could we expect ourselves? Our attentions may be useful to them but are oftener noxious to them; thus far goes our interference. Should we credit this to chance? But chance is inconstant; it would not bring about the same thing twice in similar circumstances and we always see the bees follow the rules which have been prescribed to them.

All that we see done by the bees is the work of power and kindness. Let this thought always follow you among your hives and elsewhere and let it bring you back constantly to the Author of all things, the only being from whom we may expect true happiness.

About Propolis—How the Bees Strengthen Their Combs with Threads of Propolis, in the Angles of the Cell Walls. To Miss Elisa De Portes, Lausanne, July 10, 1830

As I wish to inform you about an observation with which I have been greatly interested and of which I have not yet spoken, I must first bring you to the level of already acquired information when I began to study bees, and what I did to ascertain that my forbears had spoken according to nature.

It is about propolis that I wish to write. This word, of Greek origin, is applied to a substance intended to surround or fortify a city or village. The bees have built, under my eyes, bastions Vauban fashion, composed of this matter and of pure wax, and use it also to protect their homes from any noxious thing, by varnishing the walls with it.

You have perhaps already seen propolis, on the legs of your bees or on the glass of the observing hives; the red color was noticed by you. They say, chemically speaking, that it is a gum-resin; my own tests have taught me that it is in the nature of gum and of rosin; but did the bees take it from the Lombardy poplars? Their odor struck me as resembling the odor of propolis. To make sure of it, I made the following experiment:

In a fine day of July, I took from some Lombardy poplars a few branches with their buds. To see them more at ease, I had them taken to my study; they were placed by the side of a glassed hive which had no outside opening. The bees, attracted by the odor of those buds, were not long in coming out and showing us that they were interested in them. They began by removing the bracts and taking with their mandibles that which covered them; they loaded with it their pollen baskets and withdrew to their hive.

Those same bees paid no attention to branches of other trees which we had mixed with the poplar branches. This experience, repeated, left no doubt that the Lombardy poplars can furnish propolis to the bees, but were they the only plants upon which they could gather it? I cannot decide it.

Observation on a peculiar use of propolis.

Tardigrade speed is my speed, and this is not astonishing, in view of my circumstances; it would be still more astonishing if I had made much progress with the means and the instruments at my disposal.

The principal or even unique purpose of the care the bees take is to give their work the greatest strength possible, and to prevent entirely the fall of the combs and the ruin of the colony.

In 1801, I lived at my children's in the vicinity of Lausanne. I had brought my bees with me... The first swarms which I had at Ouchy were hived in glass hives, of which the ceilings as well as the sides were transparent. The observations which we made with them were only the repetition and confirmation of those described by Reaumur, but they had for us the merit of novelty.

One day, however, the hive which drew our attention happened to be in a light which enabled us to see a peculiarity which we had never yet seen.

A great number of bees, having upon their legs some bright substance, and running to and fro, came in great numbers into this glass hive. We saw distinctly that it was in the pollen baskets that they were bringing the bright substances which had caught our eyes; their color would have caused youthful eyes to take them for rubies, but we could not be fooled in this: it was propolis which these bees were bringing; we caught some of them as they were entering the hive. It was enough to touch these pretended rubies to recognize the gum-resin which was known to the ancients and which the name given to it by them showed that they knew its use.

In its fresh condition, before it is dried, this substance has a property similar to that of all glutinous substances, that of stretching at will, in threads; it is soft, malleable and does not break. It was through this property that the bees made use of it in this occasion under our eyes.

1. Among the great number of bees using this material, we select those that we can best see; hanging to the comb, with their heads toward the cells, they appear to feel with their antennae the propolis which they have just deposited there.

2. The greater number of them feel with their mandibles those little propolis balls.

3. They do even more; they manipulate with their teeth this gummy matter, which the warmth of the spot and their manipulations have softened.

4. After many efforts and twitching, we see them leave the little pellets, carrying away in their jaw what they have removed from them.

5. Examining them with a magnifying glass, those objects appear to be threads of propolis of different lengths.

6. As if they were intending to measure them by the length of the cell, they carry them into the hexagonal tubes. What they do within the cell is entirely hidden by their body. When they come out, we sometimes see them coming back with empty hands, it is when the thread of propolis has proven of proper length; in that case it is easy to perceive that the worker has laid it at the joint of the two faces of the hexagonal tube and that she has stretched it by pressing it into the place which it is to strengthen.

7. It often happens that the little thread of propolis is not of proper length; if it is too long, a nip shortens it; in the opposite case, the little pellet supplies what is missing.

8. That which astonishes me is to see that it is not the same worker who finishes what she began; each one that successively does it takes up the work where the previous one has left it without any irregularity being caused by this change of hands.

9. We have not seen the bees strengthen the pyramidal bases of the cells, as we saw them fix the hexagonal tubes, this was impossible, but the dissecting of the bases showed us that they had been treated in the same manner in all parts of the hive.

10. When the work in wax is interrupted by drought, and by any bad weather which prevents the secretion. of honey in the flowers, the first symptom of this suspension is indicated by a rim of propolis with which the bees strengthen the rims of the cells which have not been built out at full length, and as these interruptions in the work take place at different times each

summer, one may learn their number by that of the rings of propolis which rim their edges evidently with the view of protecting the cells from any defacement.

11. Reaumur knew too well the lightness of the cells and their extreme fragility not to understand that the bees would look after it; he had ascertained that their edges were thinner than a sheet of paper; so when they were new the trace of the fingers was noticeable upon the combs and the least added weight was sufficient to break them. It was through new wax added in the weak places that the workers averted this danger and gave their combs additional strength.

12. One now sees that they strengthen them still more by adding propolis, the threads of this material, arranged in shape of buttresses inside of the cells and artistically placed in the points of contact of their trapezes, are that which is best to tie more intimately the wax with the propolis and give the bees' work all necessary strength.

13. In order to see this ingenious artifice, it was necessary to detect them when they were busy with it; it would not have passed unobserved by Reaumur. This becomes invisible when the angles of the inside prisms are covered with the silky shells which the nymphs leave behind in the cells when they come out as adult bees: the number of shells which are left successively in them without interruption necessarily destroys their transparency. Swammerdam counted 17 of them in a single cell.

To see this new feature in the history of our bees one should: 1. Separate a cell; 2. put in on the surface of water; 3. heat it. The wax, more readily fusible than propolis, will melt at about 50° Reaumur (145° F 63° C); propolis will not melt at this degree, the prism will preserve its shape; the shells, having assumed the shape of the cell within which they were formed, will retain the edges that could be perceived before the melting away of the wax.

***Necessity of Sheltering the Hives From The Sun—The
Conclusion that Pollen is not The Element Producing Wax.
To Miss Elisa De Portes, Lausanne, Aug. 26, 1829***

Judging by reasons which appeared very good to me, I had long believed, as Reaumur did, that wax was produced from the fecundating dust of flowers or pollen, which I designated under the name of crude wax, in my first edition. I might have changed this designation in my second edition, but I did not wish to do so; you will forgive me for this; you will see in it my respect towards my dear and venerated master. I refer Elisa to the beautiful memoirs of Reaumur, whenever she wishes to know how much we are indebted to this excellent naturalist and whether I was wrong in believing in his views; in order to justify myself I need only to narrate to her what happened to me and what led me to discover a fact which I did not suspect in the least and which I accepted only after mature examination. One day I was examining the bee of a great apiary which did not belong to me, and which the tenant of the country place in which I lived had left exposed, as usual, to the noon sunshine. The actions of those bees, their extraordinary humming attracted our attention; we noticed that they did not fly far away from their hives, that the number of those who did so and came back loaded, with pollen and perhaps with honey, was very limited as compared to that of the bees who brought in nothing and who appeared to be only trying to take exercise or to escape the too great heat of the interior of the hive. Repeating this observation with my own bees, I saw that my conjecture was right, those which were exposed to the sun showed no increase in weight, while those which were in the shade had increased by several ounces in the same lapse of time.

Those observations, repeated sufficiently, convinced me that the hives should be preserved from the direct influence of the sun's rays; this was already believed in the time of Virgil. He advises, in his Georgics, to *shade them under a palm tree or under some great olive tree*:

"Palma que vestibulum aut ingens oleaster adumbret."

The weather was cloudy on the following day, the sun did not shine, but the mildness of the air still permitted the bees to go to the fields and to seek their usual harvest upon the flowers of our meadows; it was much greater than on the previous day; all that flew away came back with the fruits of their labor, without having lost time in flying about their home.

We were in the season of swarming, at least one-third of the colonies had already swarmed; the new colonies appeared much more active than the old ones, the bees that lived in the latter brought back a great deal of pollen, those of the new swarms came home with their pollen baskets absolutely empty and carried only the pollen which had been gathered by the hairs with which their body was covered, without any design of their own.

Being somewhat astonished to see the behavior of the bees in this occasion, who brought so much pollen in the old colonies and almost none in the new, we began to doubt the use of pollen in wax making, for in empty hives wax is of absolute necessity; they need it to receive the eggs of the queen. The delicate texture of the eggs is such that the least touch destroys them, even by the workers. They can bear so little pressure that, to fasten them in the bottom of the cells, the queen appears to depend entirely upon the gluten with which they are surrounded as they pass through her ovaries. Whenever you wish to transfer an egg from one cell into another, beware of taking it with pincers of any kind; in spite of your dexterity you would surely break it. To transfer it safely it is sufficient to only touch it on its side with the pincers; it fastens to the metal as to a magnet and sticks to it through the gluten which I mentioned.

It is, therefore, absolutely necessary that these eggs be at once deposited in the cells, so as to prevent accidents. The shape of the cells and their material procure to those little beings everything that the best managed motherhood could desire.

The first duty of bees, at their arrival in their new home, is doubtless to prepare cradles for the young, which their queen, in a hurry to lay, must deposit in them, and it is of wax that they are made. An instant of observation, or rather of consideration, had just taught me that I had been mistaken, as were all my predecessors, in believing that bees found the elements of their wax in the stamen's dust. Our guide, Reaumur, had noticed that bees, confined to the hive by bad weather and unable to secure pollen, nevertheless constructed beautiful combs of wax. I had seen this many times in similar circumstances, but I had not stopped farther than my master, perhaps I had not dared to do so.

When you read this, you will have seen many bees swarm. The trouble and confusion which prevail in the hives at the time preceding the exit of the bees, the astonishing hurry with which the bees leave a home which appeared so dear to them, will have caused you to think, as it did me, that the bees then think of nothing but leaving and do not worry about any other cares. But it is otherwise and the bees themselves gave me the proof of it.

When I recognized the uselessness of pollen as original material in the production of wax, I sought for it in the honey, the only substance which (with the exception of pollen) belonged in the bees' household. The first idea that would come to you would be to put this to a decisive test, by enclosing the bees within hives where they would find only honey enough for their consumption and see what would follow.

If, after a few days of confinement, you should find beautiful combs of wax in all your hives, would you not conclude that your bees had built this out of honey? You would then have thought of reversing the test, that is, to substitute pollen for honey, and see what the bees would do with it in their prison, giving them a few sweet fruits and a little water so that they would not suffer from hunger or thirst. I can predict to you that you would never have found an atom of wax in the hives in which they were confined.

Suspecting that it was the sweet or sugared part of honey which has this astonishing property, you would wish to know what would happen if you gave your bees nothing but sugar dissolved in water and you would consider this suspicion as proven when you found your bees changing the sugar into wax, as if it were honey.

Seeing that honey, or its sweet part, was the primary substance for wax and that pollen did not contribute to it in any way, you would wish to know of what use this pollen might be to the bees, since its harvest seemed so important to them. It is the workers who care for the young; their duty is to feed them. I would expect you to make sure of this matter by a few direct tests; you would remove all the combs of honey from the hives, leaving only those that contained pollen and in which young bees have been hatched. Complete success would be the result. With the help of a magnifying glass you would see: 1st, the eggs enlarging in the bottom of the cells; 2nd, the young larvae also growing, requiring more room in the cells than they did the previous day; 3rd, a few of those larvae would already be changing to the nymph state, life everywhere. Then the pollen has proven to be the milk from which they were fed, and we need seek no farther the great importance of this crop.

The Bee of Mexico

While I occupy your interest, my dear Elisa, with the insects of the New World, which we have known through a celebrated English traveler, Captain Basil Hall, my main aim will be, as always, to put under your eyes some of the marvels of Nature which I have been permitted to observe, and especially the variety of means which Nature employs to attain her aim. You know what my desire was when I spoke to you of the bees; the beings which are now in question which are indigenous to Mexico, owe to their resemblance with our own honeybees and their products to be called by a similar name.

Upon the reading of the work of Captain Hall, which interested me deeply, I noticed, however, some dissimilar features, which caused me to doubt whether my new acquaintances were really bees. With the help of a few friends and some of their correspondents in Mexico, I was able to import from Tepico some bees taken from hives similar to those that the observer whom I have mentioned had examined. This first attempt failed completely, on account of the very precaution taken to insure its success. Our correspondent had drowned all those bees in the liquid which ought to have secured their preservation. The bottles, carelessly closed, allowed the liquid to evaporate, and the length of the trip joined to the heat sustained, caused all those little beings to ferment and putrefy without exception; not a single one reached me that might have been recognized by our best anatomists. Mayor helped my son in this occasion and was no luckier. Mr. Basil Hall having noticed that the Tepico bees had stung no one when their hives were opened, took it for granted that they had no sting, but this did not seem to me to be sufficiently proved.

For that reason I did not abandon the idea of doing all I could to ascertain so important a point; this was the purpose of my second attempt. You will hardly believe that I was indiscreet enough to try it over with such new friends and to ask them to serve my fancy once again.

Veri sacra fames quid non mortalia pectora cogis! (Holy love of truth, how you lead the hearts of those who feel your charm!)

Far from being discouraged by the ill success of the first attempt, I depended upon their kindness so far as to ask them to buy for me a Mexican hive and send it to me as soon as possible, without disturbing anything in it, leaving it just as it would be found at the time of departure. Here is something that you may have difficulty in believing, but which is, however, true: I forgot to recommend not to close the hive and to leave the imprisoned bees a free access of air, under penalty of seeing them asphyxiate and perish miserably. My Mexican friends thought of it no more than I did, the hive which I had asked for was purchased, shipped to Europe, addressed at London to J. L. Prevost, who received it, unpacked it, opened it with my permission; but seeing that the entrance had been solidly closed, he feared that which had happened, that the bees were dead. Legions of mites were the only living beings that he saw in this hive and which we found also in it on its arrival at Yverdon. Excepting this, my son found everything in the best possible condition and exactly as had been seen and described by Mr. Hall. I will soon send you the narration of this part of his voyage. You may then believe, as if you should see it yourself: 1. That the bees of Tepico gather as much honey in Mexico as our bees do in Europe; that this is fully as good and more aromatic than that of our real honeybees; 2. that they know how to convert a part of it into beeswax and produce considerably of it; 3. I tell you farther what they do with it. In regard to this the inhabitants of that country are as well off as we are. You may think they are even better off, when you learn that I was lucky enough to confirm the conjecture of the first observer and to ascertain its truth. As Mr. Hall has observed, the bees of Mexico are deprived of sting, or of any offensive arm. One may, therefore, observe them without danger and take away their treasures without any cost. You are too fair, my dear Elisa, not to take interest in these strangers and admire the ways in which Providence makes them worthy of your interest and of the regard of the inhabitants of another hemisphere. The sequel of this letter will tell you what I was able to see besides. God be with you, my dear children.

(Notice of Mr. Basil Hall relating to bees which he noticed in Tepico and of which I find an account in the second volume of his voyage to Chili, Peru, and Mexico (page 238) in 1820, 1821, 1822. The author was an office in the Royal Navy; it was under its orders that this voyage was undertaken.)

"From the market square, we went to a house where there was a hive of the native bees, which they opened in our presence. The bees, honey and the hive differ much from those of England. The hive is usually made of a hollow log, two or three feet long and eight or ten inches in diameter, hollowed out and terminated at the ends with circular openings, carefully closed with wood, though opened at will."

"Instead of this coarse wooden container, some people have cylindrical hives, in baked earth, ornamented with figures an circular rings. These hives serve as ornaments on the porches of houses, to the roofs of which they are suspended in front of the village huts. On one of the sides of the hive, half way between the ends, is a small hole, large enough to permit a loaded bee to pass through, with a sort of portico to shelter the hives from the rain; this hole usually resembles the mouth of a human being or some animal, the head of which is shaped in relief upon the hive."

"One bee is entrusted with a duty which is not all profit. She is constantly at the door, which is so narrow that when a bee enters this one goes either inside or outside and at once returns to her post. Experience has proven, they told me, that the same bee remains at this watch the whole day."

"When the weight indicates that the hive is full, they remove the end and take out the honey. The hive which they opened before us was not entirely filled which permitted us to examine its inside more freely. The honey is not placed in hexagonal cells as in our hives, but in wax bags not quite as large as an egg. Those sacks or bladders are suspended around the sides of the hive and appear to be about half filled. It is probable that the quantity is for the purpose of the wax being able to sustain the weight without breaking down. The sacks placed at the bottom are stronger and consequently better filled than those near the top."

"In the center of the lower part of the hive was an irregular mass of combs built with cells similar to those of our bees and in which the young bees were resting, which appeared to be already strong. They removed these cells to liberate them and they took flight. While we were examining this hive, someone removed the combs and the honey. Confusion was seen among these little folks, but not one of us was strung, although our hands and faces were covered with them. There is in this same country a meaner race; but the kind which we saw appears to have neither the will nor the power to do any harm. Our friends told us that they were always "many manao," very tame, and that they never sting. They honey has an aromatic odor and in taste differs entirely from that of our climes."

"Descriptions of the Domestic Melipone: The bees of Mexico are of the genus Melipone; their head is somewhat square, their body rounded and hairy like that of our bumblebees, and not angular like that of our domesticated bees. When we look at them from the underside, there are some inconspicuous bands; their size is one-third less than that of the Europe-an bees; however, they secrete wax, but probably in the man-ner of our field bumblebees."

"They have pollen baskets and the brush, but they do not have the spur which serves our bees to extract the wax plates, as they do not need them."

You may think me heedless when you hear that I was not the only one who had planned to bring into Europe some interesting beings which it would have been difficult to observe in their native country. No, others have had similar ideas, but it is our own bees which they have dared to take to America. They even claim to have succeeded.

Miss De Vegobre, who allowed me to talk to her of every-thing that interested me, said to me one day that it would not be very difficult to have bees sent to us from Guadalupe, to compare them with ours and see through this first observation whether the ones were similar to the others and might have originated from the same country. Thanks to this good friend, few months were required, by the person who accepted the trust, to bring to me in Geneva a few hundred bees taken at the entrance of Guadaloupe hives and which turned out to be in every part similar to those of our own hives. It is on that ac-count that I thought I might hope that Mexican honeybees could be brought here as readily as those of Europe had been imported to America. To make sure of it, however, it was nec-essary to make the test. I trust for this in the young observers who may feel the need of it.

The Bees of Mexico. To Miss Elisa De Portes, Lausanne, July 4, 1831

My Dear Elisa: While I was soliciting your interest con-cerning my new acquaintances from across the sea, you have probably understood that I had a reason to desire you to share my sentiment concerning them.

After I had made sure, through the inspection of this un-lucky hive, which had come from such a distance, that the first observer who had made them known to me had spoken truly in telling of their possible usefulness and especially of their gentleness in their connection with us, the idea came to me that it would be doing a good service to the inhabitants of our southern provinces, and perhaps to friends that I have in those happy regions, to advise them to import them and encourage their multiplication. But before speaking of this to any one, I desired to know what would be the opinion concerning it of one of my best friends, Mr. Manoel de Vegobre, and especially consult him on the best precautions to take in order to insure the success of an enterprise which seemed to me a little hazardous, perhaps even foolhardy. Here is what seemed to me the most important: 1. One had to make sure, before the departure of the melipones, that they had sufficient food for so long a trip, and in case they did not, then give them such honey and pollen as would be necessary. 2. It was necessary to prevent the hives from following the pitching of the vessel in stormy weather and inclining to the right or to the left outside of the vertical position; it was necessary for this to employ the same means that are used to maintain the compass in proper position. 3. At all times preserve free access to air in the hives, by leaving their entrances open to prevent its alteration. Illustrious examples show us that it is not always in fine order that the naturalists of our days receive samples of the objects of our studies. See where Cuvier, Brognart and others have found the specimens which have rendered them immortal; it was in digging in the deepest cavities of our terrestrial caverns that they perceived the more or less altered debris of beings whose existence must belong only to the very remotest times and perhaps nearest or contemporaneous with the catastrophes of all sorts which have overwhelmed our planet. Yet, in those altered and reduced beings, almost in dust, these savants recognized the fossil remains of gigantic animals, differing from all that we knew in the animal kingdom. Anatomy, studied as it had never been studied, caused them to recognize, in their family traits, those to which they had belonged. Thanks to Cuvier we have under our eyes the inhabitants of a world which no longer exists and but distantly related to those that live with us. The first steps of our ancient geologists have brought others still more interesting; our race had escaped the first researches, others have found petrified human bones in the grottoes of Montpellier and other places; those bones, they say, are mixed in the layers with debris of objects which were evidently manufactured and worked upon by the hand of men who are probably of the same antiquity. These researches will lead to others, we still have much light to seek and to hope for, from the sagacity and zeal with which our young geologists are enthused. They will undoubtedly unite with the previous works of the sages who preceded them and they will not be forgotten. Their share of glory will still be fine enough.

I, also, need to investigate the laws which have ruled the beings of which we have only the dead remains. Since Mr. Cuvier was able to discover so many things on their customs, may we not also, after inspection and autopsy of the numerous corpses which have come to us from Mexico, get a glimpse of the physiology and the habits of the Mexican bees?

If this name is proper for the beings which we are studying, the differences which may be noted between the common honeybees and the honeybees of Mexico, without permitting us to place them in different families, still require between them a separation. I spoke of it in the note which followed my previous letter. In this I will call your attention to still greater differences. You are aware of the function which the sting fills in the European bees; all the order of the hive appears to hinge upon this. Their queens are dominated by an instinct of which they show the only example in natural history. This jealous disposition is so pronounced in them that infanticide, which everywhere is abhorrent to nature, is very common among European mother-bees. We know that it is with their sting that they kill their young in the cradle. The bees of Mexico, deprived of this offensive weapon, are exempt from this atrocity (this is detailed in my letters upon swarming).

There is a time when our bees, seized with a rage, show towards the males of the race unequivocal demonstrations of the hate which they inspire in them. It is also with the sting that they succeed in getting rid of them, destroying beings which have thus far been the objects of the most tender care. Is it as useless and consequently dangerous members that the drones, which consume a great deal of honey and bring in nothing that might increase the stores, invite upon themselves such rigorous treatment, of which I have described all the phases? We would not find the determining cause in their advanced age, for even their eggs and their youngest larvae do not escape the prescription. I have often seen cases when the deposing of the queen, through her old age or her sterility, causes the massacre of the drones to be delayed and sometimes even not to take place.

The deprivation of the sting must assuredly change the character and the habits of the beings which are deprived of it, so we must find more peaceableness and gentleness among the Mexican bees than among our own. The melipones do not show such differences. I have not found, in the ruins of their hive, either queens or drones; if they have any, which is not to be doubted, these must show nothing which will cause them to be readily distinguished from the workers. The dissection of those bodies would have settled the question, if putrefaction had not taken place. But beings which have lost their shape may yet be a subject of study, since a graveyard may yet reveal interesting peculiarities on the habits and customs of people which are buried there.

Mr. de Vegobre addressed to me a number of interesting questions upon the melipones; I replied to the best of my ability. But I will speak of these later. I wish to quote now some of his remarks upon the subject:

"An observation which has struck me is their harmlessness and the evil consequences which would result from them, if they should be transported into our country."

"You know better than anyone the sagacity of our bees to discover, even at a great distance, a store of honey, and the furious passion they have for it. I saw an example of it two years ago at Plainpalais. If a Mexican colony should be brought to this country, would there not be danger that all the bees of the country which sooner or later would become informed of its defenselessness, should rob it entirely so that there would be no chance of preserving it? You say that Mexican bees are a little smaller than ours; this suggests to me an idea to parry the danger that I mention; it would be to hive our strangers in hives of which the entrances would be composed of a number of small holes, as many as necessary, but each of them too small to allow the passage of one of our bees. Another observation is that it would be frightful for those poor Americans if one devised the importation into their country of our European tyrants (which you love so much)."

You will approve as I did the method that our good adviser found to nullify the objection which he himself had found and without which my plan would certainly be unpracticable. The bees of Europe also have enemies to fear, they have been trained to give the entrances to their holes such dimensions as will enable them to prevent their invasions.

Nature! Nature! Your good inventions are always ahead of ours. Let us admire her and not be jealous.

Treatment of Bee Stings—Condition Necessary for an Observing Hive. To Miss Elisa De Portes, Lausanne, Aug. 4, 1831

The Killing of Drones

Have you been stung, my dear Elisa? I guessed it, or rather felt it, when reading your last letter, and I regretted my failure to put enough weight upon the precautions that you must take against the bees in those narrow observing hives in which their instinct is so greatly thwarted as to cause their ill-humor. I should have given you the only remedy which I have seen Burnens use, and which was not of his own invention. He first extracted the sting from the wound, for he had very well noticed that it continues a spasmodic motion after it has been separated from the body of the bee, widening the wound and rendering it more painful. He would then rub the wounded spot with freshly cut grass; this pressure forced out some venom and lessened the swelling and the pain. You must remember it for a future time.

The Observing Hive

To make sure of seeing the queen, the narrow hive should not permit her to disappear from our eyes for a single instant, so the panes of glass which enclose the comb must not be more than 1 ¾ inches apart; the average thickness of a comb being about an inch, the rest of the space, divided between the two sides, will furnish to the bees a space sufficient to cover both sides of the comb without giving them enough room to cluster together so as to incommode the observer. I advise you to keep within these limits, which have always been successful with me. When you build another observing hive, do not inspect them until they have strengthened everything in their new home and are accustomed to it. I advise you, also, in order to protect yourself against stings, that the hive be enclosed in a glass closet, so that the bees be not able to go in and out except by a passage made in the window sill, which will not prevent the latter from being opened or closed; the bees will then be able to go back and forth without being disturbed and without annoying you.

About Drones

Let us now come back to our conversation concerning the drones of the species; they are worthy of our attention for a moment. They are, like all the young of the bees, the object of the most assiduous care during their early youth; the common workers are in charge of this and acquit themselves worthily. You know that they have neither legs nor feet and that, in order to crawl about their cell, they must twist themselves around a spiral, with the help of their rings, the folds of which serve as feet. This slow way of crawling is so well proportioned with the space to be traveled that the young larva terminates it only when it reaches the mouth of the cell, at the time when it is to transform into nymph, when it no longer needs to eat and can get along without the care of the kind workers who have so far served it as nurses. But their work is not at end; the adult male depends upon the care of its guards; not one of his organs can help him to feed himself, or to do any work whatever. You must therefore not accuse him of laziness when you see him idle; nature wills it so. The hive is only his bedroom; his dinner is always ready. Our greatest lords never had more waiters doing their work and hurrying to help them; the care of their nurslings occupies them constantly. One cannot watch them a single moment without seeing some bees busy rubbing them or brushing them with their proboscis, which serves as a broom (a more proper name for this instrument than the name which has been given to it, for the proboscis is not a sucker).

Grant a little more attention to these little beings. As they emerge from their childhood, they are, as you see, dependent upon their keepers; but they have liberty in addition; they can, without opposition, emerge from the hive and return at any hour. In the fine days it is from nine to ten o'clock in the morning until four in the afternoon that you will see them run, fly and sport about their home; no winged insect is as lively or as happy as a drone. Their number may be as great as a thousand to twelve hundred in each colony, and their very sonorous humming fills the atmosphere and cheerfully animates the surroundings of our apiaries. This condition usually lasts three or four weeks from their emergence from the cell out of which they hatched, and gives to the observer the sweet idea of a happy people; but you probably know that this will soon change; the first time I saw it I was very much impressed. To see these same workers pass almost suddenly to hostile demonstrations towards creatures upon which they had lavished that which is most tender in maternity, to see them chase them out of their retreats with the greatest fierceness and force them to descend upon the alighting board to suffer death! This distressing spectacle could be still more so; it came to that when I made sure that the proscription of the males was extended to the eggs, the larvae and the nymphs, which might have perpetuated their race and which were all destroyed under my eyes. It was then with good reason that Mr. de Reaumur had called this happening "a frightful massacre, a horrible slaughter."

I do not know whether you have seen all this with your own eyes, my dear Elisa; spending the summer in the country and having hives of your own, you will witness scenes such as I have just described; my duty is to cause you to see things just

as they are and not allow access in your mind for unjust prejudices.

It is usually in the beginning or in the middle of summer
that the bees change in their behavior and that the drones of
the race become the objects of their hate. Let us examine
whether the time is well chosen.

If the drones were killed sooner, the order and the regu-
lation of the hives might be deranged, as regards fecundation;
if they were killed later, the crops of the hives might suffer, the
workers then not having enough time left to fill their store-
rooms with honey and supply new stores for those that would
have been consumed by the drones, who have become at that
time useless members of the society. The time chosen by the
bees to kill them is therefore the best. The second blooming of
the meadows, that of especially, sainfoin (Onobrychis sativa) as
well as that of buckwheat, permit them to gather still as much
food and more than has been consumed by the drones during
their short stay among the workers who have killed them. The
destruction which aroused us, instead of being as grievous as
appeared to us, is advantageous instead, since the safety of
the race results from it; the wish of nature is thus accomplished, as it is generally. That which happens, in the hives that
are under your control, happens in all the hives in existence.

The first time that I witnessed it, when I could no longer
have any doubts upon the violent death which they suffered,
being ignorant at that time of the generality of the law of which
I saw the effect, I thought, as Mr. Bonnet did, that Reaumur
might be mistaken and that the massacre of the drones which
he had so well described might be but the result of an accidental cause, still unknown. Might it not be (for example) that
the drones thus observed should have acquired some fault or
vicious habits, with age, that caused them to be disliked by
those same bees which had been thus far their faithful nurses?
This gratuitous supposition was soon abandoned by me when
all my country neighbors informed me that this fact, which
astonished me and almost scandalized me, was not thus considered by them, since they knew already, by tradition, that
this massacre, which I saw, took place every year, at the same

date and in all the hives of the country. The entire masculine gender could not then be suspected of the infirmity of advanced age as a cause. Among the great number of drones, of which none was spared, there were doubtless some very young ones which had become adults only for a few days or a few hours; but that which proved, still better, that their proscription was not caused by age and infirmities resulting from it was that the eggs and larvae of all ages were taken out of their cells and thrown to the ditch. I learned afterwards, through my correspondents and through the works that treat of bees, that the proscription of the males and their extermination were known everywhere and that I was probably the only one to be astonished of it. This fact, unknown to me until then, assumed a new aspect in my eyes, that of a law of Nature. But what was its purpose? In order to know this, I needed to know its results, and I gave my attention to it. I interrogated the farmers who kept bees and whose experience worthy of respect could give me information that my own efforts would not secure for me. The majority of them said to me that their bees, usually very tractable, became less so at certain times, and that they were never meaner (these are their own words) than when they were richest—that is, when honey was plentiful in their storerooms. It was, according to these men, to defend their treasures and prevent them from being dilapidated by the males that they killed them.

I will give here only the result of numerous observations which I made, and from which I am much inclined to believe that the years of abundance or of dearth are not the aim or the cause of the massacres of the drones, which are committed by the bees almost periodically in all the hives, for I have seen these cruel dispatches take place in hives that October were not rich and had hardly enough honey for their daily subsistence. I persist, therefore, in the belief that there is another cause for the phenomenon observed in the behavior of the bees, but if we cannot define it we are allowed to judge of it by our sentiments, and it is to this that I send you, my dear girl; the ideas of kindness, greatness and wisdom do not permit me to doubt of your being on a path upon which we will meet.

Wasps and Bumblebees. To Miss Elisa De Portes, Lausanne, Aug. 10, 1831

Are you willing that we should talk another moment, my dear correspondent upon the subject which I have broached in my previous letters? I do not pretend to solve it in its entirety; my knowledge is limited to the profound admiration of the ways of Providence, however severe they may appear to us, which always serve the purpose intended. Here, the aim is no other than the perpetuation of the species; the sacrifice of the individuals was its proper and inevitable consequence. The extermination of the males among bees is not the only example that Nature offers to us of the rigor of its laws. Without looking out of that family, see what happens to wasps, hornets, woolly bumblebees, etc. It is to their females alone that the conservation of the race is entrusted, when the race is considered necessary.

At the opening of cold weather, all perish in the nests of wasps and bumblebees, the females alone surviving the great rigors of winter. As that season does not furnish them food any longer, they are enabled to do without it; then they become torpid and wake up only when milder temperature puts within their reach the beings that have also been benumbed as they were and which serve for their food. These females, fecundated during the previous summer, have no other need than giving birth to the future race; but before their first bringing forth, they must prepare a proper spot to serve as a cradle. The female who is about to become a mother knows the duty which is imposed upon her and acquits herself worthily of it; we have seen the lodges which they know how to make for their young before their appearance and during their solitude.

Among the bumblebees, as among the wasps, each nest has in the fall several fecundated females. They do not gather together to spend the winter; they isolate themselves, on the contrary, and each must pass the winter in a different spot. The successive layings of the mother will soon surround her with a sufficient number of helpers, the care of building will no longer be her duty, but the species will be preserved. What will be the limit of its existence? We are as ignorant of it as of our own. The disciples of our Lord asked him for the date of his happy return to the earth. He replied that this was the secret of God himself, and that the important thing was to be always ready to receive Him, that is to say, to be well received by Him (Gospel St. Matthew, Chapter XXIV). Being seated on the Mount of Olives his disciples addressed him particularly and said: "Tell us when those things will happen and what will be the sign of your coming and of the end of the centuries?" Jesus replied: "Beware that none seduce you. As to that day and hour, no one knows it, not even the angels in the heavens, but my Father alone knows it."

Neither you nor I are unjust enough, my dear Elisa, or selfish enough to pass judgment upon the beings which now interest us. Honey, beeswax and silk are doubtless very precious gifts, but the bees and the silkworm which put these into our hands must not secure all our attention and our recognition. Allow me, therefore, to seek in the natural history of those poor wasps which are not accustomed to our homage, some proofs of the infinite kindness, which all nature proclaims, and, to estimate them at their true value, let us use the same balance (if we can do so) as the hand of the Creator.

The wasps, as you know, do not make any store-rooms for the needs of the future or for another season; this future, this other season do not exist for them. At the first cold weather of fall, the entire family must perish, the mother alone excepted. This female, which has become fertile before that date, what becomes of her in this occurrence? Will she remain in her palace, deserted by all and in which she would be exposed to the cold of winter and to the attacks of enemies, mice, gophers, etc. No, she is the trustee of the future race; those germs (in every way precious in the eyes of Providence, which makes no exceptions), preserved within her body and needing, at the last, only the mild warmth of their mother's body, are ready to take advantage like herself of a still milder temperature and to become eggs of which spring causes the farther development. I have several times discovered some of these females, which had nested in the straw mats designed to preserve my fig trees and other plants from the cold. Their torpidness was not very profound, holding them for a moment in my band was sufficient to waken them, had I not placed them back in the spot where I had found them and where they had to wait until the spring be advanced enough to put within their reach the insects upon which they feed.

Do you not think, as I do, that these are quite sufficient proofs of the infinite kindness of which these beings are the object?

Does a patient see, in the cares which are given him by the physician, anything but kindness, no matter what remedies are necessary to bring him back to health?

When the season has no longer any danger of rigors, the females feel it, within their shelter, they leave it never to return; but where do they go? Will it be in the nest in which they lived the previous season? No, they go elsewhere to seek a suitable spot for a new establishment. It is there, as I have said, that the female, still solitary, constructs the niches in which her first egg is to be deposited. Is the dispersion of those females, in the fall, intended for the purpose of keeping their homes apart from each other, at respectable distances? This would remind us of the care the bees take of scattering their swarms apart, when they are permitted to do so.

Travel Supplies of Swarms. To Miss Elisa De Portes, Lausanne, August 24, 1831

You will be astonished, dear friend, of the discovery which I am about to entertain you. You will gain without trouble a beautiful and satisfying idea, quite in agreement with those that you have already, concerning the police and the rules which divine wisdom and kindness have given to those beings that you love, and from which they cannot swerve; or, still more astonishing, to which we see them come back when they have swerved from them. I have spoken to you of the queen occupied with a sole object, the disquietude caused in her by her young rivals, which leaves to her no other desire than that of leaving her home, but she does not wish to separate herself from a people which is composed solely of her children. Watch her running as in delirium through all parts of the hive, crawl over the bodies of her companions, touch them, strike them with ·her antennae and give them to understand, in a way which she cannot express otherwise, her desire to leave and the order to follow her. One cannot doubt that this order, this wish, is understood, for obedience is immediate; she transmits her agitation to the entire tribe. By the restlessness which is stirred in her wake, you may know that she passed by; when it is at its height she rushes to the entrance of her hive and sometimes goes out alone, as if she did not care whether she is followed or not. The entrance is often too narrow for all that come to pass through at the same time; they must wait till it be possible, but the queen does not delay, in her turn, to join them and take flight. This is all I knew when I caused to be published my "Letters upon the Swarms." On the 15th of May, 1816, I had sixteen colonies, strong, well stocked, and whose queens were all a year old; they were therefore ready to swarm. I caused them to be watched carefully so as not to lose the opportunity of reviewing facts as singular as those which I have just mentioned and of which no one had spoken. I did not hope to see new ones, but I was mistaken as you will see. The charivari (rough music) which we heard about us informed us that there were some swarms out in the vicinity. We went at once to my garden, so as not to lose those that might come out of our own hives. After a quarter of an hour of expectation, one swarm came out, which we judged to be strong, by the noise that it produced. Its queen came back to the hive two or three times (as if she had forgotten something), but she could not go in on account of the entrance being obstructed by the great number of males and workers that were also trying to escape and mingle with the bees of the swarm that were already out of the hive and had preceded the queen. We enlarged the entrance to facilitate their egress; they came out then with the impetuosity of a torrent. Being eager to see what was happening inside of that hive, while the swarm was going out, we opened the blind that covered the outside comb. When placing our hand on the glass, we found it extraordinarily warm; this was caused by the affluence of the bees which covered this outside comb almost entirely and by the excitement which existed among them. As they showed us only their backs, we could not distinguish exactly what they were doing; it was necessary to disturb them by passing a leafy branch over them or by bringing towards the glass a lighted candle, the warmth of which would compel them to move; these expedients were successful; we saw, to our great satisfaction and to our surprise, that the cells which were sealed that morning and entirely full of honey had been opened and the honey removed. I will not depict the pleasure I received from this sight; you know my sentiments; it was of the safety of the bees and of the providential care of them that I was making sure. Without that, without the foresight, or rather the astonishing presence of mind of the bees, who always do at the proper time what needs to be done, what should have become of that swarm, coming out of a well furnished home to go into one deprived of everything? What would have happened if had weather had overtaken it at its arrival in a new habitation and had prevented it from going out during the first days of its establishment? The impossibility of harvesting any crop would have deprived it of honey, without which they could not feed themselves, nor produce wax, nor build the cells where the eggs of the queen must be deposited. You have seen how this was provided for.

This observation was soon confirmed; another hive in the same condition, the swarm of which was about to issue, showed us also its outside comb covered with bees that were hurrying to remove the honey from barely opened cells. As they were less crowded than the first which had shown us the same action, we were not compelled to disturb them in order to better see their actions; for three or four minutes during which they remained in the hive, under our eyes, they did nothing other than what we had seen before. Their eagerness to gorge with honey was evident, but the haste which they used in this was a proof that the need and the desire to join the emigrating bees was occupying them also.

On the morning of that day and the preceding days, we had seen honey spread about in all parts of the hive; it appeared then that they had removed it to keep it safe from robbers, or perhaps they had wanted to gather it at the back of the hive so as to have it more handy at the time of the departure of the swarm (this supposition appears to me to be the more likely).

The Swarm Carries Supplies

The agitation of the queen, communicated to the entire tribe, was therefore to end in giving them the idea of flight with which she was herself possessed, but to leave empty-handed would have been running to ruin. Such was not the aim which Nature proposed; her aim was more material. They had the positive order never to swarm without taking along with them, to their new home, enough honey for their subsistence which could alone enable them to construct new combs, to serve as cradles for the new generation and as store-rooms for the crop.

You will want to see all this yourself, my dear girl; the experiments which I have published in my memoir which treats of the origin of beeswax will lead you, and I advise you to read it all over. I suppose that you will make a swarm in a glass hive; you will be doing only what the bees do themselves when, obeying their instinct, they leave their native hive and go seek at their peril, and sometimes at quite a distance, a new domicile. Continue to imitate them; you saw that they do not leave empty-handed. So let your swarm find in its new home a good dose of honey and a little water in a sponge, a few ounces; you then put this swarm in the position of a natural swarm which has been overtaken by bad weather at its arrival in its new home and the bees of which, kept within by rain, are not able to harvest anything on the flowers, a situation which you will imitate by closing them up in their home, taking care, however, to supply them with air. On the evening of the first day of their imprisonment, the panes of glass of your hive will allow you to see the swarm suspended in the upper part and very quiet in appearance; the interior of the duster formed by the chains or garlands of bees suspended to the ceiling will be hidden from you and you will not see what is happening within; you will see distinctly the surrounding curtain which envelopes this cluster, and which, composed of workers joined to each other by the claws of their feet, surrounds it with a veil or a movable curtain. The natural swarm and the artificial swarm would give you the same picture. Your ear pressed consecutively against the glass partition of either hive would perceive a sound resembling a sort of chattering produced by the jaws of the workers occupied with the preparatory work of their architecture, a work which is performed upon beeswax only.

The process which you follow in your experiment brings you the same results which have been achieved by the bees of a natural swarm, and I may compliment you upon having succeeded as well as Nature herself.

Other tests, made at the same time, taught me that pollen furnished to the bees the only food suitable for their young. Honey or sugar, used without being mixed with the pollen of stamens, is not suitable. I have witnessed the death of the young when I tried to confine them upon this food. Their death was always followed by the desertion of the bees.

My new tests confirm the preceding ones fully; the natural swarms produce wax by means of the honey they find in the flowers as the swarms which I may call artificial produce it also by the same means or through the honey which I supply to them myself; up to this time, I have seen no difference in the results of the tests. The natural swarms which enabled me to make this discovery showed me all that Nature had done for their preservation.

Youth Recollections—Salutary Influences of Nature Study— the Sense of Scent in the Bees—the Language of Animals. To Miss Elisa De Portes, Lausanne, Nov. 1, 1831
I have spoken to you sufficiently of our domestic bees and of those which, in our hives, may assume the name of "Sisters of Charity," you will recognize, under a name to which you have some rights, the true "worker" bees.

It is of the drones that I would like to speak to you, for they have a great role in their history, but you consider them as sluggards, do-nothings, fops, solely occupied in playing and frolicking, and almost laughing, and I do not wish to attempt their defense as long as you have this prejudice; it would be taking the defense of the vices of which they are accused; allow me, however, to ask you to suspend your judgment towards them, as long as it is not proved that they deserve your contempt.

I also have had, as you have, some large and small fowl yards to watch. My father had a passion for birds; he possessed all those that we knew best because of their musical talent. The nightingale, the warbler, the canary, etc., had at Plainpalais a great aviary; a few trees and a brook preserved them there almost in a state of nature. They roosted in their aviary and appeared to be as happy as those that had no shelter but the trees of our gardens or of our orchards. It was there that your little friend still clothed in long dresses, spent all the time that he could filch from the occupations required by his age and the will of his parents. It was there also that he acquired a taste for natural history and that his young mind was opened to beauties which have lost none of the charms that he found in them so close to the cradle.

Some friends of my father upbraided him one day before me, for leaving me too much time, according to their idea, for idling and amusing myself. I still thank the Lord that he inspired into my beloved father the willingness of permitting me to follow my taste for natural history. "Could he live in better company?" said he. "What does he hear from those innocent voices, those little beaks so pretty, even from those big ugly beaks, however homely they may appear? Is there any risk of their corrupting his little heart of spoiling his mind?" This jesting was not a jest; after a whole life I see in it an accomplished prophecy, if you will permit me so to speak. Did I already find a true revelation in what I could see and hear from those beings that had no other teachers than their fathers? Their language, which gave nothing to me but pure thoughts, was it not more intelligible and more lovable than if it had contained more wisdom? At the time of this writing, I have here, near me, two representatives of those that instructed my childhood, almost from the swaddling clothes and I have the honor to be able to say to you with truth that I understand

them now as I did then, and that they are still for me representatives of "August Truth."

I would like to be sure that you pardon me for making
my own self the subject of these observations. I know surely
better than those who have had only a glimpse of beautiful
nature, all the influence that it may have upon those whose
principal study it has been during their whole life; that which I
feel appears to me to be likely to encourage those who listen to
me and do good to them, as it does to me.

My musical ear is known to you. It did not give me any
better service than those of the physiologists who have most
studied the music of birds. Our savants ascertained before I did
that it was possible for us to imitate only distantly the language
of those small beings who have more or less the gift of charm-
ing us.

My pupil does not doubt that her old teacher has done all
he could to ascertain the cause of this difference. I believe that
I have found out, and I am not alone in that conclusion, that
the birds do not have the same scale of music that we have.

The nightingale has a greater connection with our har-
monic scale than any other; of all the birds that sing well, it is
the easiest to imitate. The nations of the North (I am sure of it)
have also a scale which differs much from ours. Strike upon
your harpsichord the sharps only, those five notes are the only
ones that we hear in the old tunes of the Caledonians. Louis
Necker (Note: Louis Necker, oldest son of Mrs. Necker-de-Saussure,
the author of 'L'Education Progressive,' grand-nephew of the Minister
of Finances of Louis XVI, was a professor at the Academy of Geneva,
where he taught geology and mineralogy. He spent the 20 last years
of his life in the Hebrides, in the Island of Skye, which offers great
interest in regard to mineralogy, and where he found gratification for
his taste for natural sciences. He published a book on the birds of
Switzerland, which is greatly appreciated for the information that it
gives on the migration of birds, etc.-Ed.), your dear relative, asserted it to me and made the experiment of it, before me, upon
his bagpipe. You know that this instrument is the one which the
Scotch Highlanders use to lead their soldiers to battle and often
to victory. Another notion which I believe to be correct and

which I also owe to my formerly good ears, is the difference observed in the scale of the songs of birds, that is, in the distance between the notes of those songs following one another; this does not prevent them from singing in tune; in all my life I never heard them give a false note.

Am I prejudiced? If there are beings so unfortunately organized that neither their heart nor their mind can understand the language that nature uses to please them, to charm them, to console them by that which is produced in the natural concerts, in those of which the wildest woods give us such pleasant sensations, we must pity them and be the more thankful that this source of pleasure has not to be withheld from us; I hope that some great compensation has been granted to them.

You will understand, dear Elisa, that it is of botany that I am thinking now. Allow me, in spite of my age, to offer you a bouquet; let it be composed in such a way that you will find nothing to criticize in the harmony of the colors with which the flowers that compose it are adorned.

Those colors, their diverse shades, are the fundamental notes of their scale; their distribution upon the petals is calculated for our enjoyment. Man, and man alone, is qualified for the enjoyments that a masterly hand has seen fit to prepare for him. You have had children to care for and to make happy, my dear girl; remember how often a bouquet, a single blossom has given them pleasure. Those little creatures were also provided for, by giving their mother a voice and more readiness than to their brothers or to their husbands for entertaining, for consoling of their little sorrows this immense portion of the human race. No, no that one of all the beings which are most enriched through so many favors must not be what he sometimes appears to be—ungrateful!

While seeking to ascertain the effect of odors upon insects, I found only the bees among which they are worthy of note; that of the honey attracts them particularly; you now that which is left exposed is very soon discovered by those insects. That which is more singular and less known is that they keep for a long time the remembrance of their discoveries. Some bees, that had found honey scattered upon a window sill, came back six months later to seek that which might have been left at the same spot. This observation was made at Yverdon and deserves to be retained as the first proof that we have had that our favorite insects have been granted the gift of memory.

The odor of pollen, imperceptible to our senses, is probably perceivable by those of the insects which find in the fecundating dusts, the food which suits their young best and which are accustomed to seek them. The more odoriferous flowers hardly seem to attract them when their pollen is not visible or is not in their reach.

If a few of the odors, among those that appear the most pleasant to us, reach them without fail, all those that displease us and that I have tried, repel them and cause them to fly away as soon as they perceive them.

It is rather curious to see at the same moment the two opposite effects which equally prove this assertion.

Spread a little honey upon your window sill. The bees which take notice of your gift will soon come to enjoy it; you will see them stretch out their tongue and dip its extremity in the honey. Seize that moment to cover this honey with pulverized camphor; the bees will take flight at once. This spectacle may become still more curious and more instructive: Cover only a part of the honey with camphor, which they dislike; the bees will not fly away; you will see them turn as far as they can away from the mixture, which attracts and repulses them equally. They will behave in such a way that only the extremity of their proboscis will reach the uncovered honey. This experiment deserves to be repeated and varied with the use of other attracting and repelling substances. It may at least amuse you.

The voice: The early travelers who spoke to us of the animals inhabiting the islands of the South Sea asserted that they are dumb. Has this been confirmed? I do not know it, but what you and I know very well is that those who are born is Europe, Asia, Africa or America are not dumb, but are on the contrary endowed with organs that facilitate their intercourse with their own kind as well as with their young. If we are ignorant of the language of animals inhabiting strange countries, we can ascertain in our cows and in their mates that nature has furnished to them, as to any other animals with which we are acquainted, the means of telling each other all they need to know, and especially to be understood by their young. This has been confirmed by travelers to different parts of the world, where animals that are strangers to us exist. I have never heard them, but you have no more doubts than I have that the lioness and the tigress can inform their young of what is suitable or harmful for them, and that their speech has mutual charms for them, even though the terror that such voices cause may be the only effect which they have upon the human organs.

Alterations to the Leaf hive. To. C.F. Petitpierre, Ouchy, October, 12, 1800

Sir:—I have just received your letter of September 15th. It has been nearly a month in reaching me, as you see—having been directed to Pregny, which place I left nearly eight years ago. I am flattered, sir, with the confidence you so freely place in me. My observations in Natural History have disclosed a method which may be of advantage to beekeepers. I promised myself to be the first to test it; but the circumstances in which I, as well as so many others have been placed have not permitted me to give any consistency to my speculations.

Some persons have given my leaf hive a trial, and because they did not take all the necessary precautions, or were not seconded by skill of their assistants, it has not proved in their hands as great a success as Burnens found it, and as I was too ready to believe all others would. This method then has certainly the disadvantage of requiring both skill and courage in those who practice it or to whom it is entrusted. But when these qualities are united I venture to assert that it promises more advantages than any others that have been proposed. I advise those persons then, who have done me the honor to consult me, and whose assistants possess only ordinary skill and intelligence, to adhere to the hive and system of M. de Gelieu (published in "A new method of making artificial swarms in 1779) With very slight alterations it can be adapted to the formation of artificial swarms. Its construction is very simple, its size handy, and it has this further advantage over mine—that its success has been confirmed by time.

M. de Gelieu can reply much better than I to most of your questions; but since you place some value in my opinion, I will give it you. Asking only a little time for reflection. I only write you to-day sir, to announce my reply and to prevent you from deeming me guilty of negligence towards you of which I am innocent. I will do my utmost to prove to you the interest I take in your success. Rest assured of this, sir, and believe in my devotion-F. Huber

P.S. if you have the courage to try the leaf hive, you must first try it on a small scale. It is enough perhaps, for the first year, to have four or five of this style, which will answer for instructing your employees in the necessary manipulations. Experience and observation have compelled me to make two alterations in the construction of this hive. The first does away with the hinges which have a disadvantage which I will explain to you another time. The second is in the entrances which I have placed at the bottom of each leaf. Instead of these you must make one, about an inch longer in each of the two boards which chose the small sides of the hive fitting to it Palteau's entrance regulator. If you expect to stock five leaf hives next spring, it will be advisable to have ten made this winter. The extra frames, you see will answer for alternating empty frames between full ones. Cylindrical hives would be good if they were not too difficult to make accurately. Therefore, I prefer square frames dovetailed together (From ABJ Vol VII No. 11, May, 1872. translated by Dr. Ehrick Parmley.)

Dead queen in front of hive and alterations to the leaf hive. To. C.F. Petitpierre, Ouchy, November, 12, 1800
I thank you, sir, for the many kind expressions contained in your letter. I feel fully the worth of your confidence and hope to merit it, but in matters of rural economy, as well as in others, we must rely upon experience, and therefore I spoke to

you of Mr. Gelieu, for whose character and knowledge I have a profound respect, and who has not been so devoted as I have to the theory. But since you are determined to have my opinions I will talk to you about bees as much as you wish, on condition only that you attach no more value to what I say than I do.

Most of the questions you ask me are yet to be solved: we will give them attention in order, and I will give you my ideas (if any occur to me), on the means to be employed to solve them.

I am highly pleased, sir, to learn that you do not entrust the care of your bees to others. The experiments you have made prove that you are fully qualified to handle them with impunity. You are the first to confirm what I have stated: that the only requisite is gentleness, and the firm conviction that the sting is only a formidable weapon to those who treat them roughly, and who make awkward blunders through fear. It also gives me great pleasure to learn that you are prosecuting investigations that I have not been able to pursue. I will assuredly contribute to your success by every means in my power.

The fact that you have noticed is very extraordinary; that queen found dying near your hives and not recognized by any of your bees, might she not have been a stranger queen abandoned and who came to seek the shelter and the subjects she had lost?

Queens cease laying when they approach the end of their lives; their hive decreases in population daily, and the colony reduced at last to a very small number, leaves the queen and never returns to the natal hive; the workers attracted to happier homes, enter and are sometimes well received; but the fate of the queen is very different. The bees of the hive she attempts to enter envelope her as you have seen, hug her in their midst, and exhaust her and cast her on the ground, when hunger or the hugging she has received renders her incapable of renewing the attempt.

The beginning of this account is only conjectural. I have never been so fortunate as to be able to follow a queen from her birth to her natural death; neither do I yet know what is the length of the life of a queen. Probably you, sir, will be able to tell us that.

This inquiry is useful as well as curious, and I commend it to you. If I have not seen queens die of old age in my own hives, I have often been visited by strange ones that come from I know not where, either alone or poorly accompanied, at the beginning or end of autumn; most frequently these old queens have been found dead at the foot of my hives; at other times I have found them alive on some neighboring stake, having about them fifty or more of their workers. I have seen them pass several days in the open air, and as they also remained there during the night, I may conclude they had no home, and that this small number of workers were all that remained of the family they had presided over.

Only once have we seen the attempt of an aged queen to enter one of my hives succeed. She at first offered herself to others who gave her a poor reception, because they had a queen; but she then entered without any difficulty a hive that had lost their queen. Her dark color and the slenderness of her body indicated old age, of which her sterility was a still surer indication. She did not lay an egg in the hive that adopted her at the latter part of autumn and she died at the end of winter without having laid a single egg, and as queens begin laying the latter part of January, the old age of this one was proven by her sterility. I am more disposed to believe that the queen found at the foot of your hives was a stranger to them, than that she went away from one of those you operated upon October 14th; which even if wounded or dying would not have been unrecognized.

The queen cell found in this hive proves that it had been queenless for some days. Did you discover it on the 14th of October, or later? This circumstance may help to decide the question. The agitation which you noticed would lead one to think that this hive had just lost its queen, and in this case that one you offered, it was not probably the queen it had lost.

To be able to explain a fact in natural history, one must know well the accompanying circumstances, without which any decision is too hazardous. This calls to mind a trait in the fidelity of bees that I must relate to you.

One day I took from a colony a virgin queen that I had given it, to see how the workers would behave under the circumstances. As there was no brood in the hive the loss of the queen was irreparable. I was curious to see what they would do, but I could not perceive any agitation among them, nor anything that led me to suspect that they regretted her loss, or even knew of her absence. I was about to conclude that their indifference arose from her sterility and I found it quite natural that they should have no affection for a mother that was of no use to them; but this human reasoning was not the reasoning of the bees, and I was soon undeceived.

The next day I found the queen numb from cold or hunger, in the box where I had put her. I therefore placed her in the hive; as soon as they perceived her on the table where she was lying, I saw a few workers range themselves around her, caress her, fawn over her with their proboscis, offer her honey which she did not take, and brush her with their feet; all this was useless; she was dead.

Their care did not diminish from ten o'clock in the morning to eight o'clock in the evening; I then took her away, and without any object in view, placed her on the window sill of my study, in which the hive was. Returning there at ten o'clock in the morning, I was much surprised to find my dead queen surrounded by bees, circling about her in the way you know, and giving to her dead body their customary honor.

The night was not warm nevertheless the dead queen was not abandoned, and on the morrow I found her faithful guard lavishing upon her the same care they had rendered during her life.

I once more returned her body to the hive and at the same time introduced a young fertile queen, not doubting but that the bees would instantly appreciate the value of my gift, and would prefer the mother I had given them to the dead virgin queen from whom they could expect nothing; another reasoning, also human and quite ad pitiable as the preceding. The bees who do not reason and who perhaps are none the worse for it, treated the strange queen very rudely; they held her in the middle of a mass of bees so that she could not move, and kept her thus over eighteen hours. At this state the knot of bees reached the entrance of the hive; it was larger than a nut; the bees that formed it imparted to it such movement, that we saw it roll like a ball which it resembled in form, to the edge of the stand on which the hive rested. Arrived there, a continuation of the same movement caused it to fall on the floor without altering its form; we extricated the queen just as you did; she had not received a sting but she was very weak; we succeeded in restoring her by returning her to her natal hive.

The bees I have been speaking to you of obstinately cared for the dead body of their queen during two days and a half; I then took her away and gave them young larvae that they nursed, and from which they procured another queen.

From this and other similar examples, I am inclined to believe the second supposition of no value, and that the queen which was not received by any of your hives was certainly a stranger to them all.

I have dispensed with the hinges of the leaf hive with regret; it is very convenient to open the hive like a book, but when it comes to shutting it up, there is an objection that compelled me to abandon this way. In closing the frames the bees get in the angle formed by two frames, and as the angle grows smaller, one unavoidably crushes those which persist in remaining in this dangerous situation. Burnens, with all his skill, could not avoid often killing them in this way and it is he who asked me to get rid of the hinges and proved the necessity of it.

You understand, sir, that you run no risk at all of crushing the bees when the frames are not fastened to each other—you can bring them close together without forming any angle, and can give the bees time to dispose of themselves on the faces of the two combs.

The invention you have made for uniting four frames, appears to me excellent; but the leaf hive must have a cover to protect it from changes of wet and dry, which will after a time warp the wood of the frames. It is not then enough, as I have formerly said, to bind together the hive with a cord or twine; such a band is too weak, and does not prevent the hive from bursting open. I might have foreseen this, but can one think if everything?

You will receive in a few days, sir, a small box containing a model of a hive and a little memoir, which I thought to add to this letter &c. but as the rest is not ready, I cannot longer delay to reply to yours, and to assure you of my devotion. I have the honor to be Yours, very respectfully, Francis Huber. (From ABJ Vol VII No 12 June 1872)

Alterations to the Leaf Hive. To C.F. Petitpierre, January 20, 1801

Sir:—I have this moment received your letter of the 10th. I will not reply to it now, but wait until after I received your promised letter. I admire your skill in manipulations, and your sagacity; which gives me hope that the history of the bee may be pursued further. Study constantly the book of nature, it will teach you more than all the romances that have been written on the bee. You understand Sir, that this little memoir is only for your eye. I have counted upon your indulgence in writing it, and do not wish it to go out of your hands, as I hope some day to publish these observations. I have the honor to be yours very devotedly—F. Huber

P.S.—I see by your letter that you have anticipated the doing away with the bottom piece of the frames of the leaf hive. It was only after long experience that I felt the inconvenience of the full frames. The cross piece that I put in the middle of the frames should be narrower than the upright pieces. It may be an inch in breadth and a quarter of an inch in thickness. To compel the bees to build their combs parallel to the small side of the hive, it is not sufficient to put a piece of comb in one of the frames; success is more surely attained by cutting a clean old comb into pieces, six inches long by one or two broad. Fasten them to the first piece firmly in the top third of the frame; the second in the sixth; the third in the ninth frame, &c.; continue in this order if the hive have more than ten frames. You must also put several pieces of comb in the hives such I sent you a model of. (From ABJ Vol VIII No. 1, July 1872 Unedited Letters of Huber Translated by Dr. Ehrick Parmley.)

Notes by L.L. Langstroth: The first edition of Huber's work on bees was published in 1792. It has plates which show very clearly the construction of his hive. The tops and bottoms of his frames were about an inch and a quarter wide, and were dovetailed to uprights of the same width, thus making them close fitting, so that when put together formed the hive, the ends being closed with glass darkened by shutters.

The second edition edited by his son was published in 1820 (actually it was 1814), and although it contains much new matter, especially on the architecture of bees, it uses the same cuts of the hive with the first edition. But for these letters which have so unexpectedly come to the knowledge of the bee-world, we should never have known that Huber made or even contemplated any changes in the construction of his hives. In the June No. of the Journal, his reasons for dispensing with the hinging of his frames were given and now we find him discarding the bottom pieces of his frames. To those who have no experience with the slow advances usually made in inventions, it may appear almost unaccountable that Huber did not, from the very start, see how greatly the close fitting bottom strips impeded the manipulations of his frames. As no smoke was used in pacifying the bees, nothing indomitable courage and patience of a Burnens was equal to the task of managing such a hive.

The method employed by Huber of fastening his guide combs by small pegs, was far inferior to the subsequent device of securing them by melted wax, or a composition of melted rosin and beeswax.

The Abbe Della Rocco, whose work on bees in three volumes (*Traite complet sur les abeilles*) was published in 1790, used at first methods still ruder than those of Huber. His recommending the placing of a sharp angled edge on the under side of his bars would seem to be an anticipation in the date of publishment at least, of the device of the celebrated English surgeon, John Hunters, who in a memoir read in 1792 before the London Royal Philosophical Society, advised the use of a salient angle or beveled edge, to induce bees to build their combs in any desired direction.

Memoir on the substances which server for the nutriment of bees and on those which are of use in the structure on their dwellings. To C.F. Petitpierre.

Sir, I do not pretend to give you advice, but in return for the confidence you so kindly repose in me, I will narrate to you two observations which I have made since my letters were published.

Maybe you think as I do, that they are not without interest, and that it is not to be wondered at that the economical science of beekeeping is yet in its infancy; seeing that today that which is most important to know is still unknown.

Distracted by other inquiries, I had given no attention whatever to various matters which are a source of nourishment to bees, or which enter into the formation of their comb. I thought, as did Reaumur and all naturalists who have followed him, that the fertilizing powders of flowers were the primary substance of wax, and that the honey served only for the nourishment of the colony. It was not until 1793 that I began to doubt the truth of these two propositions; although they seemed sanctified by time and testimony of naturalists, both ancient and modern, still I thought I might take the liberty to examine them, and there are the experiments which seemed to me the best suited to throw light on the whole matter.

On June 28th 1793, I transferred a swarm from a glazed hive into an empty basket-hive, and gave them from 5 to 6 ounces (150 to 180 grains) of honey in a cup. I put into another a wet sponge, and shut them up in such a manner that only air could get to them.

That year the months of May and June had been rainy and cold. For several days the bees on which I was trying this experiment, had not left the hive, and consequently had not gathered anything. Therefore they had no pollen at all on their hair or on their thighs, and as that matter must needs be excluded, I thought this moment favorable for an experiment, which I wished to make with all the exactness of which it was capable.

The first of July the temperature had changed considerably; it was exceedingly warm. I could not see what was going on within my hive, but its opaque sides did not prevent me from hearing very distinctly the noise or cracking sound, which the bees make when they are constructing comb. You can imagine my impatience, but I had sentenced the creatures to five days' imprisonment, and I would not free them one minute sooner than that; so that it was not till July 3rd, that I determined, not without some fears, to lift up the hive and see if my conjectures had an reality.

First of all I saw that all my honey had disappeared, and I had still greater pleasure in discovering large pieces of comb of the most beautiful wax, placed and made with regularity by the prisoner bees. I might already have concluded, from this observation, that this comb had been made from the honey which I had given the bees when I imprisoned them; but yet there was one doubt in my mind. I was certain that the bees had brought no pollen on their hair into the empty prison-hive, but there was a good supply of it in the cells of the glazed hive which they have formerly inhabited: so that it was possible that they had eaten some of it the 28th of June, the day when I began my experiment, and that this matter elaborated in their stomach had furnished them with the elements of the wax which formed the combs they made during their imprisonment. To remove this doubt from my mind another experiment was needed, and here it is.

The hive had been opened and looked in a room, the windows of which were securely shut; therefore, no bee could have gone to the fields. Attracted by the light they had clustered in a bunch in front of one of the panes of the window. I shook the hive over a table, and thus the bees which remained upon the comb, and also the queen, were forced to abandon it, and joined their companions. I was then able to detach all the combs; they contained but little honey and no fertilizing powder at all. I did not leave an atom of wax in the interior of this hive. I rubbed it with aromatic plants. I filled the cup once more with honey and I made the bees go in again, and shut them up as in the first instance.

On the second day of their confinement I heard a noise which was a good omen. On the fifth we lifted the hive from its support and saw that the bees had not lost their time. They had constructed in their prison rows of white comb, as regular and quite as large as they had before. Now I had scarcely any doubt but that the honey with which I had supplied them had furnished them with the means to make all the wax which I had found in the hive. For was it not highly improbable that the pollen which they had eaten 11 days before, could have furnished them the elements with which to construct it? But as the fact was very important, I thought myself bound to make a more rigorous demonstration, and for that, it sufficed to repeat the same trials, with the same bees. For if they continued to produce wax, being nourished only with honey and water, there could no longer be a doubt but that the fertilizing powder was useless. Burnens then repeated five times, the same experiment which I have just stated; he did it with the exactitude of which he has given me many proofs, and the result of those subsequent trials was so exactly like that of the two first that it seemed proved, to us at least that it is from honey that bees make all the wax they need.

What then is the use of those fertilizing dusts which the bees gather so eagerly? You know sir, that they interest them to such a degree that the weather must be very bad to keep them from this work.

M. De Reaumur has estimated the amount of pollen brought in yearly by a hive of ordinary strength, to be from 16 to 18 lbs. at least. (I perhaps mistake about the quantity, not having Reaumur at hand) and even should his calculations be a little over rated it would be no less clearly proved that it is a substance of primary necessity to the bees; thus you will not wonder at my desire to get at its true use. At first, I thought that the workers fed on pollen, and that it was to satisfy their appetite, that they sought for this agreeable and necessary aliment. I have taken the small balls of pollen from the legs of the bees and found them of a sweet and tartish taste; they would have made a very good preserve, had they not left upon the tongue an impression resembling that which fine sand would have made. I needed new experiments to verify my supposition, and the following occurred to me:

July 13th, 1793, I placed a small swarm in a glazed hive; in it was placed a piece of comb full of pollen, and in addition to this, some cooked fruits so that the prisoners should not die of hunger, in case the pollen should not avail them for food. I shut the hive and made sure that only air could get to them. We watched these bees during three days. We often saw them lick the fruits we gave them, but never saw one plunge his proboscis into the cells which were full of pollen, and in fact it did not seem to have any attraction for them. These bees had formed into a cluster in the top of the hive. On the 17th we disturbed this cluster with a feather to see if it did not hide some comb, but we found nothing, and we could guarantee that the bees had not built a single cell during their captivity. From this observation I could already conclude that the workers do not feed on pollen. It corroborated the former experiments, at the same time proving in another way that they did not find the elements of their wax in the dust of the stamens. This gather of pollen then was for another purpose, and if it was not for themselves that the bees collected it during 8 or 9 months of the year, it must then needs be for the young bees of which they were not the mothers. Accordingly I sought the means of obtaining some light upon so interesting a subject in the history of these insects; the following experiment taught me what I did not know. You will be glad to have me state it in full.

I had a swarm in a leaf hive, the two small ends of which were of glass. July 17th, 1793 Burnens examined this hive thoroughly. His intention was not to leave a single cell which contained pollen. Therefore he scrupulously cut out all the comb which contained pollen and put in its place cells which contained honey only.

This hive was governed by a young queen. I had prevented her from going out to seek the drones, and hence she was infertile when I commenced this last experiment. As there was no brood in her hive I was obliged to take some from another hive which was abundantly supplied. Burnens placed this brood in the first and second frames of the hive which had none. Then he took away the virgin queen and gave her to other bees to take care of; then he closed the hive with a grating which admitted air only. He resolved to observe the conduct and actions of the prisoners in these circumstances. ON the morrow we saw nothing which we deemed extraordinary: the brood was covered with bees which seemed to be taking care of it.

On the 19th after sunset, we heard a great noise in this hive. We opened the shutters to see what caused it. The bees seemed to us to be in greatest agitation; those which we were able to see, were running about in great disorder over the combs; the majority of them had abandoned the combs and had let themselves fall on the floor of the hive, and some were gnawing at the grating which prevented their exit.

They were so anxious to get out, that I feared lest a great number of them would die if we did not allow them to go out, and as they could not at that late hour go to the flowers we gave them their liberty. All the swarm availed themselves of this, and for more than a quarter of an hour flew about the hive; afterward they re-entered. We saw them climb up upon the comb, and order was completely reestablished; we seized this opportunity of shutting them up.

First we saw that the queen cells had not been continued: there was no worm in them and we did not discover an atom of the jelly which serves for bed and food to the larvae destined to become queens. In vain too did we look for worm, eggs, and food in the worker cells; all of it had disappeared. (this ends with a "to be continued" notice but shortly after L.L. Langstroth was no longer editor of ABJ and I found no completion of this letter. From ABJ Volume VIII No 2, August 1872 Unedited Letters of Huber.)

Photos of a reproduction of Huber's Leaf Hive

The following 7 photos were taken by Don Semple of a reproduction of the Huber leaf hive built by him for this book. 3 originals are included for comparison.

Fig. 2.

Photos of Original plates from the 1814 edition of *Nouvelles Observations Sur Les Abeilles*

Note from Transcriber: I started out working on just reprinting C.P. Dadant's version of Volume I and II of Huber's book, but I ran into problems with the plates. The original C.P. Dadant book had halftones of obviously yellowed plates that resulted in very gray and indistinct reproductions. They were hard to read and any attempts at improvement failed. So I tracked down and purchased the original 1814 French version of the book with all the plates. Fortunately the pages were not yellowed and the plates were in good shape. To fit those into the purpose for which Huber made them—communicating his observations, I have attempted to make the plates in the text as readable as possible. I put the figures on a plate in order by number and put new type for the figure numbers so they were more readable on those plates as the small engraved numbers were not readable. I separated the figures, cleaned up the backgrounds and enlarged them to a full page or the maximum useful size, and left the original engraved figure numbers on these since they were large enough to be easily readable, and put them in the text where descriptions of them occurred. Even if extra white space occurred, I focused on clarity over appearance. All this, I believe added to the readability and clarity of the text. However for historical and artistic purposes I think the unretouched original plates are something a student of Huber would want to see. I straightened them by the horizontal line on the side (some appear skewed despite this because they are not entirely square. Also to give an idea of the, improvement in these plates, I have include an original plate from the the C.P. Dadant version. So here they are, flaws, ink spots and all.

Vol II Plate 4 of the C.P. Dadant version followed by all 14 original plates from the 1814 French Version:

VOLUME 2—PLATE 4.

LA RUCHE EN FEUILLETS .

Fig. 3.

Fig. 4.

Fig. 1.

Fig. 2.

Adam Sculp .

Fig. 2.

Fig. 1.

Fig. 1re. Fig. 3. Fig. 2.

Fig. 4.

Fig. 5.

DÉTAILS ANATOMIQUES.

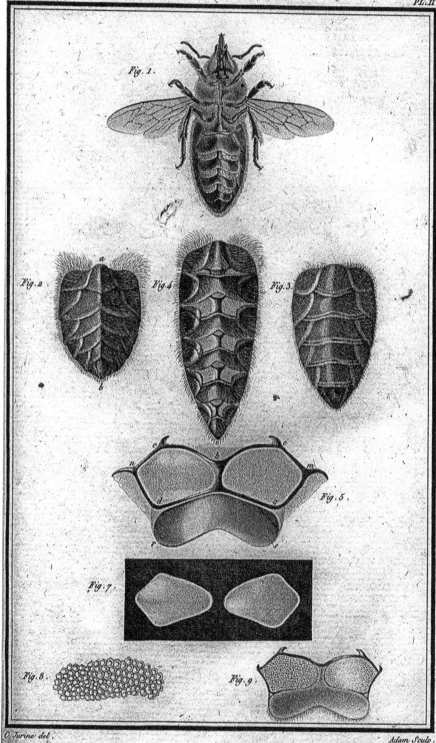

Fig. 1.

Fig. 2. Fig. 4. Fig. 3.

Fig. 5.

Fig. 7.

Fig. 8. Fig. 9.

Fig. 1. A

Fig. 2. B

Fig. 3. C

Fig. 4. A

Fig. 5. B

Fig. 6. C

C. Jurine del.

Adam Sculp.

DÉTAILS ANATOMIQUES .

Fig. 3 .

Fig. 2 .

Fig. 1 .

Fig. 4 .

Fig. 5 .

Fig. 6 .

C. Jurine del .

Fig. 9 .

Fig. 7 .

Fig. 8 .

Huber del .

Adam Sculp .

Face antérieure.

Face postérieure.

Fig. 4.

Fig. 4.*

Fig. 5.

1er Rang

2me Rang

Fig. 1re.

a

b

Fig. 3.

Fig. 2.

Fig. 11.

Fig. 6.

Fig. 7.

Fig. 8.

Fig. 9.

Fig. 10.

Fig. 9.*

Fig. 12.

Fig. 14.

Fig. 13.

Fig. 15.

Fig. 16.

Fig. 17.

Fig. 18.

Fig. 19.

P. Huber del.

Adam Sculp.

Fig. 1re

Fig. 2

Fig. 5.

Fig. 3.

Fig. 4.

P. Huber del.   Adam Sculp.

PL. VII. B.

Face antérieure.

Face postérieure.

Fig.30. Fig.29. Fig.31.

Fig.26. Fig.25. Fig.27.

Fig.24. Fig.28.

Fig.21. Fig.23. Fig.22.

N°.4. N°.1. N°.5. N°.2 et 3. N°.6. N°.2. N°.3. N°.7.

Fig.19. 19 ¾ 20 ¾ Fig.20.

N°.1.

Fig.17. Fig.18.

Face antérieure. Face postérieure.

P. Huber del.

Adam Sculp.

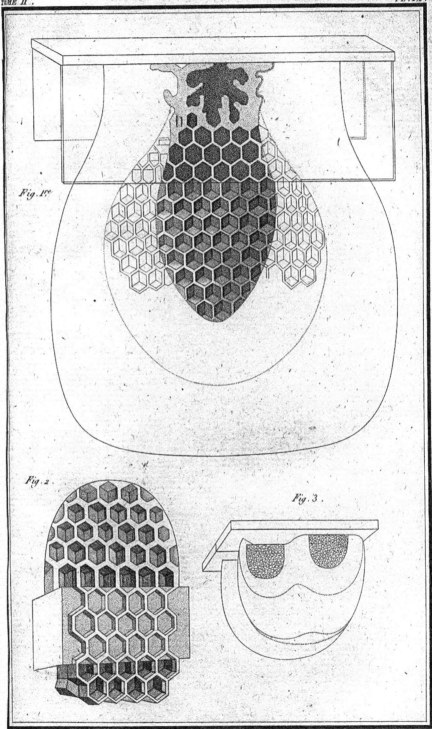

Fig. 1re.

Fig. 2.

Fig. 3.

P. Huber del.   Adam Sculp.

Fig. 1re

Fig. 4.   Fig. 3.   Fig. 2.   Fig. 5.   Fig. 6.

Fig. 7.   Fig. 8.   Fig. 9.

P. Huber del.   Adam Sculp.

Fig. 1re.

Fig. 2.

C. Jurine del.   Adam Sculp.

Francis Huber 1750-1831

Francis Huber was born on the 2nd of July 1750, of an honorable family, in which vivacity of mind and imagination seemed hereditary. His father, John Huber, had the reputation of being one of the most witty men of his day; a trait which was frequently noticed by Voltaire, who valued him for the originality of his conversation. He was an agreeable musician, and made verses which were boasted of even in the saloon at Ferney. He was distinguished for lively and piquant repartee; he painted with much facility and talent; he excelled so much in the cutting out of landscapes, that he seems to have been a creator of this art. His sculpture was better than that which those who are simply amateurs are able to execute; and to this diversity of talent, he joined the taste and art of observing the manners of the animal creation.

John Huber transmitted almost all his tastes to his son. The latter attended from his childhood the public lectures at the college, and under the guidance of good masters, he acquired a predilection for literature, which the conversation of his father served to develop. He owed to the same paternal inspiration his taste for natural history, and he derived his fondness for science from the lessons of De Saussure, and from manipulations in the laboratory of one of his relatives, who ruined himself in searching for the philosopher's stone. His precocity of talent was manifest in his attention to nature, at an age when others are scarcely aware of its existence, and in the evidence of deep feeling, at an age when others hardly betray emotions. It seemed that, destined to a submission to the most cruel of privations, he made, as it were instinctively, a provision of recollections and feelings for the remainder of his days. At the age of fifteen, his general health and his sight began to be impaired. The ardor with which he pursued his labors and his pleasures, the earnestness with which he devoted his days to study, and his nights to reading of romances by the feeble light of a lamp, and for which when deprived of its use, he sometimes substituted the light of the moon, were, it is said, the causes which threatened at once the loss of health and of sight. His father took him to Paris, to consult Tronchin, on account of his health, and Venzel on the condition of his eyes.

With a view to his general health, Ronchin sent him to a village (Stain) in the neighborhood of Paris, in order that he might be free from all disturbing occupations. There he practiced the life of a simple peasant, followed the plough, and diverted himself with all the rural concerns. This regimen was completely successful, and Huber retained, from this country residence, not only confirmed health, but a tender recollection and decided taste for a rural life.

The occultist Venzel considered the state of his eyes as incurable, and he did not think it justifiable to hazard an operation for cataract, then less understood than at present, and announced to young Huber the probability of an approaching and entire blindness. His eyes, however, notwithstanding their weakness, had, before his departure, and after his return, met those of Maria Aimée Lullin, a Daughter of one of the syndics of the Swiss Republic. They had been companions at the lessons of the dancing master, and such a mutual love was cherished as the age of seventeen is apt to produce. The constantly increasing probability, however, of the blindness of Huber, decided Mr. Lullin to refuse his consent to the union; but as the misfortune of her friend and chosen companion became more certain, the more did Maria regard herself as pledged never to abandon him. She had become attached to him at first through love, then through generosity and sort of heroism; and she resolved to wait until she had attained the lawful age to decide for herself (the age of twenty-five), and then to unite herself with Huber. The latter perceiving the risk which his infirmity would probably occasion to his hopes, endeavored to dissimulate. As long as he could discern some light, he acted and spoke as if he could see, and often beguiled his own misfortune by such a conference. The seven years thus spent made such an impression on him, that during the rest of his life, even when his blindness had been overcome with such surprising ability as to furnish one of his claims to celebrity, he was still fond of dissembling: he would boast of the beauty of a landscape, which he knew of only by hearsay or by simple recollection,—the elegance of a dress,—or the fair complexion of a female whose voice pleased him; and in his conversations, in his letters, and even in his books, he would say, *I have seen, I have seen with my own eyes.* These expressions, which deceived neither himself nor anyone else, were like so many recollections of that fatal period of his life when he was daily sensible of the thickening of the veil which was constantly spread between him and the material world, and increased his fear not only of becoming entirely blind, but of being deserted by the object of his love.

But it was not so; Miss Lullin resisted every persuasion—every persecution even—by which her father endeavored to divert her from her resolution; and as soon as she had attained her majority, she presented herself at the altar, conducted by her maternal uncle, Mr. Rilliet Fatio, and leading, if we may so term it, herself the spouse who in his happy and brilliant days had been her choice, and to whose saddened fall she was now determined to devote her life.

Madame Huber proved, by her constancy, that she was worthy of the energy which she had manifested. During the forty years of their union, she never ceased to bestow upon her blind husband the kindest attention: she was his reader, his secretary, his observer, and she removed, as far as possible, all those embarrassments which would naturally arise from his infirmity. Her husband, in alluding to her small stature, would say of her, *mens magna in corpora parvo (large mind in small body). As long as she lived,* said he also, *I was not sensible of the misfortune of being blind.*

We have seen the blind shine as poets, and distinguish themselves as philosophers and calculators; but it was reserved for Huber to give a luster to his class in the sciences of observation, and on objects so minute that the most clear-sighted observer can scarcely observe them. The reading of the works of Reaumur and Bonnet, and the conversation of the latter, directed his curiosity to the history of bees. His habitual residence in the country inspired him with the desire, first of verifying some facts, then of filling some blanks in their history; but this kind of observation required not only the use of such an instrument as the optician must furnish, but an intelligent assistant who alone could adjust it to its use. He had then a servant named Francis Burnens, remarkable for his sagacity and for the devotion he bore for his master. Huber practiced him in the art of observation, directed him to his researches by questions adroitly combined, and aided by the recollections of his youth, and by the testimonials of his wife and friends, he rectified the assertions of his assistant, and became enabled to form in his own mind a true and perfect image of the minutest facts. "I am much more certain," said he one day to me smiling, "of what I taste than you are, for you publish what your own eyes only have seen, while I take the mean among many witnesses." This is, doubtless, very plausible reasoning, but it will hardly render anyone mistrustful of his own eyes!

The publication of his observations took place in 1792, in the form of letters to Charles Bonnet, and under the title of *"Nouvelles Observations sur les Abeilles."* This work made a strong impression upon many naturalists, not only from the novelty of the facts, but from their rigorous exactness, and the singular difficulty against which the author had to struggle with so much ability. Most of the academies of Europe (and especially the Academy of Sciences of Paris) admitted Huber, from time to time, among their associates.

The activity of his researches was relaxed neither by this early research, which might have satisfied his self-love, nor by the embarrassments which he suffered in consequence of the Revolution, nor even by a separation from his faithful Burnens. Another assistant of course became necessary. His first substitute was his wife,—then his son, Pierre Huber, who began from that time to acquire a just celebrity in the history of the economy of ants, and various other insects. They form the second volume of the second edition of his work published in 1814, which was edited in part by his son.

The origin of wax was at that time a point in the history of bees much disputed by naturalists. By some it was asserted, though without sufficient proof, that it was fabricated by the bee from the honey. Huber, who had already happily cleared up the origin of the *propolis*, confirmed this opinion, with respect to the wax, by numerous observations; and showed very particularly, with the aid of Burnens, how it escaped in a laminated form from between the rings of the abdomen. He instituted laborious researches to discover how bees prepare it for their edifices; he followed step by step the whole construction of those wonderful hives, which seem, by their perfection, to resolve the most delicate problem of geometry; he assigned to each class of bees the part it takes in this construction, and traced their labors from the rudiments of the first cell to the completed perfection of the comb. He made known the ravages which the *Sphinx atropos* produces in the hives into which it insinuates itself; he even endeavored to unravel the history of the senses of the bees, and especially to examine the seat of the sense of smell, the existence of which is proved by the whole history of these insects, while the situation of the organ had never been determined with any certainty.   Finally, he prosecuted a curious research into the respiration of bees. He proved by very many curious experiments that bees consume oxygen gas like other animals,. But how can the air become renewed, and preserve its purity in a hive plastered with cement, and closed on all its sides, except at the narrow orifice which serves for a door? This problem demanded all the sagacity of our observer, and he at length ascertained that the bees, by a particular movement of their wings, agitated the air in such a way as to effect its renovation; and having assured himself by direct observation, he farther proved its correctness by means of artificial ventilation.

This perseverance of a whole life, in a given object, is one of the characteristic traits of Huber and probably one of the causes of his success. Naturalists are divided from taste, and often from position, into two series. The one love to embrace the *tout ensemble* of beings, to compare them with others, to seize the relations of their organization, and to deduce from them their classification and general laws of nature. It is this class who have necessarily at their disposal, vast collections; and they mostly dwell in large cities. The others take pleasure in the profound study of a given subject, considering it under all its aspects, scrutinizing into its minute details, and patiently following it in all its peculiarities. The latter are generally sedentary and isolated observers, living remote from collections, and far from great cities.

Huber is evidently to be placed in the school of special observers: his situation and infirmity retained him in it, and he acquired therein an honorable rank, by the sagacity and precision of his researches; but it is plainly perceptible, in reading his works, that his brilliant imagination urged him toward the region of general ideas. Unprovided with terms of comparison, he sought them in that theory of final causes, which is gratifying to every expanded and religious mind, because it appears to furnish a reason for a multitude of facts, the employment of which, however, as is well known, is prone to lead the mind into error; but we must do him the justice to acknowledge, that the use he makes of them is always confined within the limits of philosophical doubt and observation.

His style is, in general, clear and elegant; always retaining the precision requisite to the didactic, it possesses the attraction which a poetic imagination can readily confer upon all subjects; but one thing which particularly distinguishes it, and which we should least expect, is, that he describes facts in a manner so picturesque, that in reading them we fancy that we can see the very objects, which the author, alas, was never able to see! I venture also to add, that we find in his descriptions so many masterly touches, as to justify the conclusion, that if he had retained his sight he would have been like his father, his brother, and his son, a skilful painter.

His taste for the fine arts, unable to derive pleasure from forms, extended to sounds; he loved poetry, but he was more especially endowed with a strong inclination for music. His taste for it might be called innate, and it furnished him with a great source of recreation throughout his life. He had an agreeable voice, and was initiated in his childhood in the charms of Italian music.

The desire of maintaining his connection with absent friends, without having recourse to a secretary, suggested the idea of a sort of printing press for his own use; he had it executed by his domestic, Claude Lechet, whose mechanical talents he had cultivated, as he had before done those of Francis Burnens for natural history. In cases properly numbered, were placed small prominent types which he arranged in his hand. Over the lines thus composed, he placed a sheet blackened with a peculiar ink, then a sheet of white paper, and with a press, which he moved with his feet, he was enabled to print a letter which he folded and sealed himself, happy in the kind of independence which he hoped by this means to acquire. But the difficulty of putting this press into action prevented the habitual use of it. These letters, and some algebraic characters formed of baked clay, which his ingenious son, always anxious to serve him, had made for his use, were during more than fifteen years, a source of relaxation and amusement to him. He enjoyed walking, and even a solitary promenade by means of threads which he had caused to be stretched through all the rural walks about his dwelling.

Naturally endowed with a benevolent heart, how were those happy dispositions too often destroyed by the collisions of the world, preserved in him? He received from all that surrounded him nothing but kindness and respect. The busy world, the scene of so many little vexations, had disappeared from his view. His house and his fortune were taken care of, without any embarrassment to him. A stranger to public duties, he was in a great measure ignorant of the politics, the cunning, and the fraud of men. Having rarely had it in his power (without fault of his own) of being useful to others, he never experienced the bitterness of ingratitude. Jealousy, even notwithstanding his success, was silenced by his infirmity. To be happy and prosperous in a situation in which so many others are given up to continual regrets, was accounted to him as a virtue. The female sex, provided their voices were agreeable, all appeared to him as if he had seen them at the age of eighteen. His mind preserved the freshness and candor which constitute the charm and happiness of adolescence; he loved young people, for with their sentiments his own were more in accordance than with those of the aged and experiences. He took pleasure, to the very last, in directing the studies of the young, and possessed, in the highest degree, the art of pleasing and interesting them. Though fond of new acquaintance, he never abandoned his old friends. "One thing I have never been able to learn," said he in extreme old age, "that is, to forget how to love." Thus had he the good sense justly to appreciate and enjoy the balance of advantages which were furnished him, by the very condition in which he was placed.

His conversation was generally amiable and gracious; he was easily led into the humorous; he was a stranger to no kind of knowledge; he loved to elevate his thoughts to the gravest and most important subjects, as well as to descend to the most familiar sportiveness. He was learned, in the ordinary sense of the word; but, like a skilful diver, he went to the bottom of each question by a kind of tact and a sagacity of perception which supplied the place of knowledge. When anyone spoke to him on subjects which interested his head or heart, his noble figure became strikingly animated, and the vivacity of his countenance seemed, by a mysterious magic, to animate even his eyes, which had so long been condemned to darkness.

He spent the last years of his life at Lausanne, under the care of his daughter, Madame de Molin. He continued to make additions at intervals to his former labors. The discovery of bees without stings, made in the environs of Tampico by Captain Hall, excited his curiosity; and it was high satisfaction to him when his friend, Professor Prevost, procured for him at first a few individuals, and then a hive of these insects. It was the last homage which he rendered to his old friend whom he had devoted so many laborious researches, to whom he owed his celebrity, and, what is more, his happiness. Nothing of any importance has been added to their history since his time.

Huber retained his faculties to the last. He was loving and beloved to the end of his days. At the age of eighty-one, he wrote to one of his friends, "There is a time when it is impossible to remain neglectful; it is, when separating gradually from each other, we may reveal to those we love all that esteem, tenderness, and gratitude have inspired us with towards them...I say to you alone," adds he, farther on, "that resignation and serenity are blessings which have not been refused." He wrote these lines on the 20th of December 1831, and on the 22nd he was no more; his life became extinct, without pain or agony, while in the arms of his daughter.— *Abridged from "The Life and Writings of Francis Huber," by Professor De Candolle.*

ABOUT THE AUTHOR

François Huber was only fifteen years old when he began to suffer from a disease which gradually resulted in total blindness; but, with the aid of his wife, Marie Aimée Lullin, and of his servant, François Burnens, he was able to carry out investigations that laid the foundations of a scientific knowledge of the life history of the honey bee. His *Nouvelles Observations sur les Abeilles* was published at Geneva in 1792. Further observations were published as Volume II of the same in 1814. What he discovered laid the ground work for all the practical knowledge we have of bees today. His discoveries were so revolutionary, that beekeeping can be divided in two eras very easily as pre-Huber and post-Huber.

CPSIA information can be obtained
at www.ICGtesting.com
Printed in the USA
BVOW04*0910011216
468736BV00048B/41/P